T.J. PAREJA
1988

TI-59 Manual for Estimating Centrifugal Compressor Performance

Process Compressor Technology
Volume 2

Gulf Publishing Company
Book Division
Houston, London, Paris, Tokyo

TI-59 Manual for Estimating Centrifugal Compressor Performance

Process Compressor Technology
Volume 2

Ronald P. Lapina, P.E.

TI-59 Manual for Estimating Centrifugal Compressor Performance

Process Compressor Technology, Volume 2

Library of Congress Cataloging in Publication Data
(Revised for volume 2)

Lapina, Ronald P.
  Process compressor technology

  Includes bibliographies and index
  Contents: v. 1. Estimating centrifugal compressor performance—v. 2. TI-59 manual for estimating centrifugal compressor performance.
  1. Compressors—Performance—Data processing.
  2. TI Programmable 59 (Calculating-machine) I. Title.
TJ990.L367 1982   621.5'1   82-3124
ISBN 0-87201-101-1 (v. 1)
ISBN 0-87201-100-3 (v. 2)

Acknowledgments

I would like to thank the contributors to this book, namely the American Society of Heating, Refrigeration and Air-Conditioning Engineers, Inc.; the American Society of Mechanical Engineers; *Chemical Engineering,* McGraw-Hill Publications; the Compressed Air and Gas Institute; Elliott Company; the Gas Processors Suppliers Association; McGraw-Hill Book Company; Texas A&M University; Trane Company; and Transamerica DeLaval Inc.

I extend my deepest gratitude to George L. Farris of Elliott Company, who gave me considerable assistance in developing the programs in Part III of this book.

I also extend my appreciation to all those, too numerous to mention, who gave me assistance in the form of knowledge or encouragement.

And last, but certainly not the least, I thank my family, Rachel, Chris, and Kim, for their patience and understanding, and God for blessing me with them.

in memory of Harry J. Strader,
father-in-law, teacher, friend

Contents

Preface

Estimating Centrifugal Compressor Performance, Volume 1 of the series *Process Compressor Technology,* presented performance estimating procedures for centrifugal compressors. It covered compressor thermodynamics, performance estimates, performance curves, and centrifugal compressor rerates. In general, Volume 1 gave the tools necessary to size a centifugal compressor and estimate its performance for most any application.

This new volume is an extension of the first. It presents 30 calculator programs that apply the technology developed in Volume 1. The programs are written for the Texas Instrument TI-59 calculator and PC-100C printer and cover centrifugal compressor estimates, performance curves, testing, gas properties, drivers, inlet flow conversions, efficiency conversions, English-metric conversions, thrust-error analysis, and labyrinth leakage.

This book is sectioned into six parts for easy reference. Part I contains the centrifugal compressor estimating programs: the adiabatic method, the N-method, and the Mollier method. It also contains programs to determine compressor rotational speed and number of stages and pressure profiles for intercooled compressors.

Part II covers performance curves. Programs for the head curve, the pressure curve, suction throttling, and head rise to surge are presented, along with a program that will help construct a quadrant curve.

Three programs to aid in the analysis of centrifugal compressor field tests are contained in Part III. The first two determine the mass flow through the various fluid meters; the third is for determination of polytropic head and power requirement from field test data.

Part IV contains three programs for gas properties calculations. The first converts mols to mol fractions. The second calculates mixture properties—the molecular weight, critical pressure, critical temperature, and k-value. The third calculates the molecular weight and corrected massflow for air/water vapor applications.

Compressor drivers are considered in Part V. Programs are presented to estimate steam turbine performance, to check motor acceleration time, to mechanically check gears against the requirements of API 613, and to estimate the gas turbine site rating from the ISO data available in manufacturers' literature.

Part VI contains miscellaneous programs that aid in compressor selection and analysis. Inlet flow conversions, efficiency conversions, efficiency from specific speed, nozzle velocity calculations, thrust-error analysis, labyrinth leakage, and English-metric conversions are covered here.

Each program is broken into six parts: the Background, which develops the technology and presents the equations necessary to understand the program; the Program Description, which shows what the programs will do and what options are available; the Labels Used by the Program; the Program Usage, which shows step-by-step how the operator executes the program; the Sample Problem; and the Program Listing.

Each program has been constructed such that the first three storage registers are open for use by the operator without affecting program data memory. The first three steps on each program listing indicate the partition necessary for the program, unless the program uses the initial partition. While these three steps are not necessary, they serve as a reminder to repartition the calculator prior to keying in the program.

By using the programs in this book, centrifugal compressor size and performance can be estimated and checked against manufacturers' proposals for most any application. The programs will eliminate tedious and time-consuming repetitive calculations so that the engineer can devote his or her time to the more productive responsibilities of the job.

Ronald P. Lapina
Missouri City, Texas

Algebraic Nomenclature

A area

a number of gas constituents

A_L flow area through labyrinth

A_{sl} altitude

A_{tb} active area of thrust bearing

b number of compression sections

C theoretical steam velocity

C_{ap} altitude correction on power

C_d fluid meter coefficient of discharge

C_{dp} ducting-loss correction on power

C_L coefficient for labyrinth leakage

c_p specific heat at constant pressure

C_{pwr} power constant

C_{th} temperature correction on heat input

C_{tp} temperature correction on power

C_{1rc} coefficient for labyrinth radial clearance

C_{2rc} coefficient for 2 × labyrinth radial clearance

D pipe diameter upstream of fluid meter

d throat diameter of fluid meter

d_{min} minimum acceptable inlet nozzle diameter

d_n inlet nozzle diameter

d_p pinion diameter

D_s shaft diameter

D_{sd} specific diameter

d_w wheel (or impeller) diameter

F	net face width of gear
f	polytropic work factor
F_a	thermal expansion factor of fluid meter
F_{bp}	balance piston compensating load
F_r	total rotor thrust
F_{tb}	thrust bearing load
G	steam flowrate
g_c	universal gravitational constant
GAP	gap between helix faces
H_{ad}	adiabatic head
HI	heat input
H_p	polytropic head
$H_{p_{\text{nom}}}$	nominal polytropic head per stage
$\%(H_p)_s$	polytropic head rise to surge
Δh_s	isentropic enthalpy difference
$\Delta h_s'$	isentropic enthalpy difference downstream of governor valve
h_1	inlet enthalpy
h_2	discharge (exhaust) enthalpy
$h_{2'}$	side-load enthalpy
h_{2ad}	adiabatic discharge enthalpy
h_{2s}	isentropic exhaust enthalpy
h_{2s}'	isentropic exhaust enthalpy based on pressure downstream of governor valve
h_3	mixture enthalpy
J	geometry factor
J_g	gear geometry factor
J_p	pinion geometry factor
K	gear tooth pitting index
k	ratio of specific heats
k_a	average ratio of specific heats
K_{fc}	flow coefficient of orifice
k_1	inlet ratio of specific heats
k_2	discharge ratio of specific heats
L	gear width
LHV	lower heating value
L_m	mechanical losses
m	mass flow
m_a	mass flow of dry air
m_l	labyrinth leakage
m_{SL}	side-load mass flow
MW	molecular weight
MW_a	molecular weight of dry air
MW_w	molecular weight of water vapor

m_1	inlet mass flow
m_{1in}	leakage based on radial clearance for interlocking seal
m_{1rc}	leakage based on radial clearance for non-interlocking seal
m_2	discharge mass slow
m_{2in}	leakage based on 2 × radial clearance for interlocking seal
m_{2rc}	leakage based on 2 × radial clearance for non-interlocking seal
N	rotational speed
n	polytropic exponent
ΔN	speed increment
N_g	gear rotational speed
N_{nom}	nominal rotational speed
N_p	pinion rotational speed
N_{ss}	specific speed
NTP	number of throttling points
P	pressure
P_{bar}	barometric pressure
P_c	critical pressure
ΔP_{he}	heat-exchanger pressure drop
P_{nd}	normal diametral pitch
P_r	reduced pressure
$\%(\Delta P)_s$	differential pressure rise to surge
P_{tb}	thrust bearing pressure
P_w	partial pressure of water vapor
PWR	power requirement, either gas or shaft
PWR_d	gas-turbine site rated horsepower
PWR_g	gas power requirement
PWR_{gr}	gear rated horsepower
PWR_i	gas-turbine ISO rated horsepower
PWR_s	shaft power requirement
P_1	inlet pressure
P_1'	pressure downstream of governor valve
P_{12}	first-section discharge pressure
P_2	discharge pressure
P_{21}	second-section inlet pressure
P_{22}	second-section discharge pressure
$\%(P_2)_s$	discharge pressure rise to surge
P_{31}	third-section inlet pressure
P_{32}	third-section discharge pressure
q_{ad}	adiabatic head coefficient
Q_1	inlet volume flow
Q_{1a}	average inlet volume flow
$\%(Q_1)_s$	percent inlet volume flow at surge
Q_2	discharge volume flow

R gas constant
Re_t Reynolds number at throat of fluid meter
Re_1 pipe Reynolds number upstream of fluid meter
r_g gear ratio
r_p pressure ratio
$\%(r_p)_s$ pressure-ratio rise to surge
$r_{P\text{SECT}}$ sectional pressure ratio
$(r_p)_1$ first-section pressure ratio
$(r_p)_2$ second-section pressure ratio
$(r_p)_3$ third-section pressure ratio
r_t temperature ratio
r_v volume ratio
SF service factor
SFC specific fuel consumption
SH specific humidity
SHI site rated specific heat input
SHI_i ISO rated specific heat input
SR steam rate
S_t bending stress number
SVF standard volume flow
$SVFM$ metric standard volume flow
T temperature
t acceleration time
T_a ambient temperature
T_c critical temperature
T_{ic} intercool inlet temperature
T_r reduced temperature
$TSPA$ tooth spacing for labyrinths
T_1 inlet temperature
T_{12} first-section discharge temperature
T_2 discharge temperature
T_{2A} approximate discharge temperature
T_{22} second-section discharge temperature
T_{32} third-section discharge temperature
u blade velocity
v specific volume
V_a inlet velocity
$V_{\max}$ maximum acceptable inlet velocity
V_{rat} velocity ratio
v_1 inlet specific volume
v_2 discharge specific volume
W_t transmitted load through gear
WK^2 inertia of rotating string

x mol fraction
x_a mol fraction of air
x_w mol fraction of water vapor
Y_N expansion factor for flow nozzles and venturi meters
Y_O expansion factor for orifices
Z compressibility
Z_a average compressibility
Z_1 inlet compressibility
Z_2 discharge compressibility
β diameter ratio of fluid meters
δ radial clearance
η_{ad} adiabatic efficiency
η_b base steam-turbine efficiency
η_c base steam-turbine efficiency corrected for steam-path losses
η_g gear efficiency
η_{im} isometric efficiency
η_p polytropic efficiency
η_{st} steam-turbine efficiency
η_t efficiency related to total exhaust and total inlet pressures
θ speed-of-sound index
μ_1 absolute viscosity upstream of fluid meter
τ torque
$\%\tau$ percent torque
τ_a available torque
Ψ helix angle

Subscripts:

bc base performance curve
C compressor
i ith constituent
M motor
mix   mixture
r rated (Program 11 only)
s surge (Program 11 only)
std   standard
us upstream of valve

Program Data Summary

Notes on Program Data Summary

1. The "Partition" column shows the partition the calculator must be in to use the program. Note that 479.59 is the initial partition of the calculator.
2. Each program has registers 00–02 open for usage outside of the program.
3. "Number of Sides" stands for the number of card sides necessary for recording program.
4. "Continuous Usage" stands for continuous usage, without the need for complete data reentry. Those programs indicated by "yes" only require reentry of the data the operator wishes to change prior to program reexecution. The "(Q)" in the column stands for qualifications. Those programs signified by "(Q)" have qualifications upon which the program is set up for continuous usage. In these cases, refer to individual programs.

Program Data Summary

Program Number	Abbreviated Program Name	Partition	Registers Not Used	Total Steps	Number of Sides	Continuous Usage
1	Adiabatic Method	479.59	00–02, 16, 20–59	419	2	yes
2	N-Method	719.29	00–02, 24, 27–29	691	3	yes
3	Mollier Method	479.59	00–02, 22–59	478	2	no
4	Speed and Number of Stages	479.59	00–02, 17–59	479	2	yes
5	Intercool Pressure Profile	719.29	00–02, 26–29	717	3	yes
6	Power Savings from Cooling	719.29	00–02	691	3	yes
7	Fan-Law—Head	479.59	00–02, 40–44, 48–59	394	2	yes
8	Fan-Law—Pressure (psi)	559.49	00–02, 48–49	558	3	yes
9	Fan-Law—Pressure (H_2O)	559.49	00–02, 44, 48–49	551	3	yes
10	Suction Throttling	559.49	00–02, 43, 48–49	549	3	yes
11	Head Rise to Surge	719.29	00–02, 29	714	3	no
12	Quadrant Curve	479.59	00–02, 14–59	332	2	yes
13	Varying P_1 for Constant P_2	479.59	00–02, 14–59	240	1	yes (Q)
14	Mass Flow from a Nozzle	479.59	00–02, 21–59	476	2	yes (Q)
15	Mass Flow from an Orifice	479.59	00–02, 16, 23–59	479	2	yes (Q)
16	Compressor Performance Test	479.59	00–02, 21–59	438	2	yes
17	Mols to Mol Fraction	479.59	00–02	204	1	no
18	Gas Properties	479.59	00–02, 13–59	239	1	no
19	Air/Water Vapor	479.59	00–02, 11–59	322	2	yes
20	Steam-Turbine Estimates	719.29	00–02, 25–29	720	3	yes
21	Motor Acceleration Time	479.59	00–02, 37–59	416	2	no
22	Gear Mechanical Check	719.29	00–02	709	3	no
23	Gas-Turbine Site Rating	479.59	00–02, 17–59	476	2	yes
24	Inlet Flow Conversions	799.19	00–02, 17–19	790	4	yes
25	Efficiency Conversions	479.59	00–02, 15–59	366	2	yes (Q)
26	Efficiency from Specific Speed	479.59	00–02, 10–59	197	1	yes
27	Inlet Nozzle Velocity	479.59	00–02, 13–59	363	2	yes
28	Thrust-Error Analysis	479.59	00–02, 11–59	235	1	yes
29	Labyrinth Leakage	479.59	00–02, 21–59	450	2	yes (Q)
30	English-Metric Conversions	719.29	00–02, 15–59	627	3	yes

Part I

Estimating Centrifugal Compressor Performance

Program 1

Adiabatic Method Compressor Calculation Procedure

Background

A reversible adiabatic process is of the form:

$$Pv^k = \text{constant} \tag{1-1}$$

where:

P = pressure
v = specific volume
k = ratio of specific heats

By considering Equation 1-1 and the ideal gas equation given in Equation 1-2:

$$Pv = RT \tag{1-2}$$

where:

R = gas constant and is a function of the molecular weight, MW
T = temperature

the compression ratio equations can be derived for an isentropic process (therefore the efficiency is equal to 100%). They are as follows:

$$r_p = r_v^k \tag{1-3}$$

$$r_v = r_p^{1/k} \tag{1-4}$$

3

$$r_p = r_t^{k/(k-1)} \tag{1-5}$$

$$r_t = r_p^{(k-1)/k} \tag{1-6}$$

$$r_v = r_t^{1/(k-1)} \tag{1-7}$$

$$r_t = r_v^{k-1} \tag{1-8}$$

where:
r_p = pressure ratio = P_2/P_1
r_v = volume ratio = v_1/v_2
r_t = temperature ratio = T_2/T_1 (with T in °R)

By further considering the integral flow work equation for a steady-state, steady-flow process,

$$H_{ad} = \int v dP \tag{1-9}$$

and the real gas equation,

$$Pv = ZRT \tag{1-10}$$

the adiabatic head equation can be derived as given in Equation 1-11:

$$H_{ad} = Z_1 R T_1 \left(\frac{k}{k-1}\right)[r_p^{(k-1)/k} - 1] \tag{1-11}$$

where:
H_{ad} = adiabatic head, ft-lbf/lbm
Z_1 = inlet compressibility factor
R = gas constant, ft-lbf/lbm-°R (= $1545/MW$)
T_1 = inlet temperature, °R
r_p = pressure ratio = P_2/P_1
k = ratio of specific heats

The k-value used in Equation 1-11 is the average value, k_a. It can be determined either by calculating the k-value at the average compression temperature or by averaging the inlet and discharge k-values. Note that for low-pressure air service, where the adiabatic procedure is normally used, the k-value does not vary much, so use of the inlet k-value is normally satisfactory.

Since the process defined by Equation 1-1 is reversible adiabatic, and therefore isentropic, the equation for the discharge temperature does not follow directly from the temperature ratio equation given in Equation 1-6. It must be modified by including the adiabatic efficiency, as shown in Equation 1-12:

$$T_2 = \frac{T_1(r_p^{(k-1)/k} - 1)}{\eta_{ad}} + T_1 \tag{1-12}$$

where:
  T_2 = discharge temperature, °R
  η_{ad} = adiabatic efficiency

The inlet volume flow to the compressor is a function of the mass flow and the inlet specific volume:

$$Q_1 = mv_1 \tag{1-13}$$

where:
  Q_1 = inlet volume flow, ICFM
  m = mass flow, lbm/min
  v_1 = inlet specific volume, ft^3/lbm

The specific volume is given by the following:

$$v_1 = \frac{Z_1RT_1}{144\,P_1} = \frac{10.729\,Z_1T_1}{(MW)(P_1)} \tag{1-14}$$

where:
  P_1 = inlet pressure, psia
  MW = molecular weight, lbm/lbm-mol

Combining Equations 1-13 and 1-14 yields the inlet volume flow equation:

$$Q_1 = 10.729\,\frac{mZ_1T_1}{(MW)(P_1)} \tag{1-15}$$

The discharge volume flow can be calculated similarly:

$$Q_2 = 10.729\,\frac{mZ_2T_2}{(MW)(P_2)} \tag{1-16}$$

where the subscript 2 stands for discharge conditions. However, as stated before, the adiabatic calculation approach is normally used for low-pressure ratio air service, where the variation in the compressibility can be ignored. Thus, the discharge volume flow can be calculated from Equation 1-17:

$$Q_2 = Q_1 \left(\frac{T_2}{T_1}\right)\left(\frac{P_1}{P_2}\right) \tag{1-17}$$

The gas power requirement is a function of the adiabatic head, the adiabatic efficiency, and the mass flow:

$$PWR_g = \frac{mH_{ad}}{33,000 \, \eta_{ad}} \tag{1-18}$$

where:

PWR_g = gas power requirement, hp

The shaft power requirement results from adding the gas power requirement to the mechanical losses:

$$PWR_s = \frac{mH_{ad}}{33,000 \, \eta_{ad}} + L_m \tag{1-19}$$

where:

PWR_s = shaft power requirement, hp
L_m = mechanical losses, hp

For low-pressure ratio air services in single-stage (single impeller) compressors, the mechanical losses can be assumed to be approximately three percent of the gas power requirement, unless better data are available from a vendor.

The adiabatic head equation is applicable to about 15,000 ft-lbf/lbm, although some manufacturers will quote single-stage compressors up to 30,000 ft-lbf/lbm. The adiabatic method is not only applicable for single-stage compressors but to fan and blower applications as well.

A note of caution: The adiabatic head equation is only valid *between* cooling points, not including them. Thus, if an application requires intercooling in the compression process, the adiabatic head must be calculated for each compression step, i.e., between cooling points.

Program 1 Description

This Adiabatic Method Compressor Calculation Procedure, Program 1, calculates and prints the results of Equations 1-11, 1-12, 1-15, 1-17, 1-18, and 1-19.

In order to execute the program, the following must be known:

1. Inlet pressure, P_1
2. Discharge pressure, P_2
3. Inlet temperature, T_1
4. Mass flow, m
5. Molecular weight, MW
6. Average k-value, k_a
7. Inlet Z-value, Z_1
8. Adiabatic efficiency, η_{ad}

A manufacturer should be consulted for an applicable adiabatic efficiency based on the type of equipment investigated, i.e. fan, blower, or single-stage compressor, However, lacking any better information, an adiabatic efficiency of 75% is normally a fair assumption.

The program allows mechanical losses to be entered as a fraction of gas power requirement. A value of three percent is suggested for mechanical losses, unless better information is available.

The program is set up for continuous usage without the need for complete data reentry. Therefore the operator need only change the parameters desired before reexecuting the program.

Table 1-1 is the nomenclature printed by the program; Table 1-2 shows the data registers used by the program.

Table 1-1
Program 1: Printer Nomenclature

Program Term	Definition	Units
EFF	adiabatic efficiency	dimensionless
HEAD	adiabatic head	ft-lbf/lbm
KA	average ratio of specific heats	dimensionless
M	mass flow	lbm/min
MW	molecular weight	lbm/lbm-mol
P1	inlet pressure	psia
P2	discharge pressure	psia
PWRG	gas power requirement	hp
PWRS	shaft power requirement	hp
Q1	inlet volume flow	ICFM
Q2	discharge volume flow	CFM
T1	inlet temperature	°F
T2	discharge temperature	°F
Z1	inlet compressibility	dimensionless

Table 1-2
Data Registers Used by Program 1

00	not used	07	MW	14	$r_p^{(k-1)/k} - 1$
01	not used	08	k_a	15	H_{ad}
02	not used	09	Z_1	16	not used
03	P_1	10	η_{ad}	17	T_2
04	P_2	11	$(k-1)/k$	18	PWR_g
05	T_1	12	Q_1	19	PWR_s
06	m	13	Q_2		

Table 1-3
Program 1: Definitions of User-Defined and R/S Keys

A	P1	A'	MW
B	P2	B'	KA
C	T1	C'	Z1
D	M	D'	EFF
E	Calculate	R/S	Percent mechanical losses; continue execution.

Labels Used by Program 1

001	11	A
006	12	B
011	13	C
021	14	D
026	16	A'
031	17	B'
036	18	C'
041	19	D'
046	15	E

Program 1 Usage

Program 1 is executed by using the user-defined keys and the R/S key. The definitions of the user-defined and R/S keys are found in Table 1-3.

After the data are entered, program execution is initiated through user-defined key E. The program continues through the calculation of the gas power requirement and stops. The shaft power requirement can be calculated by entering mechanical losses as a fraction of gas power requirement and then depressing the R/S key.

Subsequent calculations can be made simply by changing only those terms desired. Reexecution is initiated through E.

Sample Problem 1-1

Consider dry air initially at 13 psia and 100°F. Nine hundred lbm/min of the dry air is to be compressed to 19 psia. Determine the inlet and discharge volume flows, the adiabatic head, the discharge temperature, and the shaft power requirement.

Assume the adiabatic efficiency is 75%, and that mechanical losses equal 3% of the gas power requirement.

Sample Problem 1-1: User Instructions

Step	Procedure	Enter	Press	Display
1.	Load program.			
2.	Enter inlet pressure.	13	A	13
3.	Enter discharge pressure.	19	B	19
4.	Enter inlet temperature.	100(°F)	C	560(°R)
5.	Enter mass flow.	900	D	900
6.	Enter molecular weight.	28.96	2nd A′	28.96
7.	Enter average k-value.	1.4	2nd B′	1.4
8.	Enter inlet Z-value.	1.0	2nd C′	1
9.	Enter adiabatic efficiency.	0.75	2nd D′	0.75
10.	Calculate.		E	
11.	Enter % mechanical losses as a fraction (3% unless better data available).	0.03	R/S	

Sample Problem 1-1: Program Printout

```
ADIABATIC METHOD

      13.      P1
      19.      P2
     100.      T1
     900.       M
   28.96       MW
     1.4       KA
       1.       Z1
     0.75      EFF

   14363.      Q1
   11328.      Q2
     186.      T2
   11975.      HEAD
     435.      PWRG
     449.      PWRS
```

Program 1 Listing

000	76	LBL	050	01	1	100	65	×
001	11	A	051	95	=	101	43	RCL
002	42	STO	052	55	÷	102	09	09
003	03	03	053	43	RCL	103	65	×
004	91	R/S	054	08	08	104	01	1
005	76	LBL	055	95	=	105	05	5
006	12	B	056	42	STO	106	04	4
007	42	STO	057	11	11	107	05	5
008	04	04	058	01	1	108	55	÷
009	91	R/S	059	00	0	109	43	RCL
010	76	LBL	060	93	.	110	07	07
011	13	C	061	07	7	111	65	×
012	85	+	062	02	2	112	43	RCL
013	04	4	063	09	9	113	05	05
014	06	6	064	65	×	114	95	=
015	00	0	065	43	RCL	115	42	STO
016	95	=	066	06	06	116	15	15
017	42	STO	067	65	×	117	43	RCL
018	05	05	068	43	RCL	118	14	14
019	91	R/S	069	09	09	119	65	×
020	76	LBL	070	65	×	120	43	RCL
021	14	D	071	43	RCL	121	05	05
022	42	STO	072	05	05	122	55	÷
023	06	06	073	55	÷	123	43	RCL
024	91	R/S	074	43	RCL	124	10	10
025	76	LBL	075	07	07	125	95	=
026	16	A'	076	55	÷	126	85	+
027	42	STO	077	43	RCL	127	43	RCL
028	07	07	078	03	03	128	05	05
029	91	R/S	079	95	=	129	95	=
030	76	LBL	080	42	STO	130	42	STO
031	17	B'	081	12	12	131	17	17
032	42	STO	082	43	RCL	132	55	÷
033	08	08	083	04	04	133	43	RCL
034	91	R/S	084	55	÷	134	05	05
035	76	LBL	085	43	RCL	135	65	×
036	18	C'	086	03	03	136	43	RCL
037	42	STO	087	95	=	137	03	03
038	09	09	088	45	Yˣ	138	55	÷
039	91	R/S	089	43	RCL	139	43	RCL
040	76	LBL	090	11	11	140	04	04
041	19	D'	091	75	−	141	65	×
042	42	STO	092	01	1	142	43	RCL
043	10	10	093	95	=	143	12	12
044	91	R/S	094	42	STO	144	95	=
045	76	LBL	095	14	14	145	42	STO
046	15	E	096	65	×	146	13	13
047	43	RCL	097	43	RCL	147	43	RCL
048	08	08	098	11	11	148	06	06
049	75	−	099	35	1/X	149	65	×

Program 1 Listing continued

150	43	RCL	200	03	3	250	69	OP
151	15	15	201	03	3	251	06	06
152	55	÷	202	02	2	252	03	3
153	03	3	203	01	1	253	00	0
154	03	3	204	06	6	254	69	OP
155	00	0	205	00	0	255	04	04
156	00	0	206	00	0	256	43	RCL
157	00	0	207	00	0	257	06	06
158	55	÷	208	00	0	258	69	OP
159	43	RCL	209	69	OP	259	06	06
160	10	10	210	04	04	260	03	3
161	95	=	211	69	OP	261	00	0
162	42	STO	212	05	05	262	04	4
163	18	18	213	69	OP	263	03	3
164	98	ADV	214	00	00	264	69	OP
165	69	OP	215	98	ADV	265	04	04
166	00	00	216	98	ADV	266	43	RCL
167	01	1	217	03	3	267	07	07
168	03	3	218	03	3	268	69	OP
169	01	1	219	00	0	269	06	06
170	06	6	220	02	2	270	02	2
171	02	2	221	69	OP	271	06	6
172	04	4	222	04	04	272	01	1
173	69	OP	223	43	RCL	273	03	8
174	01	01	224	03	03	274	69	OP
175	01	1	225	69	OP	275	04	04
176	03	3	226	06	06	276	43	RCL
177	01	1	227	03	3	277	08	08
178	04	4	228	03	3	278	69	OP
179	01	1	229	00	0	279	06	06
180	03	3	230	03	3	280	04	4
181	03	3	231	69	OP	281	06	6
182	07	7	232	04	04	282	00	0
183	02	2	233	43	RCL	283	02	2
184	04	4	234	04	04	284	69	OP
185	69	OP	235	69	OP	285	04	04
186	02	02	236	06	06	286	43	RCL
187	01	1	237	03	3	287	09	09
188	05	5	238	07	7	288	69	OP
189	00	0	239	00	0	289	06	06
190	00	0	240	02	2	290	01	1
191	03	3	241	69	OP	291	07	7
192	00	0	242	04	04	292	02	2
193	01	1	243	43	RCL	293	01	1
194	07	7	244	05	05	294	02	2
195	03	3	245	75	-	295	01	1
196	07	7	246	04	4	296	69	OP
197	69	OP	247	06	6	297	04	04
198	03	03	248	00	0	298	43	RCL
199	02	2	249	95	=	299	10	10

(continued on next page)

Program 1 Listing continued

300	69	OP	340	04	4	380	58	FIX
301	06	06	341	06	6	381	00	00
302	98	ADV	342	00	0	382	69	OP
303	03	3	343	95	=	383	06	06
304	04	4	344	58	FIX	384	22	INV
305	00	0	345	00	00	385	58	FIX
306	02	2	346	69	OP	386	69	OP
307	69	OP	347	06	06	387	00	00
308	04	04	348	22	INV	388	91	R/S
309	43	RCL	349	58	FIX	389	65	×
310	12	12	350	02	2	390	43	RCL
311	58	FIX	351	03	3	391	18	18
312	00	00	352	01	1	392	85	+
313	69	OP	353	07	7	393	43	RCL
314	06	06	354	01	1	394	18	18
315	22	INV	355	03	3	395	95	=
316	58	FIX	356	01	1	396	42	STO
317	03	3	357	06	6	397	19	19
318	04	4	358	69	OP	398	03	3
319	00	0	359	04	04	399	03	3
320	03	3	360	43	RCL	400	04	4
321	69	OP	361	15	15	401	03	3
322	04	04	362	58	FIX	402	03	3
323	43	RCL	363	00	00	403	05	5
324	13	13	364	69	OP	404	03	3
325	58	FIX	365	06	06	405	06	6
326	00	00	366	22	INV	406	69	OP
327	69	OP	367	58	FIX	407	04	04
328	06	06	368	03	3	408	43	RCL
329	22	INV	369	03	3	409	19	19
330	58	FIX	370	04	4	410	58	FIX
331	03	3	371	03	3	411	00	00
332	07	7	372	03	3	412	69	OP
333	00	0	373	05	5	413	06	06
334	03	3	374	02	2	414	22	INV
335	69	OP	375	02	2	415	58	FIX
336	04	04	376	69	OP	416	69	OP
337	43	RCL	377	04	04	417	00	00
338	17	17	378	43	RCL	418	91	R/S
339	75	-	379	18	18	419	00	0

Program 2

N–Method Compressor Calculation Procedure*

Background

The N-method compressor calculation procedure is so named because the polytropic exponent, n, is used to calculate the polytropic head and discharge temperature.

A polytropic process is of the form:

$$Pv^n = \text{constant} \tag{2-1}$$

where:
    n = polytropic exponent

and:
    $n = k$ (ratio of specific heats) for a reversible adiabatic process
    $n = 1$ for an isothermal process (constant temperature)
    $n = 0$ for an isobaric process (constant pressure)
    $n = \infty$ for an isometric process (constant volume)

By considering Equation 2-1 and the ideal gas equation given in Equation 1-2:

$$Pv = RT \tag{1-2}$$

---

*This procedure was originally developed by Elliott Company, Jeannette, PA but is applicable to all centrifugal compressors.

the compression ratio equations for the polytropic process can be derived. They are as follows (note that unlike the adiabatic (isentropic) compression ratio equations developed in Program 1, these are all applicable as presented):

$$r_p = r_v^n \tag{2-2}$$

$$r_v = r_p^{1/n} \tag{2-3}$$

$$r_p = r_t^{n/(n-1)} \tag{2-4}$$

$$r_t = r_p^{(n-1)/n} \tag{2-5}$$

$$r_v = r_t^{1/(n-1)} \tag{2-6}$$

$$r_t = r_v^{n-1} \tag{2-7}$$

By further considering the integral-flow work equation for a steady-state, steady-flow process,

$$H_p = \int vdP \tag{2-8}$$

and the real gas equation,

$$Pv = ZRT \tag{1-10}$$

the polytropic head equation can be derived as given by Equation 2-9:

$$H_p = Z_a RT_1 \left(\frac{n}{n-1} \right) [r_p^{(n-1)/n} - 1] \tag{2-9}$$

where:
H_p = polytropic head, ft-lbf/lbm
Z_a = average compressibility

The n-value in Equations 2-2 through 2-7 and 2-9 is derived from the k-value of the gas and from the polytropic efficiency:

$$\frac{n}{n-1} = \frac{k}{k-1} \eta_p \tag{2-10}$$

where:

η_p = polytropic efficiency

Equation 2-9 shows the use of average compressibility instead of inlet compressibility, as was used in Program 1. The polytropic approach is normally used for multi-stage compressors. The head developed by each stage (impeller) is a function of the inlet compressibility to that stage. Since the approach here is to calculate an overall head for several impellers, an average inlet compressibility is needed. A reasonable compromise for an average inlet compressibility is the average of the inlet and discharge compressibilities. Note that this compromise becomes more accurate with increasing numbers of impellers.

The k-value, and therefore the n-value, used in the calculation of Equation 2-9 is also the average value. The temperature is the true inlet temperature.

The discharge temperature can be calculated from the temperature ratio equation:

$$r_t = r_p^{(n-1)/n} \tag{2-5}$$

By substituting T_2/T_1 for r_t, the discharge temperature equation becomes:

$$T_2 = T_1 \, (r_p)^{(n-1)/n} \tag{2-11}$$

By using the inlet k-value, one can estimate an n-value from Equation 2-10 and thereby estimate a discharge temperature from Equation 2-11. With the estimated discharge temperature, a discharge k-value can be estimated and an average k-value determined. A good approximation of the actual discharge temperature results from the average k-value and, therefore, from the average n-value.

The inlet volume flow is given by Equation 1-15, presented here for convenience:

$$Q_1 = 10.729 \, \frac{mZ_1T_1}{(MW)(P_1)} \tag{1-15}$$

The discharge volume flow is given by Equation 1-16:

$$Q_2 = 10.729 \, \frac{mZ_2T_2}{(MW)(P_2)} \tag{1-16}$$

Table 2-1
Approximate Mechanical Losses as a Percentage
of Gas Power Requirement*

Gas Power Requirement (hp)	Mechanical Losses (%)
0–3000	3
3000–6000	2.5
6000–10,000	2
10,000+	1.5

*There is no way to estimate mechanical losses from gas power requirements. This table will, however, ensure that mechanical losses are considered and yield useful values for estimating purposes.

The gas power requirement is a function of the polytropic head, the polytropic efficiency, and the mass flow:

$$PWR_g = \frac{mH_p}{33,000 \; \eta_p} \tag{2-12}$$

The shaft power requirement results from adding the gas power requirement to the mechanical losses, L_m, as in Equation 2-13. The mechanical losses for multi-stage compressors can be estimated from Table 2-1.

$$PWR_s = \frac{mH_p}{33,000 \; \eta_p} + L_m \tag{2-13}$$

One final equation is considered in the N-method program, that for the speed of sound index, θ. The speed of sound index can be used to determine the maximum feasible polytropic head per stage (impeller). This information is necessary to determine the minimum number of stages required to perform a compression duty. The value θ is given by Equation 2-14:

$$\theta = \sqrt{\frac{26.1 \; MW}{k_1 Z_1 T_1}} \tag{2-14}$$

where:
  θ = speed of sound index

and the subscript 1 refers to inlet values. Once the value of θ is known, the maximum polytropic head per stage can be estimated from Figure 2-1.

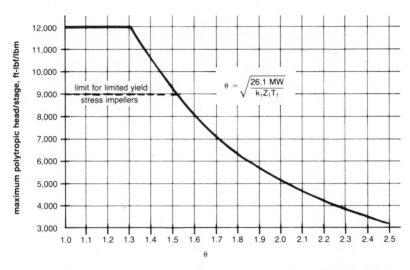

Figure 2-1. Maximum polytropic head per stage for estimating purposes.

A note of caution: The polytropic head equation is only valid *between* cooling points, not including them. Thus, if an application requires inter-cooling in the compression process, the polytropic head must be calculated for each compression step, i.e. between cooling points.

Program 2 Description

This *N*-Method Compressor Calculation Procedure, Program 2, calculates and prints the results of Equations 2-9, 2-11, 1-15, 1-16, 2-12, 2-13, and 2-14.

In order to execute the program, the following must be known:

1. Inlet pressure, P_1
2. Discharge pressure, P_2
3. Inlet temperature, T_1
4. Mass flow, m
5. Molecular weight, MW
6. Inlet k-value, k_1
7. Inlet Z-value, Z_1
8. Polytropic efficiency, η_p

The polytropic efficiency can be estimated from Table 2-2, although manufacturer's data should be used when available.

Table 2-2
Typical Centrifugal Compressor Frame Data*

Frame	Nominal Inlet Volume Flow (ICFM)	Nominal Polytropic Head (ft-lbf/lbm)	Nominal Polytropic Efficiency (%)	Nominal Rotational Speed (rpm)	Nominal Impeller Diameter (in)
A	1,000–7,000	10,000	76	11,000	16
B	6,000–18,000	10,000	76	7,700	23
C	13,000–31,000	10,000	77	5,900	30
D	23,000–44,000	10,000	77	4,900	36
E	33,000–65,000	10,000	78	4,000	44
F	48,000–100,000	10,000	78	3,300	54

*While this table is based on a survey of currently available equipment, the instance of any machinery duplicating this table would be purely coincidental.

Notes:

1. Actual flow ranges for the various frame sizes available on the market vary from one manufacturer to another. The values tabulated in Table 2-2 should be regarded as typical only.

2. The nominal inlet volume flows are what might be expected at the tabulated nominal speed. The fan-law relationships indicate that flow is directly proportional to speed: For applications requiring higher speeds, the flow range will increase proportionally; for applications requiring lower speeds, the flow range will decrease proportionally.

3. The actual polytropic efficiency will be a function of the actual impellers a manufacturer selects. Efficiencies will vary from impeller to impeller and from manufacturer to manufacturer. Those in Table 2-2 are typical for the frame sizes.

4. The nominal speed is a typically required rotational speed to produce 10,000 ft-lbf/lbm of polytropic head per stage.

5. The nominal impeller diameters in Table 2-2 are typical diameters for the nominal speeds and flow ranges listed.

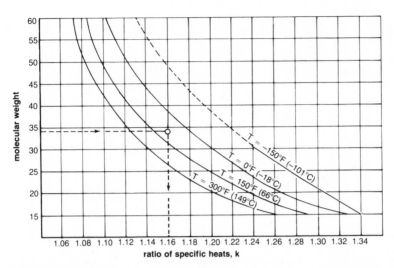

Figure 2-2. Quick estimate for ratio of specific heats for hydrocarbon mixtures. (Redrawn by permission of Compressed Air and Gas Institute, Vol. 13, No. 2; and *Chemical Engineering,* McGraw-Hill Publications Company, Feb. 8, 1982.)

The program will first calculate an approximate discharge temperature from the inlet k-value. This allows the operator to determine discharge k- and Z-values for further program execution. These values can be estimated from Figures 2-2 and 2-3 or from another source in the literature. The program will then calculate the actual discharge temperature from the average k-value, the inlet and discharge volume flows from the respective Z-values, the polytropic head from the average Z-value, the gas power requirement, the value of θ, and, upon entering the mechanical losses in percent from Table 2-1 (as a fraction), the shaft power requirement.

The program allows continuous usage by the operator without requiring recalculation of the approximate discharge temperature. Thus, to calculate required compressor performance for several values of, say, discharge pressure, simply change the discharge pressure and reexecute the program. The program allows for this approach for variations in inlet pressure, discharge pressure, inlet temperature, mass flow, molecular weight, and polytropic efficiency. The only caution is that the program will use the average k-value and the inlet, discharge, and average Z-values calculated in the first part of the program.

Table 2-3 shows the nomenclature printed by the program; Table 2-4 shows the data registers used by the program.

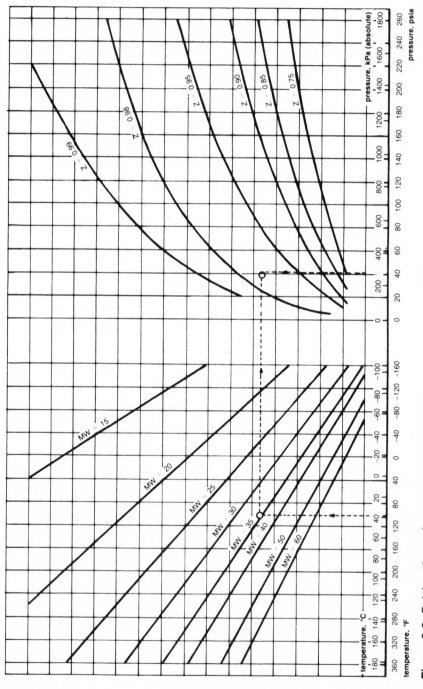

Figure 2-3. Quick estimate for compressibility of hydrocarbon mixtures. (Redrawn by permission of Compressed Air and Gas Institute, Vol. 13, No. 2; and *Chemical Engineering*, McGraw-Hill Publications Company, Feb. 8, 1982.)

Table 2-3
Program 2: Printer Nomenclature

Program Term	Definition	Units
EFF	polytropic efficiency	dimensionless
HEAD	polytropic head	ft-lbf/lbm
KA	average ratio of specific heats	dimensionless
K1	inlet ratio of specific heats	dimensionless
K2	discharge ratio of specific heats	dimensionless
M	mass flow	lbm/min
MW	molecular weight	lbm/lbm-mol
P1	inlet pressure	psia
P2	discharge pressure	psia
PWRG	gas power requirement	hp
PWRS	shaft power requirement	hp
Q1	inlet volume flow	ICFM
Q2	discharge volume flow	CFM
T1	inlet temperature	°F
T2	discharge temperature	°F
T2A	approximate discharge temperature	°F
THET	speed of sound index, θ	dimensionless
ZA	average compressibility	dimensionless
Z1	inlet compressibility	dimensionless
Z2	discharge compressibility	dimensionless

Table 2-4
Data Registers Used by Program 2

00	not used	09	MW	18	ENTER (title)
01	not used	10	k_1	19	k_a
02	not used	11	Z_1	20	Z_a
03	k_2	12	η_p	21	H_p
04	Z_2	13	Q_1	22	Q_2
05	P_1	14	$n/(n-1)$	23	PWR_g
06	P_2	15	T_{2A} and T_2 (°F)	24	not used
07	T_1 (°R)	16	r_p	25	PWR_s
08	m	17	k_1 and k_a	26	θ

Labels Used by Program 2

```
004    11   A          044   19   D'
009    12   B          049   15   E
014    13   C          326   10   E'
024    14   D          654   34   ГX
029    16   A'
034    17   B'
039    18   C'
```

Table 2-5
Program 2: Definitions of User-Defined and R/S Keys

A	P1	A'	MW
B	P2	B'	K1
C	T1	C'	Z1
D	M	D'	EFF
E	Calculate (initial)	E'	Calculate (subsequent)
		R/S	Percent mechanical losses; continue execution.

Program 2 Usage

Program 2 is executed by using the user-defined keys and the R/S key and by following instructions prompted by the program. The definitions for the user-defined and R/S keys can be found in Table 2-5.

After all data are entered, the initial calculation is made through user-defined key E. The program calculates the approximate discharge temperature and stops. The operator follows the instructions prompted by the program, entering the discharge k- and Z-values, storing them respectively in registers 03 and 04, and depressing the R/S key. Program execution then continues through the calculation of the gas power requirement and stops. The operator has the option of calculating the shaft power requirement. To do this, enter mechanical losses as a fraction of gas power requirement and depress the R/S key.

Provided the k-value and Z-values are satisfactory, subsequent N-method estimates can be made by changing only those terms desired. User-defined key E' is used for subsequent calculations.

Note that the calculator must be repartitioned to 719.29 before loading or keying in the program.

Sample Problem 2-1

Consider a 30 molecular weight gas initially at 17 psia and 100°F. Twenty-five hundred lbm/min of the gas is to be compressed to 75 psia. Determine the inlet and discharge volume flows, the polytropic head, the discharge temperature, and the shaft power requirement.

Figures 2-2 and 2-3 can be used to estimate the inlet k-value and the inlet compressibility, respectively. From these figures:

$k_1 = 1.175$

$Z_1 = 0.99$

For the first iteration, assume a polytropic efficiency of 76%. This can be refined by reference to Table 2-2 once the inlet volume flow is calculated.

As can be seen from the sample problem printout following the user instructions, the inlet volume flow is 29,158 ICFM. Reference to Table 2-2 shows that for this flow the polytropic efficiency would be on the order of 77%. Therefore, the program was rerun for a change of efficiency only. This was accomplished simply by entering the new efficiency, then D', and finally E'.

Sample Problem 2-1: User Instructions

Step	Procedure	Enter	Press	Display
1.	Partition calculator.	3	2nd OP 17	719.29
2.	Load program.			
3.	Enter inlet pressure.	17	A	17
4.	Enter discharge pressure.	75	B	75
5.	Enter inlet temperature.	100(°F)	C	560(°R)
6.	Enter mass flow.	2500	D	2500
7.	Enter molecular weight.	30	2nd A'	30
8.	Enter inlet k-value.	1.175	2nd B'	1.175
9.	Enter inlet Z-value.	0.99	2nd C'	0.99
10.	Enter polytropic efficiency.	0.76	2nd D'	0.76
11.	Calculate.		E	
12.	Enter k_2 from Figure 2-2.	1.145	STO 03	1.145
	Enter Z_2 from Figure 2-3.	0.987	STO 04	0.987
	Continue		R/S	
13.	Enter % mechanical losses from Table 2-1, as a fraction.	0.025	R/S	
14.	Enter better value for polytropic efficiency from Table 2-2, based on computed value for Q_1; then enter E' to recalculate.	0.77	2nd D' 2nd E'	0.77
15.	Enter % mechanical losses from Table 2-1, as a fraction.	0.025	R/S	

Sample Problem 2-1: Program Printout

```
N - METHOD                1.145    K2        1.096    THET
                          0.987    Z2        4962.    PWRS
                          1.160    KA
                          0.989    ZA          17.    P1
     17.     P1                                75.    P2
     75.     P2             17.    P1         100.    T1
    100.     T1             75.    P2         271.    T2
     30.     MW            100.    T1          30.    MW
    1.175    K1            273.    T2        2500.     M
    0.99     Z1             30.    MW       29158.    Q1
    289.     T2A         2500.     M         8596.    Q2
                        29158.    Q1        48473.    HEAD
                         8626.    Q2          0.770   EFF
ENTER K2 STO 03         48562.    HEAD       4769.    PWRG
ENTER Z2 STO 04          0.760    EFF        1.096    THET
ENTER R/S               4841.     PWRG       4888.    PWRS
```

Program 2 Listing

000	03	3	030	42	STO	060	00	0
001	69	OP	031	09	09	061	00	0
002	17	17	032	91	R/S	062	02	2
003	76	LBL	033	76	LBL	063	00	0
004	11	A	034	17	B'	064	00	0
005	42	STO	035	42	STO	065	00	0
006	05	05	036	10	10	066	03	3
007	91	R/S	037	91	R/S	067	00	0
008	76	LBL	038	76	LBL	068	69	OP
009	12	B	039	18	C'	069	02	02
010	42	STO	040	42	STO	070	01	1
011	06	06	041	11	11	071	07	7
012	91	R/S	042	91	R/S	072	03	3
013	76	LBL	043	76	LBL	073	07	7
014	13	C	044	19	D'	074	02	2
015	85	+	045	42	STO	075	03	3
016	04	4	046	12	12	076	03	3
017	06	6	047	91	R/S	077	02	2
018	00	0	048	76	LBL	078	01	1
019	95	=	049	15	E	079	06	6
020	42	STO	050	43	RCL	080	69	OP
021	07	07	051	10	10	081	03	03
022	91	R/S	052	42	STO	082	69	OP
023	76	LBL	053	17	17	083	05	05
024	14	D	054	71	SBR	084	98	ADV
025	42	STO	055	34	ГX	085	98	ADV
026	08	08	056	69	OP	086	03	3
027	91	R/S	057	00	00	087	03	3
028	76	LBL	058	03	3	088	00	0
029	16	A'	059	01	1	089	02	2

Program 2 Listing continued

090	69	◻P	140	06	06	190	03	3	
091	04	04	141	04	4	191	06	6	
092	43	RCL	142	06	6	192	69	◻P	
093	05	05	143	00	0	193	02	02	
094	69	◻P	144	02	2	194	03	3	
095	06	06	145	69	◻P	195	07	7	
096	03	3	146	04	04	196	03	3	
097	03	3	147	43	RCL	197	02	2	
098	00	0	148	11	11	198	00	0	
099	03	3	149	69	◻P	199	00	0	
100	69	◻P	150	06	06	200	00	0	
101	04	04	151	03	3	201	01	1	
102	43	RCL	152	07	7	202	00	0	
103	06	06	153	00	0	203	04	4	
104	69	◻P	154	03	3	204	69	◻P	
105	06	06	155	01	1	205	03	03	
106	03	3	156	03	3	206	69	◻P	
107	07	7	157	69	◻P	207	05	05	
108	00	0	158	04	04	208	04	4	
109	02	2	159	43	RCL	209	06	6	
110	69	◻P	160	15	15	210	00	0	
111	04	04	161	58	FIX	211	03	3	
112	43	RCL	162	00	00	212	00	0	
113	07	07	163	69	◻P	213	00	0	
114	75	-	164	06	06	214	03	3	
115	04	4	165	22	INV	215	06	6	
116	06	6	166	58	FIX	216	69	◻P	
117	00	0	167	98	ADV	217	02	02	
118	95	=	168	69	◻P	218	03	3	
119	69	◻P	169	00	00	219	07	7	
120	06	06	170	01	1	220	03	3	
121	03	3	171	07	7	221	02	2	
122	00	0	172	03	3	222	00	0	
123	04	4	173	01	1	223	00	0	
124	03	3	174	03	3	224	00	0	
125	69	◻P	175	07	7	225	01	1	
126	04	04	176	01	1	226	00	0	
127	43	RCL	177	07	7	227	05	5	
128	09	09	178	03	3	228	69	◻P	
129	69	◻P	179	05	5	229	03	03	
130	06	06	180	42	STO	230	69	◻P	
131	02	2	181	18	18	231	05	05	
132	06	6	182	69	◻P	232	69	◻P	
133	00	0	183	01	01	233	00	00	
134	02	2	184	02	2	234	43	RCL	
135	69	◻P	185	06	6	235	18	18	
136	04	04	186	00	0	236	69	◻P	
137	43	RCL	187	03	3	237	01	01	
138	10	10	188	00	0	238	03	3	
139	69	◻P	189	00	0	239	05	5	

(continued on next page)

Program 2 Listing continued

240	06	6	290	43	RCL	340	43	RCL
241	03	3	291	04	04	341	07	07
242	03	3	292	69	OP	342	55	÷
243	06	6	293	06	06	343	43	RCL
244	00	0	294	02	2	344	09	09
245	00	0	295	06	6	345	55	÷
246	69	OP	296	01	1	346	43	RCL
247	02	02	297	03	3	347	05	05
248	69	OP	298	69	OP	348	95	=
249	05	05	299	04	04	349	42	STO
250	91	R/S	300	43	RCL	350	13	13
251	43	RCL	301	19	19	351	43	RCL
252	03	03	302	58	FIX	352	19	19
253	85	+	303	03	03	353	42	STO
254	43	RCL	304	69	OP	354	17	17
255	10	10	305	06	06	355	71	SBR
256	95	=	306	22	INV	356	34	ΓX
257	55	÷	307	58	FIX	357	43	RCL
258	02	2	308	04	4	358	20	20
259	95	=	309	06	6	359	65	×
260	42	STO	310	01	1	360	01	1
261	19	19	311	03	3	361	05	5
262	43	RCL	312	69	OP	362	04	4
263	04	04	313	04	04	363	05	5
264	85	+	314	43	RCL	364	55	÷
265	43	RCL	315	20	20	365	43	RCL
266	11	11	316	58	FIX	366	09	09
267	95	=	317	03	03	367	65	×
268	55	÷	318	69	OP	368	43	RCL
269	02	2	319	06	06	369	07	07
270	95	=	320	22	INV	370	65	×
271	42	STO	321	58	FIX	371	43	RCL
272	20	20	322	69	OP	372	14	14
273	98	ADV	323	00	00	373	65	×
274	02	2	324	98	ADV	374	53	(
275	06	6	325	76	LBL	375	43	RCL
276	00	0	326	10	E'	376	16	16
277	03	3	327	01	1	377	45	YX
278	69	OP	328	00	0	378	43	RCL
279	04	04	329	93	.	379	14	14
280	43	RCL	330	07	7	380	35	1/X
281	03	03	331	02	2	381	75	-
282	69	OP	332	09	9	382	01	1
283	06	06	333	65	×	383	54	)
284	04	4	334	43	RCL	384	95	=
285	06	6	335	08	08	385	42	STO
286	00	0	336	65	×	386	21	21
287	03	3	337	43	RCL	387	43	RCL
288	69	OP	338	11	11	388	04	04
289	04	04	339	65	×	389	65	×

Program 2 Listing continued

390	01	1	440	09	09	490	03	3
391	00	0	441	55	÷	491	07	7
392	93	.	442	43	RCL	492	00	0
393	07	7	443	10	10	493	03	3
394	02	2	444	55	÷	494	69	OP
395	09	9	445	43	RCL	495	04	04
396	65	×	446	11	11	496	43	RCL
397	53	(	447	55	÷	497	15	15
398	43	RCL	448	43	RCL	498	58	FIX
399	15	15	449	07	07	499	00	00
400	85	+	450	95	=	500	69	OP
401	04	4	451	34	ΓX	501	06	06
402	06	6	452	42	STO	502	22	INV
403	00	0	453	26	26	503	58	FIX
404	54	)	454	98	ADV	504	03	3
405	55	÷	455	03	3	505	00	0
406	43	RCL	456	03	3	506	04	4
407	06	06	457	00	0	507	03	3
408	55	÷	458	02	2	508	69	OP
409	43	RCL	459	69	OP	509	04	04
410	09	09	460	04	04	510	43	RCL
411	65	×	461	43	RCL	511	09	09
412	43	RCL	462	05	05	512	69	OP
413	08	08	463	69	OP	513	06	06
414	95	=	464	06	06	514	03	3
415	42	STO	465	03	3	515	00	0
416	22	22	466	03	3	516	69	OP
417	43	RCL	467	00	0	517	04	04
418	08	08	468	03	3	518	43	RCL
419	65	×	469	69	OP	519	08	08
420	43	RCL	470	04	04	520	69	OP
421	21	21	471	43	RCL	521	06	06
422	55	÷	472	06	06	522	03	3
423	03	3	473	69	OP	523	04	4
424	03	3	474	06	06	524	00	0
425	00	0	475	03	3	525	02	2
426	00	0	476	07	7	526	69	OP
427	00	0	477	00	0	527	04	04
428	55	÷	478	02	2	528	43	RCL
429	43	RCL	479	69	OP	529	13	13
430	12	12	480	04	04	530	58	FIX
431	95	=	481	43	RCL	531	00	00
432	42	STO	482	07	07	532	69	OP
433	23	23	483	75	-	533	06	06
434	02	2	484	04	4	534	22	INV
435	06	6	485	06	6	535	58	FIX
436	93	.	486	00	0	536	03	3
437	01	1	487	95	=	537	04	4
438	65	×	488	69	OP	538	00	0
439	43	RCL	489	06	06	539	03	3

(continued on next page)

Program 2 Listing continued

540	69	OP	591	02	2	642	43	RCL
541	04	04	592	69	OP	643	25	25
542	43	RCL	593	04	04	644	58	FIX
543	22	22	594	43	RCL	645	00	00
544	58	FIX	595	23	23	646	69	OP
545	00	00	596	58	FIX	647	06	06
546	69	OP	597	00	00	648	22	INV
547	06	06	598	69	OP	649	58	FIX
548	22	INV	599	06	06	650	69	OP
549	58	FIX	600	22	INV	651	00	00
550	02	2	601	58	FIX	652	91	R/S
551	03	3	602	03	3	653	76	LBL
552	01	1	603	07	7	654	34	ГX
553	07	7	604	02	2	655	75	-
554	01	1	605	03	3	656	01	1
555	03	3	606	01	1	657	95	=
556	01	1	607	07	7	658	35	1/X
557	06	6	608	03	3	659	65	×
558	69	OP	609	07	7	660	43	RCL
559	04	04	610	69	OP	661	17	17
560	43	RCL	611	04	04	662	65	×
561	21	21	612	43	RCL	663	43	RCL
562	58	FIX	613	26	26	664	12	12
563	00	00	614	58	FIX	665	95	=
564	69	OP	615	03	03	666	42	STO
565	06	06	616	69	OP	667	14	14
566	22	INV	617	06	06	668	43	RCL
567	58	FIX	618	22	INV	669	06	06
568	01	1	619	58	FIX	670	55	÷
569	07	7	620	69	OP	671	43	RCL
570	02	2	621	00	00	672	05	05
571	01	1	622	91	R/S	673	95	=
572	02	2	623	65	×	674	42	STO
573	01	1	624	43	RCL	675	16	16
574	69	OP	625	23	23	676	45	YX
575	04	04	626	85	+	677	43	RCL
576	43	RCL	627	43	RCL	678	14	14
577	12	12	628	23	23	679	35	1/X
578	58	FIX	629	95	=	680	65	×
579	03	03	630	42	STO	681	43	RCL
580	69	OP	631	25	25	682	07	07
581	06	06	632	03	3	683	75	-
582	22	INV	633	03	3	684	04	4
583	58	FIX	634	04	4	685	06	6
584	03	3	635	03	3	686	00	0
585	03	3	636	03	3	687	95	=
586	04	4	637	05	5	688	42	STO
587	03	3	638	03	3	689	15	15
588	03	3	639	06	6	690	92	RTN
589	05	5	640	69	OP	691	00	0
590	02	2	641	04	04	692	00	0

Program 3

Mollier Method Compressor Calculation Procedure

Background

The Mollier method compressor calculation procedure is so named because a Mollier chart is used to calculate the head and discharge temperature. The Mollier method is primarily used for pure gases, for which Mollier charts are readily available. However, Mollier charts can be constructed for gas mixtures. When these are available, the Mollier method is more accurate than the N-method.

The Mollier method uses the inlet and adiabatic discharge state-point enthalpies to calculate an adiabatic head. The polytropic head is then derived from the adiabatic head by ratioing the polytropic and adiabatic efficiencies. The gas power requirement is calculated as in Program 2, and the discharge temperature is read directly from the Mollier chart.

The inlet volume flow evolves from Equation 3-1:

$$Q_1 = m_1 v_1 \tag{3-1}$$

where:
m_1 = inlet mass flow, lbm/min

and where the inlet specific volume, v_1, is read directly from the Mollier chart, having plotted the inlet state point of known inlet pressure and inlet temperature.

The inlet enthalpy, h_1, can also be read directly from the Mollier chart at the inlet state point. If a constant entropy line is followed to the required discharge pressure, the resultant intersection of required discharge pressure and inlet entropy defines the adiabatic discharge state point. The enthalpy at this point is the adiabatic discharge enthalpy, h_{2ad}. The difference between the adiabatic discharge enthalpy and the inlet enthalpy defines the adiabatic head, as in Equation 3-2:

$$H_{ad} = 778 \; (h_{2ad} - h_1) \tag{3-2}$$

where:

h_{2ad} = adiabatic discharge enthalpy, Btu/lbm
h_1 = inlet enthalpy, Btu/lbm
778 = conversion from Btu/lbm to ft-lbf/lbm

Note that this process is not only adiabatic but isentropic. The term adiabatic has been used to define a reversible adiabatic, and therefore an isentropic, process. This is a common use of the term in compressor terminology. Therefore, when anyone speaks of adiabatic head, he really means reversible adiabatic, or isentropic, head.

The polytropic head is related to the adiabatic head through the ratio of the polytropic and adiabatic efficiencies, as in Equation 3-3:

$$H_p = H_{ad} \left(\frac{\eta_p}{\eta_{ad}} \right) \tag{3-3}$$

The polytropic efficiency in Equation 3-3 can be estimated from Table 2-2 once the inlet volume flow is known, although manufacturer's data should be used when available. The adiabatic efficiency can be determined from Equation 3-4:

$$\eta_{ad} = \frac{r_p^{(k-1)/k} - 1}{r_p^{(k-1)/k\eta_p} - 1} \tag{3-4}$$

where r_p is the ratio of the required discharge pressure to the inlet pressure.

Two thermodynamic properties must be known in order to establish the actual discharge state point. The required discharge pressure is defined by the process. It is possible to determine the actual discharge enthalpy with information developed previously. The discharge enthalpy and discharge pressure will then establish the discharge state point. The discharge enthalpy is given by Equation 3-5:

$$h_2 = \frac{h_{2ad} - h_1}{\eta_{ad}} + h_1 \tag{3-5}$$

where:

h_2 = actual discharge enthalpy, Btu/lbm

Once the actual discharge state point is plotted, the discharge temperature can be read directly from the Mollier chart.

The general equations for the gas power requirement and the shaft power requirement are Equations 2-12 and 2-13, respectively, presented here for convenience:

$$PWR_g = \frac{mH_p}{33,000 \ \eta_p} \qquad (2\text{-}12)$$

$$PWR_s = \frac{mH_p}{33,000 \ \eta_p} + L_m \qquad (2\text{-}13)$$

The Mollier method is often used for side-load compressors. A side-load compressor has some additional gas injected through an intermediate nozzle of the compressor after partial compression. (Note that an extraction of gas after partial compression can also be considered.) For such cases it is necessary to determine a mixture enthalpy, which will become the inlet enthalpy to the downstream compressor section. The mixture enthalpy and the pressure at which the mixture takes place define the inlet state point to the downstream section. The mixture enthalpy is calculated from Equation 3-6:

$$h_3 = \frac{m_1 h_2 + m_{SL} h_{2'}}{m_1 + m_{SL}} \qquad (3\text{-}6)$$

where:

h_3 = mixture enthalpy, Btu/lbm
m_1 = upstream section mass flow, lbm/min
h_2 = upstream section actual discharge enthalpy, Btu/lbm
m_{SL} = side-load mass flow, lbm/min
$h_{2'}$ = enthalpy of the incoming side load, Btu/lbm (normally at or near the saturation line)

The mixture enthalpy, h_3, becomes the inlet enthalpy, h_1, for the downstream section.

The pressure ratio is calculated from Equation 3-7:

$$r_p = P_2/P_1 \qquad (3\text{-}7)$$

The discharge mass flow is calculated from Equation 3-8:

$$m_2 = m_1 + m_{SL} \tag{3-8}$$

where:
m_2 = discharge mass flow, lbm/min

Program 3 Description

This Mollier Method Compressor Calculation Procedure, Program 3, calculates and prints the results of Equations 3-1, 3-2, 3-3, 3-4, 3-5, 2-12, 3-6, 3-7, and 3-8 for as many side loads or extractions as necessary.

In order to execute the program, the following must be known:

1. Inlet mass flow, m_1
2. Side-load mass flow, m_{SL}
3. Inlet pressure, P_1
4. Discharge pressure, P_2
5. Inlet specific volume, v_1
6. Inlet enthalpy, h_1
7. Adiabatic discharge enthalpy, h_{2ad}
8. Side-load enthalpy, $h_{2'}$
9. Polytropic efficiency, η_p
10. Average k-value, k_a

It is imperative that a Mollier chart be available, since most of the required input is read directly from the chart.

The polytropic efficiency can be estimated from Table 2-2 if manufacturer's data are not available; however, the reader will first have to determine the inlet volume flow manually from Equation 3-1. Since most applications for which the Mollier approach is used fit in a single compressor body, the efficiency estimated for the first section can be used for the remaining compression sections.

Once the data are entered, the program procedes through the calculation of the discharge enthalpy and stops to allow the operator to enter the side-load enthalpy. Upon entering the side-load enthalpy, the program continues to calculate the mixture enthalpy, the inlet volume flow, the polytropic head, and the gas power requirement.

The program also calculates a discharge mass flow, which is the sum of the inlet mass flow and the side-load mass flow.

Upon completing the calculation, the program automatically transfers the discharge mass flow to the inlet mass flow register, the discharge pressure to the inlet pressure register, and the mixture enthalpy to the inlet enthalpy

Table 3-1
Program 3: Printer Nomenclature

Program Term	Definition	Units
EFFA	adiabatic efficiency	dimensionless
EFFP	polytropic efficiency	dimensionless
H1	inlet enthalpy	Btu/lbm
H2	actual discharge enthalpy	Btu/lbm
H2′	side-load enthalpy	Btu/lbm
H3	mixture enthalpy	Btu/lbm
H2AD	adiabatic discharge enthalpy	Btu/lbm
HDAD	adiabatic head	ft-lbf/lbm
HDP	polytropic head	ft-lbf/lbm
KA	average ratio of specific heats	dimensionless
M1	inlet mass flow	lbm/min
M2	discharge mass flow	lbm/min
MSL	side-load mass flow	lbm/min
P1	inlet pressure	psia
P2	discharge pressure	psia
PWRG	gas power requirement	hp
Q1	inlet volume flow	ICFM
RP	pressure ratio	dimensionless
SV1	inlet specific volume	ft³/lbm

Table 3-2
Data Registers Used by Program 3

00	not used	08	k_a	15	H_{ad}
01	not used	09	η_p	16	h_2
02	not used	10	P_1 and P_2	17	Q_1
03	m_1 and m_2	11	m_{SL}	18	H_p
04	h_1 and h_3	12	$h_{2'}$	19	PWR_g
05	v_1	13	$(k-1)/k$	20	m_2
06	h_{2ad}	14	η_{ad}	21	P_2
07	r_p				

register. The program is thus ready to calculate the next compression section.

Table 3-1 shows the nomenclature printed by the program; Table 3-2 shows the data registers used by the program.

Labels Used by Program 3

001	11	A	053	17	B′
033	12	B	058	18	C′
038	13	C	063	19	D′
043	14	D	068	15	E
048	16	A′	347	10	E′

Table 3-3
Program 3: Definitions of User-Defined Keys

A	M (title)	A'	KA
B	H1	B'	EFFP
C	SV1	C'	P1
D	H2AD	D'	MSL
E	P2, Calculate	E'	H2', Calculate

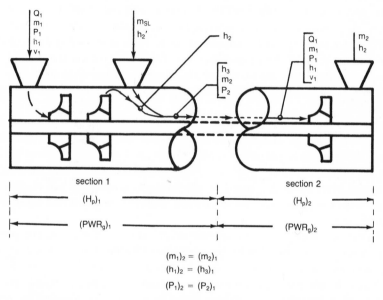

Figure 3-1. Typical compressor sectioning for the Mollier program.

Program 3 Usage

Program 3 is executed by using the user-defined keys. The definitions of the user-defined keys can be found in Table 3-3.

In order to use Program 3, the centrifugal compressor must first be sectioned as shown in Figure 3-1. Note that the gas power requirement for each section is based on the inlet mass flow, m_1, to that section. There is no significance to the number of impellers shown in the figure. The split is by nozzle location, not by the number of impellers.

Figure 3-1 shows a two-section (single side load) compressor. The same philosophy of sectioning by nozzle location would hold if sections were added, as would be the case for two or more side loads or extractions. Each section (between flanges), therefore, is handled separately.

After entering the data required by user-defined keys A through D and A′ through D′, program execution is initiated by entering the discharge pressure and depressing user-defined key E. The program continues through the calculation of the discharge enthalpy and stops. The operator then determines the side-load enthalpy and enters it through E′ to continue program execution.

After completing a section calculation, the program automatically readies itself for the next section by storing m_2 in the m_1 register, h_3 in the h_1 register, and P_2 in the P_1 register. The operator need only enter the new values for v_1, h_{2ad}, m_{SL}, and $h_{2'}$ to calculate the succeeding compression section.

When the last section is considered, there is no side load (refer to Figure 3-1 for the sketch of the second section). Therefore, for the last section, m_{SL} should be entered as zero (0), and $h_{2'}$ should be entered as the value calculated for h_2 by the program. This approach yields the correct values for m_2 and h_3.

Upon completing all compression sections, the individual section polytropic heads can be manually added to obtain the overall polytropic head. Also, the individual gas power requirements can be added to obtain the total gas power requirement. The estimated mechanical losses can then be determined from Table 2-1 based on the total gas power. As before, the sum of the total gas power and the mechanical losses is the estimated shaft power requirement.

An extraction of gas at an intermediate pressure level is a common process requirement. This can also be accommodated by Program 3. For this case, m_{SL} is entered as a negative number. Note that for an extraction, the mixture enthalpy, h_3 (the enthalpy of the gas proceeding to the next section), is equal to the preceding section discharge enthalpy, h_2. This is handled by simply entering the calculated value of h_2 for $h_{2'}$.

Sample Problem 3-1

Consider an ethylene refrigeration process. Nine hundred lbm/min of ethylene enters the compressor saturated at 17 psia. The process calls for a side load of 800 lbm/min saturated at 68 psia. The required discharge pressure is 213 psia. The average k-value is 1.24 and the polytropic efficiency is 76%.

Figure 3-2 is an ethylene Mollier chart. State point ① is plotted at 17 psia, saturated. From the Mollier chart:

$h_1 = 84$ Btu/lbm

$v_1 = 7.1$ ft^3/lbm

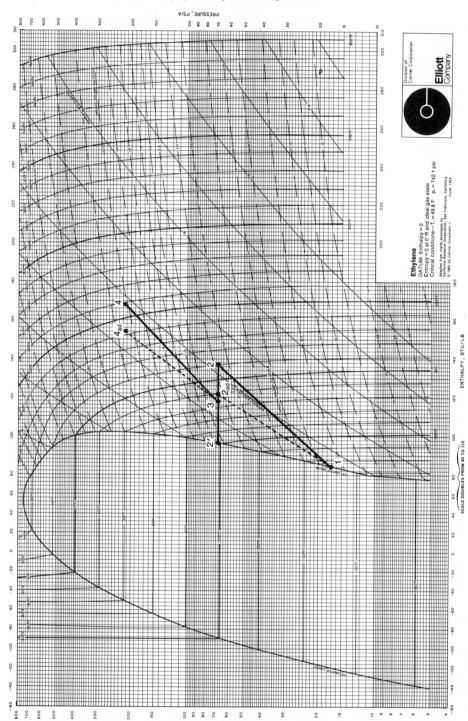

Figure 3-2. Ethylene Mollier chart for Sample Problem 3-1. Reprinted by permission of Elliott Company, Jeannette, PA, Bulletin P-25S-Rev, 1981.

Now follow a constant-entropy line to state point ② and read:

$h_{2ad} = 122$ Btu/lbm

These are the data required to calculate the first compression section.

The second section is computed similarly. Note, however, that state-point ③ on Figure 3-2 defines the inlet values for the program for the second section, and state-point ④ defines the discharge values. Therefore, the enthalpy at state-point ③ is program enthalpy h_1; the enthalpy at state-point ④ is program enthalpy h_2.

The total gas power requirement is the sum of the gas horsepowers. Therefore:

$$PWR_g = (PWR_g)_1 + (PWR_g)_2$$
$$= 1109 + 2020$$
$$= 3129 \text{ hp}$$

The mechanical losses can then be estimated from Table 2-1, based on 3129 hp.

Sample Problem 3-1: User Instructions

Step	Procedure	Enter	Press	Display
1.	Load program.			
2.	Enter inlet mass flow.	900	A	2724173500
3.	Enter inlet enthalpy.	84	B	84
4.	Enter inlet specific volume.	7.1	C	7.1
5.	Enter adiabatic discharge enthalpy.	122	D	122
6.	Enter average *k*-value	1.24	2nd A'	1.24
7.	Enter polytropic efficiency from Table 2-2.	0.76	2nd B'	0.76
8.	Enter inlet pressure.	17	2nd C'	17
9.	Enter side-load mass flow.	800	2nd D'	800
10.	Enter discharge pressure and calculate.	68	E	
11.	Enter side-load enthalpy and calculate.	96.5	2nd E'	
12.	Enter inlet specific volume @ ③.	2.35	C	2.35

(continued on next page)

Sample Problem 3-1: User Instructions continued

Step	Procedure	Enter	Press	Display
13.	Enter adiabatic discharge enthalpy @ t_{ad}.	154.5	D	154.5
14.	Enter side-load mass flow. Enter zero, since this is the last section.	0	2nd D′	0
15.	Enter discharge pressure and calculate.	213	E	
16.	Enter side-load enthalpy and calculate. Reenter discharge enthalpy, since this is last section.	168	2nd E′	

Sample Problem 3-1: Program Printout

```
MOLLIER              96.5    H2'      1700.      M2
                    117.6    H3       0.733      EFFA
  1.24    KA                         28740.     HDAD
  0.76    EFFP                        213.0      P2
 17.0     P1        6390.    Q1        3.132      RP
  7.1     SV1      30911.    HDP      168.0      H2
900.      M1       1109.    PWRG
800.      MSL
 84.0     H1                          168.      H2'
122.      H2AD      1.24    KA        168.0      H3
                    0.76    EFFP
1700.     M2       68.0     P1
  0.727   EFFA      2.35    SV1
29564.    HDAD    1700.     M1
 68.0     P2          0.    MSL       3995.      Q1
  4.000   RP       117.6    H1       29804.     HDP
136.3     H2       154.5    H2AD      2020.     PWRG
```

Program 3 Listing

```
000  76 LBL     007  03   3      014  02  02
001  11  A      008  00   0      015  02   2
002  42 STO     009  03   3      016  07   7
003  03  03     010  02   2      017  02   2
004  98 ADV     011  02   2      018  04   4
005  69 OP      012  07   7      019  01   1
006  00  00     013  69  OP
```

Program 3 Listing continued

020	07	7	070	21	21	120	02	2
021	03	3	071	55	÷	121	00	0
022	05	5	072	43	RCL	122	02	2
023	00	0	073	10	10	123	69	OP
024	00	0	074	95	=	124	04	04
025	69	OP	075	42	STO	125	43	RCL
026	03	03	076	07	07	126	05	05
027	69	OP	077	98	ADV	127	69	OP
028	05	05	078	98	ADV	128	06	06
029	69	OP	079	02	2	129	03	3
030	00	00	080	06	6	130	00	0
031	91	R/S	081	01	1	131	00	0
032	76	LBL	082	03	3	132	02	2
033	12	B	083	69	OP	133	69	OP
034	42	STO	084	04	04	134	04	04
035	04	04	085	43	RCL	135	43	RCL
036	91	R/S	086	08	08	136	03	03
037	76	LBL	087	69	OP	137	69	OP
038	13	C	088	06	06	138	06	06
039	42	STO	089	01	1	139	03	3
040	05	05	090	07	7	140	00	0
041	91	R/S	091	02	2	141	03	3
042	76	LBL	092	01	1	142	06	6
043	14	D	093	02	2	143	02	2
044	42	STO	094	01	1	144	07	7
045	06	06	095	03	3	145	69	OP
046	91	R/S	096	03	3	146	04	04
047	76	LBL	097	69	OP	147	43	RCL
048	16	A'	098	04	04	148	11	11
049	42	STO	099	43	RCL	149	69	OP
050	08	08	100	09	09	150	06	06
051	91	R/S	101	69	OP	151	02	2
052	76	LBL	102	06	06	152	03	3
053	17	B'	103	03	3	153	00	0
054	42	STO	104	03	3	154	02	2
055	09	09	105	00	0	155	69	OP
056	91	R/S	106	02	2	156	04	04
057	76	LBL	107	69	OP	157	43	RCL
058	18	C'	108	04	04	158	04	04
059	42	STO	109	43	RCL	159	58	FIX
060	10	10	110	10	10	160	01	01
061	91	R/S	111	58	FIX	161	69	OP
062	76	LBL	112	01	01	162	06	06
063	19	D'	113	69	OP	163	22	INV
064	42	STO	114	06	06	164	58	FIX
065	11	11	115	22	INV	165	02	2
066	91	R/S	116	58	FIX	166	03	3
067	76	LBL	117	03	3	167	00	0
068	15	E	118	06	6	168	03	3
069	42	STO	119	04	4	169	01	1

(continued on next page)

Program 3 Listing continued

170	03	3	220	07	07	270	06	6
171	01	1	221	45	Y×	271	01	1
172	06	6	222	53	(	272	03	3
173	69	□P	223	43	RCL	273	01	1
174	04	04	224	13	13	274	06	6
175	43	RCL	225	55	÷	275	69	□P
176	06	06	226	43	RCL	276	04	04
177	69	□P	227	09	09	277	43	RCL
178	06	06	228	54	)	278	15	15
179	98	ADV	229	75	-	279	59	INT
180	43	RCL	230	01	1	280	69	□P
181	11	11	231	54	)	281	06	06
182	85	+	232	95	=	282	43	RCL
183	43	RCL	233	42	STO	283	21	21
184	03	03	234	14	14	284	42	STO
185	95	=	235	01	1	285	10	10
186	42	STO	236	07	7	286	03	3
187	20	20	237	02	2	287	03	3
188	03	3	238	01	1	288	00	0
189	00	0	239	02	2	289	03	3
190	00	0	240	01	1	290	69	□P
191	03	3	241	01	1	291	04	04
192	69	□P	242	03	3	292	43	RCL
193	04	04	243	69	□P	293	10	10
194	43	RCL	244	04	04	294	58	FIX
195	20	20	245	43	RCL	295	01	01
196	69	□P	246	14	14	296	69	□P
197	06	06	247	58	FIX	297	06	06
198	43	RCL	248	03	03	298	22	INV
199	08	08	249	69	□P	299	58	FIX
200	75	-	250	06	06	300	03	3
201	01	1	251	22	INV	301	05	5
202	95	=	252	58	FIX	302	03	3
203	55	÷	253	07	7	303	03	3
204	43	RCL	254	07	7	304	69	□P
205	08	08	255	08	8	305	04	04
206	95	=	256	65	×	306	43	RCL
207	42	STO	257	53	(	307	07	07
208	13	13	258	43	RCL	308	58	FIX
209	43	RCL	259	06	06	309	03	03
210	07	07	260	75	-	310	69	□P
211	45	Y×	261	43	RCL	311	06	06
212	43	RCL	262	04	04	312	22	INV
213	13	13	263	54	)	313	58	FIX
214	75	-	264	95	=	314	53	(
215	01	1	265	42	STO	315	43	RCL
216	95	=	266	15	15	316	06	06
217	55	÷	267	02	2	317	75	-
218	53	(	268	03	3	318	43	RCL
219	43	RCL	269	01	1	319	04	04

Program 3 Listing continued

320	54	)	370	65	×	420	55	÷
321	55	÷	371	43	RCL	421	43	RCL
322	43	RCL	372	12	12	422	14	14
323	14	14	373	95	=	423	95	=
324	85	+	374	55	÷	424	42	STO
325	43	RCL	375	43	RCL	425	18	18
326	04	04	376	20	20	426	02	2
327	95	=	377	95	=	427	03	3
328	42	STO	378	42	STO	428	01	1
329	16	16	379	04	04	429	06	6
330	02	2	380	02	2	430	03	3
331	03	3	381	03	3	431	03	3
332	00	0	382	00	0	432	69	OP
333	03	3	383	04	4	433	04	04
334	69	OP	384	69	OP	434	43	RCL
335	04	04	385	04	04	435	18	18
336	43	RCL	386	43	RCL	436	59	INT
337	16	16	387	04	04	437	69	OP
338	58	FIX	388	58	FIX	438	06	06
339	01	01	389	01	01	439	43	RCL
340	69	OP	390	69	OP	440	18	18
341	06	06	391	06	06	441	55	÷
342	22	INV	392	22	INV	442	03	3
343	58	FIX	393	58	FIX	443	03	3
344	98	ADV	394	98	ADV	444	00	0
345	91	R/S	395	98	ADV	445	00	0
346	76	LBL	396	43	RCL	446	00	0
347	10	E'	397	03	03	447	55	÷
348	42	STO	398	65	×	448	43	RCL
349	12	12	399	43	RCL	449	09	09
350	02	2	400	05	05	450	65	×
351	03	3	401	95	=	451	43	RCL
352	00	0	402	42	STO	452	03	03
353	03	3	403	17	17	453	95	=
354	06	6	404	03	3	454	42	STO
355	05	5	405	04	4	455	19	19
356	69	OP	406	00	0	456	03	3
357	04	04	407	02	2	457	03	3
358	43	RCL	408	69	OP	458	04	4
359	12	12	409	04	04	459	03	3
360	69	OP	410	43	RCL	460	03	3
361	06	06	411	17	17	461	05	5
362	43	RCL	412	59	INT	462	02	2
363	03	03	413	69	OP	463	02	2
364	65	×	414	06	06	464	69	OP
365	43	RCL	415	43	RCL	465	04	04
366	16	16	416	15	15	466	43	RCL
367	85	+	417	65	×	467	19	19
368	43	RCL	418	43	RCL	468	59	INT
369	11	11	419	09	09	469	69	OP

(continued on next page)

Program 3 Listing continued

470	06	06	473	42	STO	476	00	00
471	43	RCL	474	03	03	477	91	R/S
472	20	20	475	69	OP	478	00	0

Program 4

Speed and Number of Stages

Background

Once the polytropic head for a compressor application is known, the next step is to calculate the rotational speed and number of compressor stages (impellers) required to perform the duty.

For this purpose, compressor applications can be grouped into two broad classifications. The first includes compressor applications where compressor rotational speed is not restricted by any of the other rotating equipment in the string. This classification, therefore, includes single compressor bodies driven by steam turbines, steam-turbine gears, motor gears, or gas-turbine gears. Note that motor and gas-turbine drivers incorporating gears are included in this classification, since the gear can be selected to allow the compressor to operate at its optimum speed.

The second classification includes compressor applications where compressor rotational speed is dictated by another rotating body in the string. Such applications include direct-coupled motor or gas-turbine drives, where the driver dictates the speed of the string, and multi-body compressor strings, where the largest compressor dictates the rotational speed.

Consider the first classification, where compressor rotational speed is not restricted by other rotating bodies in the string.

The number of compressor stages required to perform a given compression duty is given by Equation 4-1:

$$\text{no. stages} = \frac{H_p}{\max H_p/\text{stage}} \qquad (4\text{-}1)$$

The max H_p/stage comes from Figure 2-1 once the value of θ is known.

With the number of compressor stages defined, the required rotational speed of the compressor is given by:

$$N = N_{\text{nom}} \sqrt{\frac{H_p}{H_{p_{\text{nom}}} \times \text{no. stages}}} \qquad (4\text{-}2)$$

where:

N = rotational speed, rpm

N_{nom} = nominal rotational speed, rpm

$H_{p_{\text{nom}}}$ = polytropic head per stage at the nominal rotational speed, ft-lbf/lbm

The actual polytropic head per stage is:

$$H_p/\text{stage} = \frac{H_p}{\text{no. stages}} \qquad (4\text{-}3)$$

Now consider the fixed-speed application. By rearranging Equation 4-2, the equation for the required number of stages for a given rotational speed can be derived:

$$\text{no. stages} = \left(\frac{N_{\text{nom}}}{N}\right)^2 \left(\frac{H_p}{H_{p_{\text{nom}}}}\right) \qquad (4\text{-}4)$$

Once the number of stages is known, the actual polytropic head per stage can be calculated from Equation 4-3.

The H_p/stage for the fixed-speed case must be compared to the max H_p/stage from Figure 2-1. If the H_p/stage is less than the maximum allowable from Figure 2-1, the rotational speed and number of stages are satisfactory. If the H_p/stage is above the maximum allowable, too few stages have been calculated. Thus, the selected rotational speed is too high and must be reduced to allow for more compressor stages.

Table 4-1 shows the maximum number of stages that should be considered feasible for each compressor for various compressor arrangements. Note that Table 4-1 does not portray absolute limits. In fact, it is not always possible for compressors to accommodate the limits listed. However, Table 4-1 is an adequate feasibility limit schedule for centrifugal compressor estimates.

Program 4 Description

Program 4, Speed and Number of Stages, considers both the unrestricted-speed case and the fixed-speed case. It calculates and prints the value of θ

Table 4-1
Maximum Number of Stages Per Compressor Body

Arrangement	Max No. Stages/Body
Straight-through	9
Single intercooled	8
Double intercooled	7
1 side load or extraction	8
2 side loads or extractions	7
3 side loads or extractions	6
Double-flow	4

to allow the operator to enter the maximum polytropic head per stage, and procedes to calculate and print the results of Equations 4-1, 4-2, 4-3, and 4-4.

In order to execute the program, the following must be known:

1. Polytropic head, H_p
2. Nominal polytropic head, $H_{p\text{nom}}$
3. Inlet temperature, T_1
4. Nominal rotational speed, N_{nom}
5. Molecular weight, MW
6. Inlet k-value, k_1
7. Inlet Z-value, Z_1
8. Rotational speed, N (fixed-speed case only)

The nominal polytropic head is the polytropic head produced by an impeller at the nominal rotational speed. These values should be obtained from the compressor manufacturer. However, lacking manufacturer's information or as a means of using general data, these values can be obtained from Table 2-2.

The program first calculates the value of θ. This permits the operator to determine the maximum polytropic head per stage from Figure 2-1 and enter it into the program.

For the unrestricted-speed case, the program calculates the minimum number of compressor stages that can be used without exceeding the maximum polytropic head per stage and rounds up to the next higher whole number of stages. It then calculates the rotational speed required to produce the specified polytropic head with the calculated number of stages.

For the fixed-speed case, the program calculates the number of stages required to obtain the polytropic head at the specified speed. The program then calculates the polytropic head per stage and compares it to the maximum allowable. If the polytropic head per stage is satisfactory, the program prints out the calculated number of stages to the nearest 0.1 stages. This

Table 4-2
Program 4: Printer Nomenclature

Program Term	Definition	Units
HEAD	polytropic head	ft-lbf/lbm
HMAX	max polytropic head/stage	ft-lbf/lbm
HNOM	nominal polytropic head/stage	ft-lbf/lbm
H/ST	polytropic head/stage	ft-lbf/lbm
K1	inlet ratio of specific heats	dimensionless
MW	molecular weight	lbm/lbm-mol
N	rotational speed	rpm
NNOM	nominal rotational speed	rpm
NOST	number of stages	dimensionless
T1	inlet temperature	°F
THET	speed of sound index, θ	dimensionless
Z1	inlet compressibility	dimensionless

Table 4-3
Data Registers Used by Program 4

00	not used	06	MW	12	max H_p/stage
01	not used	07	k_1	13	HMAX (title)
02	not used	08	Z_1	14	no. stages
03	H_p	09	N	15	H_p/stage
04	$H_{p_{nom}}$	10	T_1	16	H_p/stage $-$ max H_p/stage
05	N_{nom}	11	θ		

allows the operator to choose between increasing the speed slightly to lower the number of stages or decreasing the speed slightly to raise the number of stages. Note that speed variation may not be possible, depending on the particular application. However, the manufacturer can trim some head out of one or more of the impellers simply by cutting back on the diameter. Thus, if 8.2 stages are required, the manufacturer would probably furnish 9 impellers, with several of them slightly trimmed on diameter to reduce the head output.

If the specified speed results in a polytropic head per stage higher than the allowable, the program will print the warning SPEED TOO HIGH and program execution terminates.

The program is set up to allow continuous usage by the operator, without the need for complete data reentry. Thus the program can be rerun for different conditions by changing only the parameters of interest.

Table 4-2 is the nomenclature printed by the program; Table 4-3 shows the data registers used by the program.

Labels Used by Program 4

```
001   11  A          036   18  C'
006   12  B          041   15   E
011   13  C          078   10  E'
021   14  D          123   33  X²
026   16  A'         363   34  ΓX
031   17  B'         424   45  YX
```

Table 4-4
Program 4: Definitions of User-Defined and R/S Keys

A	HEAD	A'	MW
B	HNOM	B'	K1
C	T1	C'	Z1
D	NNOM	E'	N, Calculate (fixed speed)
E	Calculate (unrestricted speed)	R/S	HMAX, Continue execution

Program 4 Usage

Program 4 is executed by using the user-defined keys and the R/S key. The definitions of the user-defined and R/S keys can be found in Table 4-4.

After all the data required by user-defined keys A through D and A' through C' are entered, calculations for the unrestricted-speed case are conducted through user-defined key E. Calculations for the fixed-speed case are conducted by entering the rotational speed and then depressing user-defined key E'. In either case, the program continues through the calculation of θ and stops. The operator then enters the max H_p/stage, as prompted by the program, and presses the R/S key to continue program execution.

Subsequent calculations can be made simply by changing only those terms desired.

Sample Problem 4-1: Unrestricted Speed

Consider the compression duty investigated in Sample Problem 2-1. The following data are given:

$$H_p = 48,600 \text{ ft-lbf/lbm}$$
$$T_1 = 100°F$$
$$MW = 30$$
$$k_1 = 1.175$$

$Z_1 = 0.99$

$Q_1 = 29,158$ ICFM

Reference to Table 2-2 shows that the volume flow places the service in a Frame D compressor. The Frame D has a nominal polytropic head of 10,000 ft-lbf/lbm and a nominal rotational speed of 4900 rpm.

Table 4-1 shows that the required number of stages will fit in a single compressor body.

Sample Problem 4-1: User Instructions

Step	Procedure	Enter	Press	Display
1.	Load program.			
2.	Enter polytropic head.	48600	A	48600
3.	Enter nominal polytropic head from Table 2-2.	10000	B	10000
4.	Enter inlet temperature.	100(°F)	C	560(°R)
5.	Enter nominal rotational speed from Table 2-2.	4900	D	4900
6.	Enter molecular weight.	30	2nd A'	30
7.	Enter inlet k-value.	1.175	2nd B'	1.175
8.	Enter inlet Z-value.	0.99	2nd C'	0.99
9.	Calculate.		E	
10.	Enter max H_p/stage based on the value of θ from Figure 2-1	12000	R/S	

Sample Problem 4-1: Program Printout

```
SPEED AND NO. STAGES            1.096    THET
     48600.    HEAD     ENTER HMAX, R/S
     10000.    HNOM
      4900.    NNOM           12000.    HMAX
       100.    T1
        30.    MW              4831.       N
      1.175    K1                 5.0    NOST
      0.99     Z1              9720.     H/ST
```

Sample Problem 4-2: Fixed Speed

Consider Problem 2-1; however, this time assume the compressor is to be directly connected to a 3600-rpm motor. Due to slip, the motor full-load speed will be approximately 3550 rpm. Since the speed is fixed, it is normal practice to subtract one percent from the speed to perform estimates. In essence, this allows for an extra two percent head in the compressor for insurance. Thus the program is executed at a speed of 3515 rpm.

Note from the program printout (Problem 4-1) that 9.4 stages are required at the fixed speed of 3515 rpm. Reference to Table 4-1 shows that for estimating purposes, nine stages should be considered maximum per pody. This application may still feasibly fit into a single compressor body if the manufacturer can install 10 impellers in a body or if he has higher-head impellers available. However, realize that this example may certainly be infringing on a limit.

Sample Problem 4-2: User Instructions

Step	Procedure	Enter	Press	Display
1–8	Refer to Problem 4-1 User Instructions			
9.	Enter rotational speed and calculate.	3515	2nd E'	
10.	Enter max H_p/stage based on the value of θ from Figure 2-1.	12000	R/S	

Sample Problem 4-2: Program Printout

```
SPEED AND NO. STAGES          1.096    THET

                      ENTER HMAX, R/S
        48600.   HEAD
        10000.   HNOM
         4900.   NNOM          12000.    HMAX
          100.   T1
           30.   MW            3515.       N
        1.175    K1             9.4      NOST
         0.99    Z1            5146.      H/ST
```

Program 4 Listing

000	76	LBL	004	91	R/S	008	04	04	
001	11	A	005	76	LBL	009	91	R/S	
002	42	STO	006	12	B				
003	03	03	007	42	STO				

(continued on next page)

Program 4 Listing continued

010	76	LBL	060	55	÷	110	95	=
011	13	C	061	43	RCL	111	42	STD
012	85	+	062	04	04	112	16	16
013	04	4	063	55	÷	113	00	0
014	06	6	064	43	RCL	114	32	X:T
015	00	0	065	14	14	115	43	RCL
016	95	=	066	95	=	116	16	16
017	42	STD	067	34	ΓX	117	77	GE
018	10	10	068	65	×	118	45	YX
019	91	R/S	069	43	RCL	119	71	SBR
020	76	LBL	070	05	05	120	34	ΓX
021	14	D	071	95	=	121	91	R/S
022	42	STD	072	42	STD	122	76	LBL
023	05	05	073	09	09	123	33	X²
024	91	R/S	074	71	SBR	124	98	ADV
025	76	LBL	075	34	ΓX	125	03	3
026	16	A'	076	91	R/S	126	06	6
027	42	STD	077	76	LBL	127	03	3
028	06	06	078	10	E'	128	03	3
029	91	R/S	079	42	STD	129	01	1
030	76	LBL	080	09	09	130	07	7
031	17	B'	081	71	SBR	131	01	1
032	42	STD	082	33	X²	132	07	7
033	07	07	083	43	RCL	133	01	1
034	91	R/S	084	09	09	134	06	6
035	76	LBL	085	35	1/X	135	69	DP
036	18	C'	086	65	×	136	01	01
037	42	STD	087	43	RCL	137	01	1
038	08	08	088	05	05	138	03	3
039	91	R/S	089	95	=	139	03	3
040	76	LBL	090	33	X²	140	01	1
041	15	E	091	65	×	141	01	1
042	71	SBR	092	43	RCL	142	06	6
043	33	X²	093	03	03	143	00	0
044	43	RCL	094	55	÷	144	00	0
045	03	03	095	43	RCL	145	69	DP
046	55	÷	096	04	04	146	02	02
047	43	RCL	097	95	=	147	03	3
048	12	12	098	42	STD	148	01	1
049	95	=	099	14	14	149	03	3
050	85	+	100	55	÷	150	02	2
051	93	.	101	43	RCL	151	04	4
052	09	9	102	03	03	152	00	0
053	09	9	103	95	=	153	00	0
054	95	=	104	35	1/X	154	00	0
055	59	INT	105	42	STD	155	03	3
056	42	STD	106	15	15	156	06	6
057	14	14	107	75	-	157	69	DP
058	43	RCL	108	43	RCL	158	03	03
059	03	03	109	12	12	159	03	3

Program 4 Listing continued

160	07	7	210	06	06	260	43	RCL
161	01	1	211	02	2	261	06	06
162	03	3	212	03	3	262	69	OP
163	02	2	213	03	3	263	06	06
164	02	2	214	01	1	264	02	2
165	01	1	215	03	3	265	06	6
166	07	7	216	02	2	266	00	0
167	03	3	217	03	3	267	02	2
168	06	6	218	00	0	268	69	OP
169	69	OP	219	69	OP	269	04	04
170	04	04	220	04	04	270	43	RCL
171	69	OP	221	43	RCL	271	07	07
172	05	05	222	04	04	272	69	OP
173	69	OP	223	69	OP	273	06	06
174	00	00	224	06	06	274	04	4
175	98	ADV	225	03	3	275	06	6
176	98	ADV	226	01	1	276	00	0
177	02	2	227	03	3	277	02	2
178	06	6	228	01	1	278	69	OP
179	93	.	229	03	3	279	04	04
180	01	1	230	02	2	280	43	RCL
181	65	×	231	03	3	281	08	08
182	43	RCL	232	00	0	282	69	OP
183	06	06	233	69	OP	283	06	06
184	55	÷	234	04	04	284	98	ADV
185	43	RCL	235	43	RCL	285	03	3
186	07	07	236	05	05	286	07	7
187	55	÷	237	69	OP	287	02	2
188	43	RCL	238	06	06	288	03	3
189	08	08	239	03	3	289	01	1
190	55	÷	240	07	7	290	07	7
191	43	RCL	241	00	0	291	03	3
192	10	10	242	02	2	292	07	7
193	95	=	243	69	OP	293	69	OP
194	34	⌜X	244	04	04	294	04	04
195	42	STO	245	43	RCL	295	43	RCL
196	11	11	246	10	10	296	11	11
197	02	2	247	75	-	297	58	FIX
198	03	3	248	04	4	298	03	03
199	01	1	249	06	6	299	69	OP
200	07	7	250	00	0	300	06	06
201	01	1	251	95	=	301	22	INV
202	03	3	252	69	OP	302	58	FIX
203	01	1	253	06	06	303	98	ADV
204	06	6	254	00	0	304	69	OP
205	69	OP	255	00	0	305	00	00
206	04	04	256	04	4	306	01	1
207	43	RCL	257	03	3	307	07	7
208	03	03	258	69	OP	308	03	3
209	69	OP	259	04	04	309	01	1

(continued on next page)

Program 4 Listing continued

310	03	3	360	98	ADV	410	69	OP
311	07	7	361	92	RTN	411	04	04
312	01	1	362	76	LBL	412	43	RCL
313	07	7	363	34	ГX	413	15	15
314	03	3	364	03	3	414	58	FIX
315	05	5	365	01	1	415	00	00
316	69	OP	366	69	OP	416	69	OP
317	01	01	367	04	04	417	06	06
318	02	2	368	43	RCL	418	22	INV
319	03	3	369	09	09	419	58	FIX
320	03	3	370	58	FIX	420	69	OP
321	00	0	371	00	00	421	00	00
322	01	1	372	69	OP	422	92	RTN
323	03	3	373	06	06	423	76	LBL
324	04	4	374	22	INV	424	45	YX
325	04	4	375	58	FIX	425	03	3
326	42	STO	376	03	3	426	01	1
327	13	13	377	01	1	427	69	OP
328	69	OP	378	03	3	428	04	04
329	02	02	379	02	2	429	43	RCL
330	05	5	380	03	3	430	09	09
331	07	7	381	06	6	431	58	FIX
332	00	0	382	03	3	432	00	00
333	00	0	383	07	7	433	69	OP
334	03	3	384	69	OP	434	06	06
335	05	5	385	04	04	435	22	INV
336	06	6	386	43	RCL	436	58	FIX
337	03	3	387	14	14	437	69	OP
338	03	3	388	58	FIX	438	00	00
339	06	6	389	01	01	439	98	ADV
340	69	OP	390	69	OP	440	03	3
341	03	03	391	06	06	441	06	6
342	69	OP	392	22	INV	442	03	3
343	05	05	393	58	FIX	443	03	3
344	69	OP	394	43	RCL	444	01	1
345	00	00	395	03	03	445	07	7
346	91	R/S	396	55	÷	446	01	1
347	42	STO	397	43	RCL	447	07	7
348	12	12	398	14	14	448	01	1
349	98	ADV	399	95	=	449	06	6
350	43	RCL	400	42	STO	450	69	OP
351	13	13	401	15	15	451	01	01
352	69	OP	402	02	2	452	03	3
353	04	04	403	03	3	453	07	7
354	43	RCL	404	06	6	454	03	3
355	12	12	405	03	3	455	02	2
356	69	OP	406	03	3	456	03	3
357	06	06	407	06	6	457	02	2
358	69	OP	408	03	3	458	00	0
359	00	00	409	07	7	459	00	0

Program 4 Listing continued

460	69	OP		467	02	2		474	69	OP
461	02	02		468	02	2		475	05	05
462	02	2		469	03	3		476	69	OP
463	03	3		470	00	0		477	00	00
464	02	2		471	00	0		478	92	RTN
465	04	4		472	69	OP		479	00	0
466	02	2		473	03	03				

Program 5

Pressure Profile
for Intercooled Compressors

Background

When compression temperatures get too high, it becomes necessary to intercool the process gas. This is accomplished by removing the gas from the compressor at some intermediate location, directing it through a heat exchanger, and reinjecting the gas for final compression. This is shown diagramatically in Figure 5-1.

The problem becomes the determination of the pressure at which cooling should be done for optimum compressor selection. The best selection will generally result if the pressure level for cooling is chosen such that the discharge temperatures from each section are equal. For practical purposes, these temperatures should be within ±10°F.

For the simple case where the inlet temperatures to both sections are equal, the preceding requirement reduces to equal pressure ratios for each section. (Refer to Equation 2-5, noting that for a given k-value and polytropic efficiency, equal temperature ratios will result in equal pressure ratios.) Thus, a good initial approximation on the pressure profile for a two-section compressor would result from Equation 5-1:

$$r_{p_{\text{SECT}}} = \sqrt{r_p} \qquad (5\text{-}1)$$

where:

$r_{p_{\text{SECT}}}$ = sectional pressure ratio

r_p = total pressure ratio across the compressor

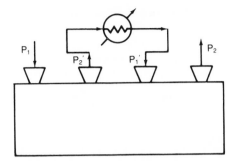

Figure 5-1. Schematic representation of a single intercooled compressor.

If Equation 5-1 is extended to consider b sections, the sectional pressure ratio becomes:

$$r_{P_{\text{SECT}}} = \sqrt[b]{r_p} \qquad (5\text{-}2)$$

where:
b = number of compression sections

In addition, the pressure drop associated with the heat exchanger and associated piping must be considered. Referring to Figure 5-1, the following equations evolve:

$$P_2' = (P_1)(r_{P_{\text{SECT}}})(1 + \Delta P_{he}) \qquad (5\text{-}3)$$

$$P_1' = \frac{P_2'}{1 + \Delta P_{he}} \qquad (5\text{-}4)$$

where:
ΔP_{he} = pressure drop through the heat exchanger and associated piping

and with P_1 and P_2 defined by process conditions.

Equations 5-3 and 5-4 can be further extended to three or more compression sections.

After the initial guess on pressure profile, the cooling pressure level should be revised by iteration until discharge temperatures within $\pm 10°F$ are obtained. The discharge temperature is calculated for each section from Equation 2-11, presented here for convenience:

$$T_2 = T_1(r_p)^{(n-1)/n} \qquad (2\text{-}11)$$

Program 5 Description

Program 5, Pressure Profile for Intercooled Compressors, calculates and prints the results of Equations 5-2, 5-3, 5-4, and 2-11 for one or two cooling points (i.e. two or three compression sections).

In order to execute the program, the following must be known:

1. Inlet pressure, P_1
2. Discharge pressure, P_2
3. Intercooler pressure drop, ΔP_{he}
4. Inlet temperature, T_1
5. Intercool inlet temperature, T_{ic} (i.e. the return temperature)
6. Number of cooling points, CLPT
7. Average k-value, k_a
8. Polytropic efficiency, η_p

The polytropic efficiency can be estimated from Table 2-2 or obtained from manufacturer's data.

The following assumptions are made by the program:

1. The average k-value for all compression sections is the same value.
2. The polytropic efficiency is constant for all sections.
3. The percent pressure drop, expressed as a fraction of section discharge pressure, is the same for each heat exchanger and associated piping.
4. The intercool inlet temperature downstream of the intermediate heat exchanger is the same for all cooled sections.

The program is set up for continuous usage, without the need for complete data reentry. Thus, the program can be rerun for different conditions by changing only the parameters of interest.

Table 5-1 is the nomenclature printed by the program; Table 5-2 shows the data registers used by the program.

Labels Used by Program 5

004	11	A	044	18	C'	408	35	1/X
009	12	B	052	19	D'	434	42	STO
014	13	C	057	15	E	575	43	RCL
024	14	D	178	34	ГX	619	52	EE
029	16	A'	257	33	X2	645	23	LNX
039	17	B'	273	55	÷			

Table 5-1
Program 5: Printer Nomenclature

Program Term	Definition	Units
CLPT	number of cooling points	dimensionless
DROP	intercooler pressure drop, expressed as a fraction of the pressure entering the cooler (i.e. the previous section discharge pressure)	dimensionless
EFF	polytropic efficiency	dimensionless
KA	average ratio of specific heats	dimensionless
P11	inlet pressure	psia
P12	first-section discharge pressure	psia
P21	second-section inlet pressure	psia
P22	second-section discharge pressure	psia
P31	third-section inlet pressure	psia
P32	third-section discharge pressure	psia
T11	inlet temperature	°F
T12	first-section discharge temperature	°F
T21	second-section inlet temperature	°F
T22	second-section discharge temperature	°F
T31	third-section inlet temperature	°F
T32	third-section discharge temperature	°F

Table 5-2
Data Registers Used by Program 5

00	not used	09	$1 + \Delta P_{he}$	18	P_{32}		
01	not used	10	η_p	19	T_{12}		
02	not used	11	$(r_p)_1$	20	T_{22}		
03	P_1	12	$(r_p)_2$	21	T_{32}		
04	P_2	13	$(r_p)_3$	22	$r_{P\text{SECT}}$		
05	T_1	14	P_{12}	23	$n/(n-1)$		
06	CLPT	15	P_{21}	24	$(n-1)/n$		
07	T_{ic}	16	P_{22}	25	$(r_p)_1$		
08	k_a	17	P_{31}				

Notes:
1. P_1 = inlet pressure to the compressor and is printed out as P11.
2. P_2 = discharge pressure from the compressor and is printed out as P22 for two-section compressors (i.e. one cool point) and P32 for three-section compressors (i.e. two cool points).
3. T_1 = inlet temperature to the compressor (stored in °R) and is printed out as T11.
4. T_{ic} = intercool inlet temperature (stored in °R) and is printed out as T21 and T31.
5. $(r_p)_1$ = first-section pressure ratio—similar for $(r_p)_2$ and $(r_p)_3$.

Table 5-3
Program 5: Definitions of User-Defined Keys

A	P1	A′	TIC (T_{ic})
B	P2	B′	KA
C	T1	C′	DROP
D	CLPT	D′	EFF
E	Calculate		

Program 5 Usage

Program 5 is executed by using the user-defined keys. The definitions for the user-defined keys can be found in Table 5-3.

After all the data are entered, program execution is initiated through user-defined key E. Subsequent calculations can be made simply by changing only those terms desired.

Note that the calculator must be repartitioned to 719.29 before loading or keying in the program.

Sample Problem 5-1

Consider a chlorine mixture initially at 12 psia and −25°F. The gas is to be compressed to 250 psia. The maximum allowable discharge temperature due to process considerations is 250°F. Determine the number of compression sections required and an optimum pressure profile for compressor selection.

The following data are known:

$$k_a = 1.3$$

$$\eta_p = 0.78$$

The pressure drop in the coolers is two percent of the entering pressure. The return temperature is 100°F.

Note from the printout that one cool point resulted in estimated discharge temperatures of 315°F, which are too high for process considerations. Two cool points resulted in acceptable discharge temperatures of 235°F and 237°F.

Sample Problem 5-1: User Instructions

Step	Procedure	Enter	Press	Display
1.	Partition calculator.	3	2nd OP 17	719.29
2.	Load program.			

Sample Problem 5-1: User Instructions continued

Step	Procedure	Enter	Press	Display
3.	Enter inlet pressure.	12	A	12
4.	Enter discharge pressure.	250	B	250
5.	Enter inlet temperature.	−25(°F)	C	435(°R)
6.	Enter intercool inlet temperature.	100(°F)	2nd A'	560(°R)
7.	Enter average k-value.	1.3	2nd B'	1.3
8.	Enter intercooler pressure drop as a fraction of intercooler inlet pressure.	0.02	2nd C'	1.02
9.	Enter polytropic efficiency.	0.78	2nd D'	0.78
10.	Enter number of cooling points.	1	D	1
11.	Calculate.		E	
12.	Enter number of cooling points for recalculation.	2	D	2
13.	Calculate.		E	

Sample Problem 5-1: Program Printout

```
INTERCOOL                  INTERCOOL


    1.3      KA                1.3      KA
   0.78      EFF              0.78      EFF
   0.02      DROP             0.02      DROP


     1.      CLPT               2.      CLPT


   12.0      P11              12.0      P11
   -25.      T11              -25.      T11
   84.8      P12              58.7      P12
   315.      T12              235.      T12
   83.1      P21              57.6      P21
   100.      T21              100.      T21
  250.0      P22             121.2      P22
   315.      T22              237.      T22
                             118.8      P31
                              100.      T31
                             250.0      P32
                              237.      T32
```

Program 5 Listing

000	03	3	050	91	R/S	100	07	7
001	69	OP	051	76	LBL	101	02	2
002	17	17	052	19	D'	102	01	1
003	76	LBL	053	42	STO	103	02	2
004	11	A	054	10	10	104	01	1
005	42	STO	055	91	R/S	105	69	OP
006	03	03	056	76	LBL	106	04	04
007	91	R/S	057	15	E	107	43	RCL
008	76	LBL	058	69	OP	108	10	10
009	12	B	059	00	00	109	69	OP
010	42	STO	060	98	ADV	110	06	06
011	04	04	061	02	2	111	01	1
012	91	R/S	062	04	4	112	06	6
013	76	LBL	063	03	3	113	03	3
014	13	C	064	01	1	114	05	5
015	85	+	065	03	3	115	03	3
016	04	4	066	07	7	116	02	2
017	06	6	067	01	1	117	03	3
018	00	0	068	07	7	118	03	3
019	95	=	069	69	OP	119	69	OP
020	42	STO	070	02	02	120	04	04
021	05	05	071	03	3	121	43	RCL
022	91	R/S	072	05	5	122	09	09
023	76	LBL	073	01	1	123	75	-
024	14	D	074	05	5	124	01	1
025	42	STO	075	03	3	125	95	=
026	06	06	076	02	2	126	69	OP
027	91	R/S	077	03	3	127	06	06
028	76	LBL	078	02	2	128	98	ADV
029	16	A'	079	02	2	129	01	1
030	85	+	080	07	7	130	05	5
031	04	4	081	69	OP	131	02	2
032	06	6	082	03	03	132	07	7
033	00	0	083	69	OP	133	03	3
034	95	=	084	05	05	134	03	3
035	42	STO	085	69	OP	135	03	3
036	07	07	086	00	00	136	07	7
037	91	R/S	087	98	ADV	137	69	OP
038	76	LBL	088	98	ADV	138	04	04
039	17	B'	089	02	2	139	43	RCL
040	42	STO	090	06	6	140	06	06
041	08	08	091	01	1	141	69	OP
042	91	R/S	092	03	3	142	06	06
043	76	LBL	093	69	OP	143	98	ADV
044	18	C'	094	04	04	144	43	RCL
045	85	+	095	43	RCL	145	08	08
046	01	1	096	08	08	146	75	-
047	95	=	097	69	OP	147	01	1
048	42	STO	098	06	06	148	95	=
049	09	09	099	01	1	149	35	1/X

Program 5 Listing continued

150	65	×	200	95	=	250	77	GE
151	43	RCL	201	42	STO	251	35	1/X
152	08	08	202	12	12	252	71	SBR
153	65	×	203	43	RCL	253	42	STO
154	43	RCL	204	14	14	254	92	RTN
155	10	10	205	55	÷	255	91	R/S
156	95	=	206	43	RCL	256	76	LBL
157	42	STO	207	03	03	257	33	X²
158	23	23	208	95	=	258	43	RCL
159	35	1/X	209	42	STO	259	04	04
160	42	STO	210	11	11	260	55	÷
161	24	24	211	45	Yˣ	261	43	RCL
162	02	2	212	43	RCL	262	03	03
163	32	X⇌T	213	24	24	263	95	=
164	43	RCL	214	65	×	264	45	Yˣ
165	06	06	215	43	RCL	265	03	3
166	77	GE	216	05	05	266	35	1/X
167	33	X²	217	95	=	267	95	=
168	43	RCL	218	42	STO	268	42	STO
169	04	04	219	19	19	269	22	22
170	55	÷	220	43	RCL	270	42	STO
171	43	RCL	221	12	12	271	11	11
172	03	03	222	45	Yˣ	272	76	LBL
173	95	=	223	43	RCL	273	55	÷
174	34	ΓX	224	24	24	274	43	RCL
175	42	STO	225	65	×	275	11	11
176	22	22	226	43	RCL	276	65	×
177	76	LBL	227	07	07	277	43	RCL
178	34	ΓX	228	95	=	278	03	03
179	43	RCL	229	42	STO	279	95	=
180	22	22	230	20	20	280	42	STO
181	65	×	231	43	RCL	281	15	15
182	43	RCL	232	19	19	282	65	×
183	03	03	233	85	+	283	43	RCL
184	95	=	234	05	5	284	09	09
185	42	STO	235	95	=	285	95	=
186	15	15	236	32	X⇌T	286	42	STO
187	65	×	237	43	RCL	287	14	14
188	43	RCL	238	20	20	288	43	RCL
189	09	09	239	77	GE	289	22	22
190	95	=	240	35	1/X	290	65	×
191	42	STO	241	43	RCL	291	43	RCL
192	14	14	242	19	19	292	15	15
193	43	RCL	243	75	-	293	95	=
194	04	04	244	05	5	294	42	STO
195	42	STO	245	95	=	295	17	17
196	16	16	246	32	X⇌T	296	65	×
197	55	÷	247	43	RCL	297	43	RCL
198	43	RCL	248	20	20	298	09	09
199	15	15	249	22	INV	299	95	=

(continued on next page)

Program 5 Listing continued

300	42	STO	350	45	Yˣ	400	52	EE	
301	16	16	351	43	RCL	401	71	SBR	
302	43	RCL	352	24	24	402	42	STO	
303	04	04	353	65	×	403	71	SBR	
304	42	STO	354	43	RCL	404	23	LNX	
305	18	18	355	07	07	405	92	RTN	
306	55	÷	356	95	=	406	91	R/S	
307	43	RCL	357	42	STO	407	76	LBL	
308	17	17	358	21	21	408	35	1/X	
309	95	=	359	43	RCL	409	43	RCL	
310	42	STO	360	19	19	410	19	19	
311	13	13	361	85	+	411	85	+	
312	43	RCL	362	05	5	412	43	RCL	
313	16	16	363	95	=	413	20	20	
314	55	÷	364	32	X:T	414	95	=	
315	43	RCL	365	43	RCL	415	55	÷	
316	15	15	366	20	20	416	02	2	
317	95	=	367	77	GE	417	55	÷	
318	42	STO	368	43	RCL	418	43	RCL	
319	12	12	369	43	RCL	419	05	05	
320	43	RCL	370	19	19	420	95	=	
321	14	14	371	75	−	421	45	Yˣ	
322	55	÷	372	05	5	422	43	RCL	
323	43	RCL	373	95	=	423	23	23	
324	03	03	374	32	X:T	424	55	÷	
325	95	=	375	43	RCL	425	43	RCL	
326	42	STO	376	20	20	426	09	09	
327	11	11	377	22	INV	427	95	=	
328	45	Yˣ	378	77	GE	428	42	STO	
329	43	RCL	379	43	RCL	429	22	22	
330	24	24	380	43	RCL	430	71	SBR	
331	65	×	381	20	20	431	34	⌐X	
332	43	RCL	382	85	+	432	92	RTN	
333	05	05	383	05	5	433	76	LBL	
334	95	=	384	95	=	434	42	STO	
335	42	STO	385	32	X:T	435	03	3	
336	19	19	386	43	RCL	436	03	3	
337	43	RCL	387	21	21	437	00	0	
338	12	12	388	77	GE	438	02	2	
339	45	Yˣ	389	52	EE	439	00	0	
340	43	RCL	390	43	RCL	440	02	2	
341	24	24	391	20	20	441	69	OP	
342	65	×	392	75	−	442	04	04	
343	43	RCL	393	05	5	443	43	RCL	
344	07	07	394	95	=	444	03	03	
345	95	=	395	32	X:T	445	58	FIX	
346	42	STO	396	43	RCL	446	01	01	
347	20	20	397	21	21	447	69	OP	
348	43	RCL	398	22	INV	448	06	06	
349	13	13	399	77	GE	449	22	INV	

Program 5 Listing continued

450	58	FIX	500	59	INT	550	06	06
451	03	3	501	69	□P	551	22	INV
452	07	7	502	06	06	552	58	FIX
453	00	0	503	03	3	553	03	3
454	02	2	504	03	3	554	07	7
455	00	0	505	00	0	555	00	0
456	02	2	506	03	3	556	03	3
457	69	□P	507	00	0	557	00	0
458	04	04	508	02	2	558	03	3
459	43	RCL	509	69	□P	559	69	□P
460	05	05	510	04	04	560	04	04
461	75	-	511	43	RCL	561	43	RCL
462	04	4	512	15	15	562	20	20
463	06	6	513	58	FIX	563	75	-
464	00	0	514	01	01	564	04	4
465	95	=	515	69	□P	565	06	6
466	59	INT	516	06	06	566	00	0
467	69	□P	517	22	INV	567	95	=
468	06	06	518	58	FIX	568	59	INT
469	03	3	519	03	3	569	69	□P
470	03	3	520	07	7	570	06	06
471	00	0	521	00	0	571	69	□P
472	02	2	522	03	3	572	00	00
473	00	0	523	00	0	573	92	RTN
474	03	3	524	02	2	574	76	LBL
475	69	□P	525	69	□P	575	43	RCL
476	04	04	526	04	04	576	43	RCL
477	43	RCL	527	43	RCL	577	19	19
478	14	14	528	07	07	578	85	+
479	58	FIX	529	75	-	579	43	RCL
480	01	01	530	04	4	580	20	20
481	69	□P	531	06	6	581	95	=
482	06	06	532	00	0	582	55	÷
483	22	INV	533	95	=	583	02	2
484	58	FIX	534	59	INT	584	55	÷
485	03	3	535	69	□P	585	43	RCL
486	07	7	536	06	06	586	05	05
487	00	0	537	03	3	587	95	=
488	02	2	538	03	3	588	45	Y×
489	00	0	539	00	0	589	43	RCL
490	03	3	540	03	3	590	23	23
491	69	□P	541	00	0	591	55	÷
492	04	04	542	03	3	592	43	RCL
493	43	RCL	543	69	□P	593	09	09
494	19	19	544	04	04	594	95	=
495	75	-	545	43	RCL	595	42	STO
496	04	4	546	16	16	596	11	11
497	06	6	547	58	FIX	597	65	×
498	00	0	548	01	01	598	43	RCL
499	95	=	549	69	□P	599	09	09

(continued on next page)

Program 5 Listing continued

600	95	=	640	22	22	680	03	3
601	42	STO	641	71	SBR	681	03	3
602	25	25	642	55	÷	682	00	0
603	43	RCL	643	92	RTN	683	04	4
604	04	04	644	76	LBL	684	00	0
605	55	÷	645	23	LNX	685	03	3
606	43	RCL	646	03	3	686	69	OP
607	03	03	647	03	3	687	04	04
608	55	÷	648	00	0	688	43	RCL
609	43	RCL	649	04	4	689	18	18
610	25	25	650	00	0	690	58	FIX
611	95	=	651	02	2	691	01	01
612	34	ГX	652	69	OP	692	69	OP
613	42	STO	653	04	04	693	06	06
614	22	22	654	43	RCL	694	22	INV
615	71	SBR	655	17	17	695	58	FIX
616	55	÷	656	58	FIX	696	03	3
617	92	RTN	657	01	01	697	07	7
618	76	LBL	658	69	OP	698	00	0
619	52	EE	659	06	06	699	04	4
620	43	RCL	660	22	INV	700	00	0
621	20	20	661	58	FIX	701	03	3
622	85	+	662	03	3	702	69	OP
623	43	RCL	663	07	7	703	04	04
624	21	21	664	00	0	704	43	RCL
625	95	=	665	04	4	705	21	21
626	55	÷	666	00	0	706	75	-
627	02	2	667	02	2	707	04	4
628	55	÷	668	69	OP	708	06	6
629	43	RCL	669	04	04	709	00	0
630	07	07	670	43	RCL	710	95	=
631	95	=	671	07	07	711	59	INT
632	45	YX	672	75	-	712	69	OP
633	43	RCL	673	04	4	713	06	06
634	23	23	674	06	6	714	69	OP
635	55	÷	675	00	0	715	00	00
636	43	RCL	676	95	=	716	92	RTN
637	09	09	677	59	INT	717	00	0
638	95	=	678	69	OP	718	00	0
639	42	STO	679	06	06	719	00	0

Program 6

Power Savings from Cooling

Background

Program 5 discussed how intercooling is used to keep compression temperatures from getting too high. Study of Equations 2-9 and 2-12 shows that the power required for compression is directly proportional to the inlet temperature. Thus, since cooling lowers the compression temperature, it also lowers the power requirement. Intercooling, then, can help improve overall compression efficiency.

It is often interesting to study the effects on a compression process due to intercooling. The equations necessary for this investigation are Equations 5-2, 2-9, and 2-12, presented here for convenience:

$$r_{P_{SECT}} = \sqrt[b]{r_p} \tag{5-2}$$

$$H_p = Z_a R T_1 \left(\frac{n}{n-1}\right) [r_p^{(n-1)/n} - 1] \tag{2-9}$$

$$PWR_g = \frac{mH_p}{33,000\ \eta_p} \tag{2-12}$$

Equation 5-2 is used to establish an approximate pressure profile. Equation 2-9 is used to calculate the polytropic head for each section. The sum of the sectional polytropic heads is the total polytropic head required for the compression process. Equation 2-12 is used to calculate the power requirement based on the total polytropic head.

This procedure can be used to estimate the power requirement for straight-through compression, one cooling point, two cooling points, etc. The power requirements can be compared and the power savings evaluated against initial equipment cost and the cost of cooling utilities.

Program 6 Description

Program 6, Power Savings from Cooling, calculates and prints the results of Equations 5-2, 2-9, and 2-12 for straight-through compression, one cooling point, and two cooling points.

In order to execute the program, the following must be known:

1. Inlet pressure, P_1
2. Discharge pressure, P_2
3. Intercooler pressure drop, ΔP_{he}
4. Inlet temperature, T_1
5. Intercool inlet temperature, T_{ic}
6. Mass flow, m
7. Polytropic efficiency, η_p
8. Molecular weight, MW
9. Average k-value, k_a
10. Average Z-value, Z_a

The polytropic efficiency can be estimated from Table 2-2.

Calculations by the program are not entirely rigorous, for the following reasons:

1. No attempt is made by the program to optimize the pressure profile beyond the calculation of Equation 5-2.
2. The program uses the same average k- and Z-values throughout the investigation, even though these would potentially change as the number of cooling points is increased.
3. The same values for mass flow and molecular weight are used throughout the investigation. With cooling, there will normally be liquid knockout in the cooler. As a result, the mass flow and molecular weight will change from one section to another. Note also that molecular-weight changes may also have an effect on k- and Z-values.

Nevertheless, the program does present a qualitative analysis of the power saved by intercooling.

The discharge temperature printed by the program is the final discharge temperature, and is therefore not necessarily the highest sectional discharge temperature. However, the intercool inlet temperature is normally higher

Table 6-1
Program 6: Printer Nomenclature

Program Term	Definition	Units
CLPT	number of cooling points	dimensionless
DROP	intercooler pressure drop, expressed as a fraction of the pressure entering the cooler (i.e. the previous section discharge pressure)	dimensionless
EFF	polytropic efficiency	dimensionless
HEAD	polytropic head	ft-lbf/lbm
KA	average ratio of specific heats	dimensionless
M	mass flow	lbm/min
MW	molecular weight	lbm/lbm-mol
P1	inlet pressure	psia
P2	discharge pressure	psia
PWRG	gas power requirement	hp
T1	inlet temperature	°F
T2	discharge temperature	°F
TIC	intercool inlet temperature	°F
ZA	average compressibility	dimensionless

than the initial inlet temperature. Should this be the case, the temperature printed will be approximately the highest discharge temperature, allowing only for the intercooler pressure drop.

The program is set up to allow continuous usage by the operator, without the need for complete data reentry. Thus, the program can be rerun for different conditions by changing only the parameters of interest.

Table 6-1 is the nomenclature printed by the program; Table 6-2 shows the data registers used by the program.

Labels Used by Program 6

```
004   11   A      029   15   E      054   19   D'
009   12   B      039   16   A'     059   10   E'
014   13   C      044   17   B'     067   33   X²
024   14   D      049   18   C'
```

Program 6 Usage

Program 6 is executed by using the user-defined keys and SBR x^2. The definitions for the user-defined keys and SBR x^2 can be found in Table 6-3.

Table 6-2
Data Registers Used by Program 6

00	not used	10	Z_a	20	T2 (title)
01	not used	11	η_p	21	HEAD (title)
02	not used	12	$n/(n-1)$	22	PWRG (title)
03	P_1	13	$(n-1)/n$	23	T_2
04	P_2	14	$Z_a\left(\dfrac{1545}{MW}\right)\left(\dfrac{n}{n-1}\right)$	24	$(r_p)_1$
05	T_1	15	$r_p = P_2/P_1$	25	P_{12}
06	m	16	H_p	26	P_{21}
07	T_{ic}	17	PWR_g	27	P_{22}
08	MW	18	$1 + \Delta P_{he}$	28	P_{31}
09	k_a	19	CLPT (title)	29	33,000

Notes:
1. $(r_p)_1$ = first-section pressure ratio, and includes the effects of the cooler pressure drop.
2. P_{12} = first-section discharge pressure.
3. P_{21} = second-section inlet pressure.
4. P_{22} = second-section discharge pressure.
5. P_{31} = third-section inlet pressure.
6. P_1 = inlet pressure to the compressor.
7. P_2 = final discharge pressure.

Table 6-3
Program 6: Definitions of User-Defined Keys and SBR x^2

A	P1	A'	MW
B	P2	B'	KA
C	T1	C'	ZA
D	M	D'	EFF
E	TIC	E'	DROP
		SBR x^2	Calculate

After all the data are entered, program execution is initiated by depressing SBR x^2. Subsequent calculations can be made simply by changing only those terms desired.

Note that the calculator must be repartitioned to 719.29 before loading or keying in the program.

Sample Problem 6-1

Consider a dry-air process with an inlet pressure of 14 psia and an inlet temperature of 90°F. Nine hundred lbm/min of the gas is to be compressed to 100 psia. If intercooling is used, the heat exchangers will return the gas to the compressor at 100°F, with a pressure drop in the exchanger of 2% of the entering pressure. Assume a polytropic efficiency of 77% and calculate the polytropic head and gas power requirement for straight-through compression, one cool point, and two cool points.

The program printout will show that cooling is definitely required, since without it the discharge temperature would be approximately 680°F. Note that the second cool point saves an extra 5% horsepower.

Sample Problem 6-1: User Instructions

Step	Procedure	Enter	Press	Display
1.	Partition calculator.	3	2nd OP 17	719.29
2.	Load program.			
3.	Enter inlet pressure.	14	A	14
4.	Enter discharge pressure.	100	B	100
5.	Enter inlet temperature.	90(°F)	C	550(°R)
6.	Enter mass flow.	900	D	900
7.	Enter intercool inlet temperature.	100(°F)	E	560(°R)
8.	Enter molecular weight.	28.96	2nd A'	28.96
9.	Enter average *k*-value.	1.4	2nd B'	1.4
10.	Enter average Z-value.	1	2nd C'	1
11.	Enter polytropic efficiency.	0.77	2nd D'	0.77
12.	Enter intercooler pressure drop as a fraction of intercooler inlet pressure.	0.02	2nd E'	1.02
13.	Calculate.		SBR x^2	

Sample Problem 6-1: Program Printout

```
PWRG-SAVE              0.      CLPT
                     681.        T2
    14.     P1     84939.      HEAD
   100.     P2      3008.      PWRG
    90.     T1         1.      CLPT
   100.     TIC      347.        T2
   0.77     EFF    71090.      HEAD
  28.96     MW      2518.      PWRG
   1.4      KA         2.      CLPT
   1.       ZA       254.        T2
   0.02     DROP   67602.      HEAD
   900.      M      2394.      PWRG
```

Program 6 Listing

000	03	3	050	42	STO	100	43	RCL	
001	69	OP	051	10	10	101	09	09	
002	17	17	052	91	R/S	102	75	-	
003	76	LBL	053	76	LBL	103	01	1	
004	11	A	054	19	D'	104	95	=	
005	42	STO	055	42	STO	105	35	1/X	
006	03	03	056	11	11	106	65	×	
007	91	R/S	057	91	R/S	107	43	RCL	
008	76	LBL	058	76	LBL	108	09	09	
009	12	B	059	10	E'	109	65	×	
010	42	STO	060	85	+	110	43	RCL	
011	04	04	061	01	1	111	11	11	
012	91	R/S	062	95	=	112	95	=	
013	76	LBL	063	42	STO	113	42	STO	
014	13	C	064	18	18	114	12	12	
015	85	+	065	91	R/S	115	35	1/X	
016	04	4	066	76	LBL	116	42	STO	
017	06	6	067	33	X²	117	13	13	
018	00	0	068	69	OP	118	35	1/X	
019	95	=	069	00	00	119	65	×	
020	42	STO	070	03	3	120	01	1	
021	05	05	071	03	3	121	05	5	
022	91	R/S	072	04	4	122	04	4	
023	76	LBL	073	03	3	123	05	5	
024	14	D	074	03	3	124	65	×	
025	42	STO	075	05	5	125	43	RCL	
026	06	06	076	02	2	126	10	10	
027	91	R/S	077	02	2	127	55	÷	
028	76	LBL	078	02	2	128	43	RCL	
029	15	E	079	00	0	129	08	08	
030	85	+	080	69	OP	130	95	=	
031	04	4	081	02	02	131	42	STO	
032	06	6	082	03	3	132	14	14	
033	00	0	083	06	6	133	43	RCL	
034	95	=	084	01	1	134	04	04	
035	42	STO	085	03	3	135	55	÷	
036	07	07	086	04	4	136	43	RCL	
037	91	R/S	087	02	2	137	03	03	
038	76	LBL	088	01	1	138	95	=	
039	16	A'	089	07	7	139	42	STO	
040	42	STO	090	00	0	140	15	15	
041	08	08	091	00	0	141	45	Yˣ	
042	91	R/S	092	69	OP	142	43	RCL	
043	76	LBL	093	03	03	143	13	13	
044	17	B'	094	69	OP	144	65	×	
045	42	STO	095	05	05	145	43	RCL	
046	09	09	096	69	OP	146	05	05	
047	91	R/S	097	00	00	147	95	=	
048	76	LBL	098	98	ADV	148	42	STO	
049	18	C'	099	98	ADV	149	23	23	

Program 6 Listing continued

150	55	÷	200	69	OP	250	69	OP
151	43	RCL	201	06	06	251	04	04
152	05	05	202	03	3	252	43	RCL
153	75	-	203	07	7	253	08	08
154	01	1	204	00	0	254	69	OP
155	95	=	205	02	2	255	06	06
156	65	×	206	69	OP	256	02	2
157	43	RCL	207	04	04	257	06	6
158	05	05	208	43	RCL	258	01	1
159	65	×	209	05	05	259	03	3
160	43	RCL	210	75	-	260	69	OP
161	14	14	211	04	4	261	04	04
162	95	=	212	06	6	262	43	RCL
163	42	STO	213	00	0	263	09	09
164	16	16	214	95	=	264	69	OP
165	65	×	215	69	OP	265	06	06
166	43	RCL	216	06	06	266	04	4
167	06	06	217	03	3	267	06	6
168	55	÷	218	07	7	268	01	1
169	03	3	219	02	2	269	03	3
170	03	3	220	04	4	270	69	OP
171	00	0	221	01	1	271	04	04
172	00	0	222	05	5	272	43	RCL
173	00	0	223	69	OP	273	10	10
174	42	STO	224	04	04	274	69	OP
175	29	29	225	43	RCL	275	06	06
176	55	÷	226	07	07	276	01	1
177	43	RCL	227	75	-	277	06	6
178	11	11	228	04	4	278	03	3
179	95	=	229	06	6	279	05	5
180	42	STO	230	00	0	280	03	3
181	17	17	231	95	=	281	02	2
182	03	3	232	69	OP	282	03	3
183	03	3	233	06	06	283	03	3
184	00	0	234	01	1	284	69	OP
185	02	2	235	07	7	285	04	04
186	69	OP	236	02	2	286	43	RCL
187	04	04	237	01	1	287	18	18
188	43	RCL	238	02	2	288	75	-
189	03	03	239	01	1	289	01	1
190	69	OP	240	69	OP	290	95	=
191	06	06	241	04	04	291	69	OP
192	03	3	242	43	RCL	292	06	06
193	03	3	243	11	11	293	03	3
194	00	0	244	69	OP	294	00	0
195	03	3	245	06	06	295	69	OP
196	69	OP	246	03	3	296	04	04
197	04	04	247	00	0	297	43	RCL
198	43	RCL	248	04	4	298	06	06
199	04	04	249	03	3	299	69	OP

(continued on next page)

Program 6 Listing continued

300	06	06	350	23	23	400	95	=	
301	98	ADV	351	75	-	401	42	STO	
302	01	1	352	04	4	402	25	25	
303	05	5	353	06	6	403	55	÷	
304	02	2	354	00	0	404	43	RCL	
305	07	7	355	95	=	405	03	03	
306	03	3	356	58	FIX	406	95	=	
307	03	3	357	00	00	407	45	Yˣ	
308	03	3	358	69	OP	408	43	RCL	
309	07	7	359	06	06	409	13	13	
310	42	STO	360	22	INV	410	95	=	
311	19	19	361	58	FIX	411	75	-	
312	03	3	362	43	RCL	412	01	1	
313	07	7	363	21	21	413	95	=	
314	00	0	364	69	OP	414	65	×	
315	03	3	365	04	04	415	43	RCL	
316	42	STO	366	43	RCL	416	05	05	
317	20	20	367	16	16	417	65	×	
318	02	2	368	58	FIX	418	43	RCL	
319	03	3	369	00	00	419	14	14	
320	01	1	370	69	OP	420	95	=	
321	07	7	371	06	06	421	42	STO	
322	01	1	372	22	INV	422	16	16	
323	03	3	373	58	FIX	423	43	RCL	
324	01	1	374	43	RCL	424	04	04	
325	06	6	375	22	22	425	55	÷	
326	42	STO	376	69	OP	426	43	RCL	
327	21	21	377	04	04	427	26	26	
328	03	3	378	43	RCL	428	95	=	
329	03	3	379	17	17	429	45	Yˣ	
330	04	4	380	58	FIX	430	43	RCL	
331	03	3	381	00	00	431	13	13	
332	03	3	382	69	OP	432	65	×	
333	05	5	383	06	06	433	43	RCL	
334	02	2	384	22	INV	434	07	07	
335	02	2	385	58	FIX	435	95	=	
336	42	STO	386	43	RCL	436	42	STO	
337	22	22	387	15	15	437	23	23	
338	43	RCL	388	34	√x̄	438	55	÷	
339	19	19	389	42	STO	439	43	RCL	
340	69	OP	390	24	24	440	07	07	
341	04	04	391	65	×	441	75	-	
342	00	0	392	43	RCL	442	01	1	
343	69	OP	393	03	03	443	95	=	
344	06	06	394	95	=	444	65	×	
345	43	RCL	395	42	STO	445	43	RCL	
346	20	20	396	26	26	446	07	07	
347	69	OP	397	65	××	447	65	×	
348	04	04	398	43	RCL	448	43	RCL	
349	43	RCL	399	18	18	449	14	14	

Program 6 Listing continued

450	95	=	500	69	OP	550	43	RCL		
451	44	SUM	501	06	06	551	25	25		
452	16	16	502	22	INV	552	55	÷		
453	43	RCL	503	58	FIX	553	43	RCL		
454	16	16	504	43	RCL	554	03	03		
455	65	×	505	22	22	555	95	=		
456	43	RCL	506	69	OP	556	45	Y×		
457	06	06	507	04	04	557	43	RCL		
458	55	÷	508	43	RCL	558	13	13		
459	43	RCL	509	17	17	559	95	=		
460	29	29	510	58	FIX	560	75	-		
461	55	÷	511	00	00	561	01	1		
462	43	RCL	512	69	OP	562	95	=		
463	11	11	513	06	06	563	65	×		
464	95	=	514	22	INV	564	43	RCL		
465	42	STO	515	58	FIX	565	05	05		
466	17	17	516	43	RCL	566	65	×		
467	98	ADV	517	15	15	567	43	RCL		
468	43	RCL	518	45	Y×	568	14	14		
469	19	19	519	03	3	569	95	=		
470	69	OP	520	35	1/X	570	42	STO		
471	04	04	521	95	=	571	16	16		
472	01	1	522	42	STO	572	43	RCL		
473	69	OP	523	24	24	573	27	27		
474	06	06	524	65	×	574	55	÷		
475	43	RCL	525	43	RCL	575	43	RCL		
476	20	20	526	03	03	576	26	26		
477	69	OP	527	95	=	577	95	=		
478	04	04	528	42	STO	578	45	Y×		
479	43	RCL	529	26	26	579	43	RCL		
480	23	23	530	65	×	580	13	13		
481	75	-	531	43	RCL	581	95	=		
482	04	4	532	18	18	582	75	-		
483	06	6	533	95	=	583	01	1		
484	00	0	534	42	STO	584	95	=		
485	95	=	535	25	25	585	65	×		
486	58	FIX	536	43	RCL	586	43	RCL		
487	00	00	537	24	24	587	07	07		
488	69	OP	538	65	×	588	65	×		
489	06	06	539	43	RCL	589	43	RCL		
490	22	INV	540	26	26	590	14	14		
491	58	FIX	541	95	=	591	95	=		
492	43	RCL	542	42	STO	592	44	SUM		
493	21	21	543	28	28	593	16	16		
494	69	OP	544	65	×	594	43	RCL		
495	04	04	545	43	RCL	595	04	04		
496	43	RCL	546	18	18	596	55	÷		
497	16	16	547	95	=	597	43	RCL		
498	58	FIX	548	42	STO	598	28	28		
499	00	00	549	27	27	599	95	=		

(continued on next page)

Program 6 Listing continued

600	45	Y×	631	29	29	662	58	FIX
601	43	RCL	632	55	÷	663	43	RCL
602	13	13	633	43	RCL	664	21	21
603	65	×	634	11	11	665	69	OP
604	43	RCL	635	95	=	666	04	04
605	07	07	636	42	STO	667	43	RCL
606	95	=	637	17	17	668	16	16
607	42	STO	638	98	ADV	669	58	FIX
608	23	23	639	43	RCL	670	00	00
609	55	÷	640	19	19	671	69	OP
610	43	RCL	641	69	OP	672	06	06
611	07	07	642	04	04	673	22	INV
612	75	–	643	02	2	674	58	FIX
613	01	1	644	69	OP	675	43	RCL
614	95	=	645	06	06	676	22	22
615	65	×	646	43	RCL	677	69	OP
616	43	RCL	647	20	20	678	04	04
617	07	07	648	69	OP	679	43	RCL
618	65	×	649	04	04	680	17	17
619	43	RCL	650	43	RCL	681	58	FIX
620	14	14	651	23	23	682	00	00
621	95	=	652	75	–	683	69	OP
622	44	SUM	653	04	4	684	06	06
623	16	16	654	06	6	685	22	INV
624	43	RCL	655	00	0	686	58	FIX
625	16	16	656	95	=	687	69	OP
626	65	×	657	58	FIX	688	00	00
627	43	RCL	658	00	00	689	91	R/S
628	06	06	659	69	OP	690	92	RTN
629	55	÷	660	06	06	691	00	0
630	43	RCL	661	22	INV	692	00	0

Part II

Centrifugal Compressor
Performance Curves

Program 7

Fan-Law for the Head Curve

Background

Compressor manufacturers often present the performance of their centrifugal compressors in the form of an inlet volume flow versus head and power curve. The curve is useful as it stands; however, it is often necessary to analyze compressor performance at speeds other than those plotted by the manufacturer.

Additional performance curves can be drawn by using the fan-laws. Such curves are sufficiently accurate within $\pm10\%$ of the manufacturer's curve speed. Beyond 10%, the fan-laws will begin to deteriorate, although the results obtained from them may still be useful.

The fan-law relationships are given by Equations 7-1, 7-2, and 7-3:

$$\frac{Q_1}{(Q_1)_{bc}} = \frac{N}{N_{bc}} \tag{7-1}$$

$$\frac{H_p}{(H_p)_{bc}} = \left(\frac{N}{N_{bc}}\right)^2 \tag{7-2}$$

$$\frac{PWR}{PWR_{bc}} = \left(\frac{N}{N_{bc}}\right)^3 \tag{7-3}$$

where:

bc = base curve, and refers to the manufacturer's curve
PWR = power requirement, either gas or shaft

Table 7-1
Program 7: Printer Nomenclature

Program Term	Definition	Units
HEAD	polytropic or adiabatic head	ft-lbf/lbm
N	curve speed of interest	rpm
NBC	speed of base curve	rpm
PWR	gas or shaft power requirement	hp
Q1	inlet volume flow	ICFM

Note that when using the fan-laws, each compression section should be handled separately. For example, a compressor with two side loads will have three compression sections. The manufacturer probably would furnish a curve for each section, and the fan-law should be applied to each of the sectional curves, not to an overall performance curve.

In the case of an intercooled compressor: If the only intermediate pressure drop is that associated with the intercool heat exchanger, if the liquid knockout in the exchanger is small, and if no gas is extracted or added to the process at the point of cooling, relatively accurate results can be obtained by fan-lawing the overall performance curve.

Program 7 Description

Program 7, Fan-Law for the Head Curve, calculates and prints the results of Equations 7-1, 7-2, and 7-3 for up to five curve points from a manufacturer's performance curve.

In order to execute the program, the following must be known:

1. Inlet volume flow, $(Q_1)_{bc}$
2. Polytropic or adiabatic head, $(H_p)_{bc}$ or $(H_{ad})_{bc}$
3. Power requirement, $(PWR)_{bc}$
4. Manufacturer's curve speed, N_{bc}
5. Curve speed of interest, N

After the manufacturer's curve is entered into the program, any number of curve speeds can be calculated simply by entering the new speed of interest. Reentry of the manufacturer's curve is not necessary.

Table 7-1 is the nomenclature printed by the program; Table 7-2 shows the data registers used by the program.

Note that if the power entered is gas horsepower, the program calculates gas horsepower. If the power entered is shaft horsepower, the program calculates shaft horsepower.

Table 7-2
Data Registers Used by Program 7

00	not used	16 ⎫		32 ⎫	
01	not used	17 ⎬ $(H_p)_{bc}$		33 ⎬ H_p	
02	not used	18 ⎭		34 ⎭	
03	pointer, Q_1	19		35 ⎫	
04	pointer, H_p	20 ⎫		36 ⎪	
05	pointer, PWR	21 ⎪		37 ⎬ PWR	
06	counter, number of points	22 ⎬ PWR_{bc}		38 ⎪	
07	pointer, $(Q_1)_{bc}$	23 ⎪		39 ⎭	
08	pointer, $(H_p)_{bc}$	24 ⎭		40	not used
09	pointer, PWR_{bc}	25 ⎫		41	not used
10 ⎫		26 ⎪		42	not used
11 ⎪		27 ⎬ Q_1		43	not used
12 ⎬ $(Q_1)_{bc}$		28 ⎪		44	not used
13 ⎪		29 ⎭		45	number of points
14 ⎭		30 ⎫ H_p		46	N_{bc}
15	$(H_p)_{bc}$	31 ⎭		47	N

Table 7-3
Program 7: Definitions of User-Defined Keys

A	Q1	D	N, Calculate
B	HEAD	D'	NBC
C	PWR	E'	Initialize

Labels Used by Program 7

```
001   10 E'        081   19 D'        301   35 1/X
058   11  A        108   14  D        368   34 ГX
067   12  B        178   33 X²
074   13  C        237   45 Y×
```

Program 7 Usage

Program 7 is executed by using the user-defined keys. The definitions of the user-defined keys can be found in Table 7-3.

After initializing, the program is executed by first entering the base performance curve. This is accomplished by entering the inlet volume flow and the corresponding head and power requirement through user-defined keys A, B, and C, respectively. Up to five curve points can be entered in this way. After entering the base curve, the base speed is entered through user-defined key D'.

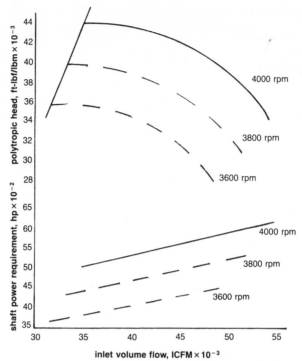

Figure 7-1. Inlet volume flow versus polytropic head and power curve for Sample Problem 7-1.

The program is then ready to calculate the performance curve for any number of speeds simply by entering the speed through D. Reentry of the base performance curve between performance-curve calculations is not necessary.

Sample Problem 7-1

Given the base performance curve in Figure 7-1 (shown by the solid line) for which the base speed is 4000 rpm, calculate the performance curves for speeds of 3800 rpm and 3600 rpm.

The following points can be read from the base curve:

$(Q_1)_{bc}$	$(H_p)_{bc}$	PWR_{bc}
35,000	44,000	5050
40,000	43,600	5350
45,000	42,100	5700
50,000	39,100	5900
54,000	34,000	6200

The dashed curves on Figure 7-1 are the calculated performance curves.

Sample Problem 7-1: User Instructions

Step	Procedure	Enter	Press	Display
1.	Load program.			
2.	Initialize.		2nd E'	0
3.	Enter base-curve inlet volume flow.	35000	A	35000
4.	Enter base-curve head.	44000	B	44000
5.	Enter base-curve power requirement.	5050	C	5050
6.	Repeat steps 3, 4, and 5 for up to five curve points.			
7.	Enter base-curve speed.	4000	2nd D'	35
8.	Enter curve speed of interest and calculate.	3800	D	
9.	For new speed, repeat step 8.	3600	D	

Sample Problem 7-1: Program Printout

```
FAN-LAW (HEAD)        **CURVE SPEED**     **CURVE SPEED**

   4000.      NBC      3800.        N      3600.        N


  35000.       Q1     33250.       Q1     31500.       Q1
  44000.     HEAD     39710.     HEAD     35640.     HEAD
   5050.      PWR      4330.      PWR      3681.      PWR

  40000.       Q1     38000.       Q1     36000.       Q1
  43600.     HEAD     39349.     HEAD     35316.     HEAD
   5350.      PWR      4587.      PWR      3900.      PWR

  45000.       Q1     42750.       Q1     40500.       Q1
  42100.     HEAD     37995.     HEAD     34101.     HEAD
   5700.      PWR      4887.      PWR      4155.      PWR

  50000.       Q1     47500.       Q1     45000.       Q1
  39100.     HEAD     35288.     HEAD     31671.     HEAD
   5900.      PWR      5059.      PWR      4301.      PWR

  54000.       Q1     51300.       Q1     48600.       Q1
  34000.     HEAD     30685.     HEAD     27540.     HEAD
   6200.      PWR      5316.      PWR      4520.      PWR
```

Program 7 Listing

000	76	LBL		050	98	ADV		100	42	STO	
001	10	E'		051	71	SBR		101	45	45	
002	98	ADV		052	34	⌐X		102	71	SBR	
003	69	OP		053	00	0		103	34	⌐X	
004	00	00		054	42	STO		104	71	SBR	
005	02	2		055	06	06		105	33	X²	
006	01	1		056	91	R/S		106	91	R/S	
007	01	1		057	76	LBL		107	76	LBL	
008	03	3		058	11	A		108	14	D	
009	69	OP		059	72	ST*		109	42	STO	
010	01	01		060	07	07		110	47	47	
011	03	3		061	69	OP		111	05	5	
012	01	1		062	27	27		112	01	1	
013	02	2		063	69	OP		113	05	5	
014	00	0		064	26	26		114	01	1	
015	02	2		065	91	R/S		115	01	1	
016	07	7		066	76	LBL		116	05	5	
017	01	1		067	12	B		117	69	OP	
018	03	3		068	72	ST*		118	01	01	
019	04	4		069	08	08		119	04	4	
020	03	3		070	69	OP		120	01	1	
021	69	OP		071	28	28		121	03	3	
022	02	02		072	91	R/S		122	05	5	
023	05	5		073	76	LBL		123	04	4	
024	05	5		074	13	C		124	02	2	
025	02	2		075	72	ST*		125	01	1	
026	03	3		076	09	09		126	07	7	
027	01	1		077	69	OP		127	00	0	
028	07	7		078	29	29		128	00	0	
029	01	1		079	91	R/S		129	69	OP	
030	03	3		080	76	LBL		130	02	02	
031	69	OP		081	19	D'		131	03	3	
032	03	03		082	42	STO		132	06	6	
033	01	1		083	46	46		133	03	3	
034	06	6		084	03	3		134	03	3	
035	05	5		085	01	1		135	01	1	
036	06	6		086	01	1		136	07	7	
037	00	0		087	04	4		137	01	1	
038	00	0		088	01	1		138	07	7	
039	00	0		089	05	5		139	01	1	
040	00	0		090	69	OP		140	06	6	
041	00	0		091	04	04		141	69	OP	
042	00	0		092	43	RCL		142	03	03	
043	69	OP		093	46	46		143	05	5	
044	04	04		094	69	OP		144	01	1	
045	69	OP		095	06	06		145	05	5	
046	05	05		096	98	ADV		146	01	1	
047	69	OP		097	98	ADV		147	00	0	
048	00	00		098	43	RCL		148	00	0	
049	98	ADV		099	06	06		149	00	0	

Program 7 Listing continued

150	00	0	200	08	08	250	47	47
151	00	0	201	69	□P	251	55	÷
152	00	0	202	06	06	252	43	RCL
153	69	□P	203	03	3	253	46	46
154	04	04	204	03	3	254	95	=
155	69	□P	205	04	4	255	33	X²
156	05	05	206	03	3	256	65	×
157	69	□P	207	03	3	257	73	RC*
158	00	00	208	05	5	258	08	08
159	98	ADV	209	69	□P	259	95	=
160	03	3	210	04	04	260	72	ST*
161	01	1	211	73	RC*	261	04	04
162	69	□P	212	09	09	262	43	RCL
163	04	04	213	69	□P	263	47	47
164	43	RCL	214	06	06	264	55	÷
165	47	47	215	98	ADV	265	43	RCL
166	69	□P	216	69	□P	266	46	46
167	06	06	217	27	27	267	95	=
168	98	ADV	218	69	□P	268	45	Yˣ
169	98	ADV	219	28	28	269	03	3
170	71	SBR	220	69	□P	270	65	×
171	45	Yˣ	221	29	29	271	73	RC*
172	71	SBR	222	97	DSZ	272	09	09
173	34	ГX	223	06	06	273	95	=
174	98	ADV	224	33	X²	274	72	ST*
175	98	ADV	225	69	□P	275	05	05
176	91	R/S	226	00	00	276	69	□P
177	76	LBL	227	43	RCL	277	27	27
178	33	X²	228	45	45	278	69	□P
179	03	3	229	42	STD	279	28	28
180	04	4	230	06	06	280	69	□P
181	00	0	231	71	SBR	281	29	29
182	02	2	232	34	ГX	282	69	□P
183	69	□P	233	98	ADV	283	23	23
184	04	04	234	98	ADV	284	69	□P
185	73	RC*	235	92	RTN	285	24	24
186	07	07	236	76	LBL	286	69	□P
187	69	□P	237	45	Yˣ	287	25	25
188	06	06	238	43	RCL	288	97	DSZ
189	02	2	239	47	47	289	06	06
190	03	3	240	55	÷	290	45	Yˣ
191	01	1	241	43	RCL	291	43	RCL
192	07	7	242	46	46	292	45	45
193	01	1	243	65	×	293	42	STD
194	03	3	244	73	RC*	294	06	06
195	01	1	245	07	07	295	71	SBR
196	06	6	246	95	=	296	34	ГX
197	69	□P	247	72	ST*	297	71	SBR
198	04	04	248	03	03	298	35	1/X
199	73	RC*	249	43	RCL	299	92	RTN

(continued on next page)

Program 7 Listing continued

300	76	LBL	332	22	INV	364	42	STD
301	35	1/X	333	58	FIX	365	06	06
302	03	3	334	03	3	366	92	RTN
303	04	4	335	03	3	367	76	LBL
304	00	0	336	04	4	368	34	ΓX
305	02	2	337	03	3	369	01	1
306	69	DP	338	03	3	370	00	0
307	04	04	339	05	5	371	42	STD
308	73	RC*	340	69	DP	372	07	07
309	03	03	341	04	04	373	01	1
310	58	FIX	342	73	RC*	374	05	5
311	00	00	343	05	05	375	42	STD
312	69	DP	344	58	FIX	376	08	08
313	06	06	345	00	00	377	02	2
314	22	INV	346	69	DP	378	00	0
315	58	FIX	347	06	06	379	42	STD
316	02	2	348	22	INV	380	09	09
317	03	3	349	58	FIX	381	02	2
318	01	1	350	69	DP	382	05	5
319	07	7	351	23	23	383	42	STD
320	01	1	352	69	DP	384	03	03
321	03	3	353	24	24	385	03	3
322	01	1	354	69	DP	386	00	0
323	06	6	355	25	25	387	42	STD
324	69	DP	356	98	ADV	388	04	04
325	04	04	357	97	DSZ	389	03	3
326	73	RC*	358	06	06	390	05	5
327	04	04	359	35	1/X	391	42	STD
328	58	FIX	360	69	DP	392	05	05
329	00	00	361	00	00	393	92	RTN
330	69	DP	362	43	RCL	394	00	0
331	06	06	363	45	45	395	00	0

Program 8

Fan-Law for the Pressure Curve (psi)

Background

Compressor manufacturers often present the performance of their centrifugal compressors in the form of an inlet volume flow versus discharge pressure (psi absolute or gauge) and power curve. The curve is useful as it stands; however, it is often necessary to analyze compressor performance at speeds other than those plotted by the manufacturer.

Additional curves can be drawn by using the fan-laws. Refer to Program 7 for accuracy and applicability.

The fan-law relationships for inlet volume flow and power are shown in Equations 7-1 and 7-3, respectively, presented here for convenience:

$$\frac{Q_1}{(Q_1)_{bc}} = \frac{N}{N_{bc}} \tag{7-1}$$

$$\frac{PWR}{PWR_{bc}} = \left(\frac{N}{N_{bc}}\right)^3 \tag{7-3}$$

The fan-law equation for discharge pressure must be derived.

Reference to Equation 7-2 shows that the head is proportional to the square of the speed.

Use the adiabatic head equation, Equation 1-11, for the derivation of the discharge-pressure equation:

$$H_{ad} = Z_1 R T_1 \left(\frac{k}{k-1}\right) [r_p^{(k-1)/k} - 1] \tag{1-11}$$

85

When fan-lawing from a point on a curve, the compressibility, molecular weight, inlet temperature, and k-value remain constant. Therefore:

$$\frac{(r_p^{(k-1)/k} - 1)}{(r_p^{(k-1)/k} - 1)_{bc}} = \left(\frac{H_{ad}}{(H_{ad})_{bc}}\right)$$

and:

$$\frac{(r_p^{(k-1)/k} - 1)}{(r_p^{(k-1)/k} - 1)_{bc}} = \left(\frac{N}{N_{bc}}\right)^2 \tag{8-1}$$

Substituting P_2/P_1 for r_p results in Equation 8-2:

$$P_2 = P_1 \left[(r_p^{(k-1)/k} - 1)_{bc} \left(\frac{N}{N_{bc}}\right)^2 + 1 \right]^{k/(k-1)} \tag{8-2}$$

Equation 8-2 was derived from the adiabatic head equation. The adiabatic head was chosen for simplicity. Had the polytropic head been chosen, Equation 8-2 would have been a function of the n-value of the gas. Thus, a polytropic efficiency would have to be known for each point. Note that while the polytropic efficiency will change from point to point along a performance curve, it will remain constant when point fan-lawing from one speed curve to another. Thus, Equation 8-2 is reasonably valid for polytropic processes. The accuracy will be within the expected accuracy of the fan-law relationships.

Program 8 Description

Program 8, Fan-Law for the Pressure Curve (psi), calculates and prints the results of Equations 7-1, 7-3, and 8-2 for up to five curve points from a manufacturer's performance curve.

In order to execute the program, the following must be known:

1. Inlet volume flow, $(Q_1)_{bc}$
2. Discharge pressure, $(P_2)_{bc}$, either absolute or gauge pressure
3. Power requirement, PWR_{bc}
4. Inlet pressure, P_1, either absolute or gauge pressure, but consistent with the units of $(P_2)_{bc}$
5. Average k-value, k_a
6. Barometric pressure, P_{bar}
7. Manufacturer's curve speed, N_{bc}
8. Curve speed of interest, N

After the manufacturer's curve is entered into the program, any number of curve speeds can be calculated simply by entering the new speed of interest. Reentry of the manufacturer's curve is not necessary.

Table 8-1 is the nomenclature printed by the program; Table 8-2 shows the data registers used by the program.

Note that if the power entered is gas horsepower, the program calculates gas horsepower. If the power entered is shaft horsepower, the program calculates shaft horsepower.

Table 8-1
Program 8: Printer Nomenclature

Program Term	Definition	Units
KA	average ratio of specific heats	dimensionless
N	curve speed of interest	rpm
NBC	speed of base curve	rpm
P1	inlet pressure	psia or psig
PBAR	barometric pressure	psia
PSI	discharge pressure—base curve	psia or psig
PSIA	discharge pressure	psia
PSIG	discharge pressure	psig
PWR	gas or shaft power requirement	hp
Q1	inlet volume flow	ICFM

Table 8-2
Data Registers Used by Program 8

00	not used	16		32	
01	not used	17	$(P_2)_{bc}$	33	P_2
02	not used	18		34	
03	pointer, Q_1	19		35	
04	pointer, P_2	20		36	
05	pointer, PWR	21		37	PWR
06	counter, number of points	22	PWR_{bc}	38	
07	pointer, $(Q_1)_{bc}$	23		39	
08	pointer, $(P_2)_{bc}$	24		40	k_a
09	pointer, PWR_{bc}	25		41	P_{bar}
10		26		42	$(k-1)/k$
11		27	Q_1	43	P_1
12	$(Q_1)_{bc}$	28		44	PSIA or PSIG (title)
13		29		45	number of points
14		30	P_2	46	N_{bc}
15	$(P_2)_{bc}$	31		47	N

Labels Used by Program 8

```
004   10 E'        103   18 C'        316   44 SUM
061   11 A         108   19 D'        374   45 Y×
070   12 B         171   14 D         458   35 1/X
077   13 C         198   15 E         517   42 STO
084   16 A'        238   34 ΓX        535   43 RCL
089   17 B'        265   33 X²
```

Table 8-3
Program 8: Definitions of User-Defined Keys

A	Q1	A'	P1
B	P2 (PSIA or PSIG)	B'	KA
C	PWR	C'	PBAR
D	N, Calculate—PSIA	D'	NBC
E	N, Calculate—PSIG	E'	Initialize

Program 8 Usage

Program 8 is executed by using the user-defined keys. The definitions for the user-defined keys can be found in Table 8-3.

After initializing, the program is executed by first entering the base performance curve. This is accomplished by entering the inlet volume flow and the corresponding discharge pressure (psia or psig) and power requirement through user-defined keys A, B, and C, respectively. Up to five curve points can be entered in this way.

The inlet pressure is entered through user-defined key A'. If the discharge pressure values for the base curve are entered in psia, the inlet pressure must also be entered in psia. If the discharge pressure values are entered in psig, so must the inlet pressure. The output will be in the same units as the input.

Note on the program printouts that the discharge pressures for the curve of interest are titled PSIA or PSIG to denote the units used. The discharge pressures for the base curve are titled PSI to indicate either psia or psig.

The average ratio of specific heats and the barometric pressure (psia) are entered through user-defined keys B' and C', respectively. Note that the barometric pressure need not be entered for cases computed in psia, unless desired for record purposes.

The base speed is entered through user-defined key D'.

The program will calculate the performance curve for any number of speeds simply by entering the speed of interest through D for curves in psia, or through E for curves in psig. Reentry of the base performance curve between performance curve calculations is not necessary.

Note that the calculator must be repartitioned to 559.49 before loading or keying in the program.

Sample Problem 8-1

Given a base performance curve in psia from which the following can be extracted:

$P_1 = 14.0$ psia

$k_a = 1.4$

$P_{bar} = 14.2$ psia

$N_{bc} = 4000$ rpm

$(Q_1)_{bc}$	$(P_2)_{bc}$	PWR_{bc}
35,000	45.0	4400
45,000	43.5	5000
50,000	41.0	5250
54,000	35.5	5450

calculate the performance curves for speeds of 3800 rpm and 3600 rpm.

Sample Problem 8-1 (psia): User Instructions

Step	Procedure	Enter	Press	Display
1.	Partition calculator.	5	2nd OP 17	559.49
2.	Load program.			
3.	Initialize.		2nd E'	0
4.	Enter inlet pressure.	14.0	2nd A'	14
5.	Enter average k-value.	1.4	2nd B'	$.2857\ldots\left(\dfrac{k-1}{k}\right)$
6.	Enter barometric pressure.	14.2	2nd C'	14.2
7.	Enter base-curve inlet volume flow.	35000	A	35000
8.	Enter base-curve discharge pressure.	45.0	B	45
9.	Enter base-curve power requirement.	4400	C	4400

Sample Problem 8-1: User Instructions continued

Step	Procedure	Enter	Press	Display
10.	Repeat steps 7, 8, and 9 for up to five curve points.			
11.	Enter base-curve speed.	4000	2nd D′	35
12.	Enter curve speed of interest and calculate.	3800	D	
13.	For new curve speed, repeat step 12.	3600	D	

Sample Problem 8-1: Program Printout

```
FAN-LAW (PSI)        **CURVE SPEED**      **CURVE SPEED**

                       3800.        N       3600.        N
        14.     P1
        14.2    PBAR
        1.4     KA      33250.      Q1     31500.       Q1
      4000.     NBC       40.8     PSIA      37.1      PSIA
                        3772.      PWR      3208.      PWR
      35000.    Q1
        45.     PSI     42750.      Q1     40500.       Q1
      4400.     PWR       39.5     PSIA      36.0      PSIA
                        4287.      PWR      3645.      PWR
      45000.    Q1
        43.5    PSI     47500.      Q1     45000.       Q1
      5000.     PWR       37.4     PSIA      34.2      PSIA
                        4501.      PWR      3827.      PWR
      50000.    Q1
        41.     PSI     51300.      Q1     48600.       Q1
      5250.     PWR       32.8     PSIA      30.3      PSIA
                        4673.      PWR      3973.      PWR
      54000.    Q1
        35.5    PSI
      5450.     PWR
```

Sample Problem 8-2

Calculate the performance curves for Sample Problem 8-1 in psig.

Plotting of the peformance curves for these two sample problems is left to the reader.

Sample Problem 8-2 (psig): User Instructions

Step	Procedure	Enter	Press	Display
1–11.	Refer to sample problem 8-1 user instructions, except that inlet and discharge pressures are entered in psig.			
12.	Enter curve speed of interest and calculate.	3800	E	
13.	For new curve speed, repeat step 12.	3600	E	

Sample Problem 8-2: Program Printout

```
FAN-LAW (PSI)      **CURVE SPEED**        **CURVE SPEED**

   -0.2      P1     3800.        N         3600.         N
   14.2      PBAR
    1.4      KA

 4000.       NBC    33250.       Q1        31500.        Q1
                       26.6     PSIG          22.9      PSIG
35000.       Q1      3772.      PWR         3208.       PWR
   30.8      PSI
 4400.       PWR    42750.       Q1        40500.        Q1
                       25.3     PSIG          21.8      PSIG
45000.       Q1      4287.      PWR         3645.       PWR
   29.3      PSI
 5000.       PWR    47500.       Q1        45000.        Q1
                       23.2     PSIG          20.0      PSIG
50000.       Q1      4501.      PWR         3827.       PWR
   26.8      PSI
 5250.       PWR    51300.       Q1        48600.        Q1
                       18.6     PSIG          16.1      PSIG
54000.       Q1      4673.      PWR         3973.       PWR
   21.3      PSI
 5450.       PWR
```

Program 8 Listing

000	05	5	004	10	E'	008	02	2
001	69	OP	005	98	ADV	009	01	1
002	17	17	006	69	OP	010	01	1
003	76	LBL	007	00	00	011	03	3

(continued on next page)

Program 8 Listing continued

012	69	OP	062	72	ST*	112	03	3
013	01	01	063	07	07	113	00	0
014	03	3	064	69	OP	114	02	2
015	01	1	065	27	27	115	69	OP
016	02	2	066	69	OP	116	04	04
017	00	0	067	26	26	117	43	RCL
018	02	2	068	91	R/S	118	43	43
019	07	7	069	76	LBL	119	69	OP
020	01	1	070	12	B	120	06	06
021	03	3	071	72	ST*	121	03	3
022	04	4	072	08	08	122	03	3
023	03	3	073	69	OP	123	01	1
024	69	OP	074	28	28	124	04	4
025	02	02	075	91	R/S	125	01	1
026	05	5	076	76	LBL	126	03	3
027	05	5	077	13	C	127	03	3
028	03	3	078	72	ST*	128	05	5
029	03	3	079	09	09	129	69	OP
030	03	3	080	69	OP	130	04	04
031	06	6	081	29	29	131	43	RCL
032	02	2	082	91	R/S	132	41	41
033	04	4	083	76	LBL	133	69	OP
034	69	OP	084	16	A'	134	06	06
035	03	03	085	42	STO	135	02	2
036	05	5	086	43	43	136	06	6
037	06	6	087	91	R/S	137	01	1
038	00	0	088	76	LBL	138	03	3
039	00	0	089	17	B'	139	69	OP
040	00	0	090	42	STO	140	04	04
041	00	0	091	40	40	141	43	RCL
042	00	0	092	75	-	142	40	40
043	00	0	093	01	1	143	69	OP
044	00	0	094	95	=	144	06	06
045	00	0	095	55	÷	145	98	ADV
046	69	OP	096	43	RCL	146	98	ADV
047	04	04	097	40	40	147	03	3
048	69	OP	098	95	=	148	01	1
049	05	05	099	42	STO	149	01	1
050	69	OP	100	42	42	150	04	4
051	00	00	101	91	R/S	151	01	1
052	98	ADV	102	76	LBL	152	05	5
053	98	ADV	103	18	C'	153	69	OP
054	71	SBR	104	42	STO	154	04	04
055	34	ГX	105	41	41	155	43	RCL
056	00	0	106	91	R/S	156	46	46
057	42	STO	107	76	LBL	157	69	OP
058	06	06	108	19	D'	158	06	06
059	91	R/S	109	42	STO	159	98	ADV
060	76	LBL	110	46	46	160	98	ADV
061	11	A	111	03	3	161	43	RCL

Program 8 Listing continued

162	06	06	212	02	2	262	05	05
163	42	STO	213	42	STO	263	92	RTN
164	45	45	214	44	44	264	76	LBL
165	71	SBR	215	71	SBR	265	33	X²
166	34	ΓX	216	42	STO	266	03	3
167	71	SBR	217	43	RCL	267	04	4
168	33	X²	218	41	41	268	00	0
169	91	R/S	219	44	SUM	269	02	2
170	76	LBL	220	43	43	270	69	OP
171	14	D	221	71	SBR	271	04	04
172	42	STO	222	44	SUM	272	73	RC*
173	47	47	223	71	SBR	273	07	07
174	43	RCL	224	45	YX	274	69	OP
175	45	45	225	71	SBR	275	06	06
176	42	STO	226	43	RCL	276	03	3
177	06	06	227	71	SBR	277	03	3
178	03	3	228	35	1/X	278	03	3
179	03	3	229	71	SBR	279	06	6
180	03	3	230	34	ΓX	280	02	2
181	06	6	231	43	RCL	281	04	4
182	02	2	232	41	41	282	69	OP
183	04	4	233	22	INV	283	04	04
184	01	1	234	44	SUM	284	73	RC*
185	03	3	235	43	43	285	08	08
186	42	STO	236	91	R/S	286	69	OP
187	44	44	237	76	LBL	287	06	06
188	71	SBR	238	34	ΓX	288	03	3
189	44	SUM	239	01	1	289	03	3
190	71	SBR	240	00	0	290	04	4
191	45	YX	241	42	STO	291	03	3
192	71	SBR	242	07	07	292	03	3
193	35	1/X	243	01	1	293	05	5
194	71	SBR	244	05	5	294	69	OP
195	34	ΓX	245	42	STO	295	04	04
196	91	R/S	246	08	08	296	73	RC*
197	76	LBL	247	02	2	297	09	09
198	15	E	248	00	0	298	69	OP
199	42	STO	249	42	STO	299	06	06
200	47	47	250	09	09	300	98	ADV
201	43	RCL	251	02	2	301	69	OP
202	45	45	252	05	5	302	27	27
203	42	STO	253	42	STO	303	69	OP
204	06	06	254	03	03	304	28	28
205	03	3	255	03	3	305	69	OP
206	03	3	256	00	0	306	29	29
207	03	3	257	42	STO	307	97	DSZ
208	06	6	258	04	04	308	06	06
209	02	2	259	03	3	309	33	X²
210	04	4	260	05	5	310	71	SBR
211	02	2	261	42	STO	311	34	ΓX

(continued on next page)

Program 8 Listing continued

312	98	ADV	362	03	3	,12	42	42
313	98	ADV	363	01	1	413	35	1/X
314	92	RTN	364	69	OP	414	95	=
315	76	LBL	365	04	04	415	65	×
316	44	SUM	366	43	RCL	416	43	RCL
317	05	5	367	47	47	417	43	43
318	01	1	368	69	OP	418	95	=
319	05	5	369	06	06	419	72	ST*
320	01	1	370	98	ADV	420	04	04
321	69	OP	371	98	ADV	421	43	RCL
322	01	01	372	92	RTN	422	47	47
323	01	1	373	76	LBL	423	55	÷
324	05	5	374	45	YX	424	43	RCL
325	04	4	375	43	RCL	425	46	46
326	01	1	376	47	47	426	95	=
327	03	3	377	55	÷	427	45	YX
328	05	5	378	43	RCL	428	03	3
329	04	4	379	46	46	429	65	×
330	02	2	380	65	×	430	73	RC*
331	01	1	381	73	RC*	431	09	09
332	07	7	382	07	07	432	95	=
333	69	OP	383	95	=	433	72	ST*
334	02	02	384	72	ST*	434	05	05
335	03	3	385	03	03	435	69	OP
336	06	6	386	73	RC*	436	27	27
337	03	3	387	08	08	437	69	OP
338	03	3	388	55	÷	438	28	28
339	01	1	389	43	RCL	439	69	OP
340	07	7	390	43	43	440	29	29
341	01	1	391	95	=	441	69	OP
342	07	7	392	45	YX	442	23	23
343	69	OP	393	43	RCL	443	69	OP
344	03	03	394	42	42	444	24	24
345	01	1	395	75	-	445	69	OP
346	06	6	396	01	1	446	25	25
347	05	5	397	95	=	447	97	DSZ
348	01	1	398	65	×	448	06	06
349	05	5	399	53	(	449	45	YX
350	01	1	400	43	RCL	450	71	SBR
351	00	0	401	47	47	451	34	ſX
352	00	0	402	55	÷	452	43	RCL
353	00	0	403	43	RCL	453	45	45
354	00	0	404	46	46	454	42	STO
355	69	OP	405	54	)	455	06	06
356	04	04	406	33	X²	456	92	RTN
357	69	OP	407	85	+	457	76	LBL
358	05	05	408	01	1	458	35	1/X
359	69	OP	409	95	=	459	03	3
360	00	00	410	45	YX	460	04	4
361	98	ADV	411	43	RCL	461	00	0

Program 8 Listing continued

462	02	2	494	05	05	526	42	STO
463	69	OP	495	58	FIX	527	43	RCL
464	04	04	496	00	00	528	45	45
465	73	RC*	497	69	OP	529	42	STO
466	03	03	498	06	06	530	06	06
467	58	FIX	499	22	INV	531	71	SBR
468	00	00	500	58	FIX	532	34	ГX
469	69	OP	501	69	OP	533	92	RTN
470	06	06	502	23	23	534	76	LBL
471	22	INV	503	69	OP	535	43	RCL
472	58	FIX	504	24	24	536	43	RCL
473	43	RCL	505	69	OP	537	41	41
474	44	44	506	25	25	538	22	INV
475	69	OP	507	98	ADV	539	74	SM*
476	04	04	508	97	DSZ	540	08	08
477	73	RC*	509	06	06	541	22	INV
478	04	04	510	35	1/X	542	74	SM*
479	58	FIX	511	98	ADV	543	04	04
480	01	01	512	98	ADV	544	69	OP
481	69	OP	513	69	OP	545	28	28
482	06	06	514	00	00	546	69	OP
483	22	INV	515	92	RTN	547	24	24
484	58	FIX	516	76	LBL	548	97	DSZ
485	03	3	517	42	STO	549	06	06
486	03	3	518	43	RCL	550	43	RCL
487	04	4	519	41	41	551	71	SBR
488	03	3	520	74	SM*	552	34	ГX
489	03	3	521	08	08	553	43	RCL
490	05	5	522	69	OP	554	45	45
491	69	OP	523	28	28	555	42	STO
492	04	04	524	97	DSZ	556	06	06
493	73	RC*	525	06	06	557	92	RTN

Program 9

Fan-Law for the Pressure Curve (in H₂O)

Background

Compressor manufacturers often present the performance of their centrifugal compressors in the form of an inlet volume flow versus discharge pressure (inches water gauge, in H₂O) and power curve. The curve is useful as it stands; however, it is often necessary to analyze compressor performance at speeds other than those plotted by the manufacturer.

Additional curves can be drawn by using the fan-laws. Refer to Program 7 for accuracy and applicability.

The reader is referred to Program 8 for the fan-law equations applicable to this type of performance curve. They are presented here for convenience:

$$\frac{Q_1}{(Q_1)_{bc}} = \frac{N}{N_{bc}} \tag{7-1}$$

$$P_2 = P_1 \left[(r_p^{(k-1)/k} - 1)_{bc} \left(\frac{N}{N_{bc}} \right)^2 + 1 \right]^{k/(k-1)} \tag{8-2}$$

$$\frac{PWR}{PWR_{bc}} = \left(\frac{N}{N_{bc}} \right)^3 \tag{7-3}$$

The only additional equation necessary for discharge pressure in inches water gauge is a conversion from inches water gauge to psig, as in Equation 9-1:

$$\text{psig} = \frac{\text{inches water gauge}}{27.72} \tag{9-1}$$

Table 9-1
Program 9: Printer Nomenclature

Program Term	Definition	Units
H2O	discharge pressure	in. H_2O gauge
KA	average ratio of specific heats	dimensionless
N	curve speed of interest	rpm
NBC	speed of base curve	rpm
P1	inlet pressure	in. H_2O gauge
PBAR	barometric pressure	psia
PWR	gas of shaft power requirement	hp
Q1	inlet volume flow	ICFM

Program 9 Description

Program 9, Fan-Law for the Pressure Curve (in H_2O), calculates and prints the results of Equations 7-1, 8-2, 7-3, and 9-1 for up to five curve points from a manufacturer's performance curve.

In order to execute the program, the following must be known:

1. Inlet volume flow, $(Q_1)_{bc}$
2. Discharge pressure, $(P_2)_{bc}$, in. H_2O
3. Power requirement, PWR_{bc}
4. Inlet pressure, P_1, in. H_2O
5. Average k-value, k_a
6. Barometric pressure, P_{bar}
7. Manufacturer's curve speed, N_{bc}
8. Curve speed of interest, N

After the manufacturer's curve is entered into the program, any number of curve speeds can be calculated simply by entering the new speed of interest. Reentry of the manufacturer's curve is not necessary.

Table 9-1 is the nomenclature printed by the program; Table 9-2 shows the data registers used by the program.

Note that if the power entered is gas horsepower, the program calculates gas horsepower. If the power entered is shaft horsepower, the program calculates shaft horsepower.

Labels Used by Program 9

004	10	E'	088	17	B'	295	33	X²
060	11	A	102	18	C'	346	42	STD
069	12	B	107	19	D'	372	45	Y×
076	13	C	170	14	D	456	43	RCL
083	16	A'	268	34	ΓX	489	35	1/X

Table 9-2
Data Registers Used by Program 9

00	not used	16	$\left.\vphantom{\begin{array}{c}1\\1\\1\\1\end{array}}\right\}$	32	$\left.\vphantom{\begin{array}{c}1\\1\\1\end{array}}\right\}$ P_2
01	not used	17	$(P_2)_{bc}$	33	
02	not used	18		34	
03	pointer, Q_1	19		35	$\left.\vphantom{\begin{array}{c}1\\1\\1\\1\\1\end{array}}\right\}$
04	pointer, P_2	20	$\left.\vphantom{\begin{array}{c}1\\1\\1\end{array}}\right\}$	36	
05	pointer, PWR	21		37	PWR
06	counter, number of points	22	PWR_{bc}	38	
07	pointer, $(Q_1)_{bc}$	23		39	
08	pointer, $(P_2)_{bc}$	24		40	k_a
09	pointer, PWR_{bc}	25	$\left.\vphantom{\begin{array}{c}1\\1\\1\end{array}}\right\}$	41	P_{bar}
10	$\left.\vphantom{\begin{array}{c}1\\1\\1\\1\\1\end{array}}\right\}$	26		42	$(k-1)/k$
11		27	Q_1	43	P_1
12	$(Q_1)_{bc}$	28		44	not used
13		29		45	number of points
14		30	$\left.\vphantom{\begin{array}{c}1\\1\end{array}}\right\}$	46	N_{bc}
15	$(P_2)_{bc}$	31	P_2	47	N

Table 9-3
Program 9: Definitions of User-Defined Keys

A	Q1	A'	P1
B	P2 (H2O)	B'	KA
C	PWR	C'	PBAR
D	N, Calculate	D'	NBC
		E'	Initialize

Program 9 Usage

Program 9 is executed by using the user-defined keys. The definitions of the user-defined keys can be found in Table 9-3.

After initializing, the program is executed by first entering the base performance curve. This is accomplished by entering the inlet volume flow and the corresponding discharge pressure (in H_2O gauge) and power requirement through user-defined keys A, B, and C, respectively. Up to five points can be entered in this way.

The inlet pressure is entered in inches water gauge through user-defined key A'. The average ratio of specific heats and the barometric pressure (psia) are entered through user-defined keys B' and C', respectively. The base speed is entered through user-defined key D'.

The program will calculate the performance curve for any number of speeds simply by entering the speed of interest through D. Reentry of the base performance curve between performance-curve calculations is not necessary.

Note that the calculator must be repartitioned to 559.49 before loading or keying in the program.

Sample Problem 9-1

Given a base performance curve with discharge pressures in inches water gauge from which the following can be extracted:

$$P_1 = -5 \text{ in. } H_2O$$

$$k_a = 1.4$$

$$P_{bar} = 14.2 \text{ psia}$$

$$N_{bc} = 4000 \text{ rpm}$$

$(Q_1)_{bc}$	$(P_2)_{bc}$	PWR_{bc}
35,000	220	1530
45,000	217	1770
50,000	200	1880
54,000	175	1940

calculate the performance curves for speeds of 3800 rpm and 3600 rpm. Plotting of the performance curves is left to the reader.

Sample Problem 9-1: User Instructions

Step	Procedure	Enter	Press	Display
1.	Partition calculator.	5	2nd OP 17	559.49
2.	Load program.			
3.	Initialize.		2nd E′	0
4.	Enter inlet pressure.	−5	2nd A′	−5
5.	Enter average k-value.	1.4	2nd B′	$.2857\ldots\left(\dfrac{k-1}{k}\right)$
6.	Enter barometric pressure.	14.2	2nd C′	14.2
7.	Enter base-curve inlet volume flow.	35000	A	35000
8.	Enter base-curve discharge pressure.	220	B	220
9.	Enter base-curve power requirement.	1530	C	1530
10.	Repeat steps 7, 8, and 9 for up to five curve points.			

(continued on next page)

Sample Problem 9-1: User Instructions continued

Step	Procedure	Enter	Press	Display
11.	Enter base-curve speed.	4000	2nd D′	35
12.	Enter curve speed of interest and calculate.	3800	D	
13.	For new curve speed, repeat step 12.	3600	D	

Sample Problem 9-1: Program Printout

```
FAN-LAW (H2O)      **CURVE SPEED**      **CURVE SPEED**
    -5.      P1      3800.        N      3600.        N
   14.2     PBAR
    1.4       KA

  4000.      NBC    33250.       Q1     31500.       Q1
                      194.8     H2O       171.5     H2O
 35000.       Q1     1312.      PWR      1115.      PWR
    220.     H2O
   1530.     PWR     42750.       Q1     40500.       Q1
                      192.1     H2O       169.2     H2O
 45000.       Q1     1518.      PWR      1290.      PWR
    217.     H2O
   1770.     PWR     47500.       Q1     45000.       Q1
                      177.2     H2O       156.2     H2O
 50000.       Q1     1612.      PWR      1371.      PWR
    200.     H2O
   1880.     PWR     51300.       Q1     48600.       Q1
                      155.3     H2O       137.0     H2O
 54000.       Q1     1663.      PWR      1414.      PWR
    175.     H2O
   1940.     PWR
```

Program 9 Listing

```
000   05   5      007   02   2      014   01   1
001   69   OP     008   01   1      015   02   2
002   17   17     009   01   1      016   00   0
003   76   LBL    010   03   3      017   02   2
004   10   E'     011   69   OP     018   07   7
005   69   OP     012   01   01     019   01   1
006   00   00     013   03   3      020   03   3
```

Program 9 Listing continued

021	04	4	071	08	08	121	03	3
022	03	3	072	69	□P	122	01	1
023	69	□P	073	28	28	123	04	4
024	02	02	074	91	R/S	124	01	1
025	05	5	075	76	LBL	125	03	3
026	05	5	076	13	C	126	03	3
027	02	2	077	72	ST*	127	05	5
028	03	3	078	09	09	128	69	□P
029	00	0	079	69	□P	129	04	04
030	03	3	080	29	29	130	43	RCL
031	03	3	081	91	R/S	131	41	41
032	02	2	082	76	LBL	132	69	□P
033	69	□P	083	16	A'	133	06	06
034	03	03	084	42	STO	134	02	2
035	05	5	085	43	43	135	06	6
036	06	6	086	91	R/S	136	01	1
037	00	0	087	76	LBL	137	03	3
038	00	0	088	17	B'	138	69	□P
039	00	0	089	42	STO	139	04	04
040	00	0	090	40	40	140	43	RCL
041	00	0	091	75	-	141	40	40
042	00	0	092	01	1	142	69	□P
043	00	0	093	95	=	143	06	06
044	00	0	094	55	÷	144	98	ADV
045	69	□P	095	43	RCL	145	98	ADV
046	04	04	096	40	40	146	03	3
047	69	□P	097	95	=	147	01	1
048	05	05	098	42	STO	148	01	1
049	69	□P	099	42	42	149	04	4
050	00	00	100	91	R/S	150	01	1
051	98	ADV	101	76	LBL	151	05	5
052	98	ADV	102	18	C'	152	69	□P
053	71	SBR	103	42	STO	153	04	04
054	34	ΓX	104	41	41	154	43	RCL
055	00	0	105	91	R/S	155	46	46
056	42	STO	106	76	LBL	156	69	□P
057	06	06	107	19	D'	157	06	06
058	91	R/S	108	42	STO	158	98	ADV
059	76	LBL	109	46	46	159	98	ADV
060	11	A	110	03	3	160	43	RCL
061	72	ST*	111	03	3	161	06	06
062	07	07	112	00	0	162	42	STO
063	69	□P	113	02	2	163	45	45
064	27	27	114	69	□P	164	71	SBR
065	69	□P	115	04	04	165	34	ΓX
066	26	26	116	43	RCL	166	71	SBR
067	91	R/S	117	43	43	167	33	X²
068	76	LBL	118	69	□P	168	91	R/S
069	12	B	119	06	06	169	76	LBL
070	72	ST*	120	03	3	170	14	D

(continued on next page)

Program 9 Listing continued

171	42	STD	221	98	ADV	271	42	STD	
172	47	47	222	03	3	272	07	07	
173	43	RCL	223	01	1	273	01	1	
174	45	45	224	69	OP	274	05	5	
175	42	STD	225	04	04	275	42	STD	
176	06	06	226	43	RCL	276	08	08	
177	05	5	227	47	47	277	02	2	
178	01	1	228	69	OP	278	00	0	
179	05	5	229	06	06	279	42	STD	
180	01	1	230	98	ADV	280	09	09	
181	69	OP	231	98	ADV	281	02	2	
182	01	01	232	71	SBR	282	05	5	
183	01	1	233	42	STD	283	42	STD	
184	05	5	234	02	2	284	03	03	
185	04	4	235	07	7	285	03	3	
186	01	1	236	93	.	286	00	0	
187	03	3	237	07	7	287	42	STD	
188	05	5	238	02	2	288	04	04	
189	04	4	239	22	INV	289	03	3	
190	02	2	240	49	PRD	290	05	5	
191	01	1	241	43	43	291	42	STD	
192	07	7	242	43	RCL	292	05	05	
193	69	OP	243	41	41	293	92	RTN	
194	02	02	244	44	SUM	294	76	LBL	
195	03	3	245	43	43	295	33	X²	
196	06	6	246	71	SBR	296	03	3	
197	03	3	247	45	Y×	297	04	4	
198	03	3	248	71	SBR	298	00	0	
199	01	1	249	43	RCL	299	02	2	
200	07	7	250	71	SBR	300	69	OP	
201	01	1	251	35	1/X	301	04	04	
202	07	7	252	71	SBR	302	73	RC*	
203	69	OP	253	34	⌈X	303	07	07	
204	03	03	254	43	RCL	304	69	OP	
205	01	1	255	41	41	305	06	06	
206	06	6	256	22	INV	306	02	2	
207	05	5	257	44	SUM	307	03	3	
208	01	1	258	43	43	308	00	0	
209	05	5	259	02	2	309	03	3	
210	01	1	260	07	7	310	03	3	
211	00	0	261	93	.	311	02	2	
212	00	0	262	07	7	312	69	OP	
213	00	0	263	02	2	313	04	04	
214	00	0	264	49	PRD	314	73	RC*	
215	69	OP	265	43	43	315	08	08	
216	04	04	266	91	R/S	316	69	OP	
217	69	OP	267	76	LBL	317	06	06	
218	05	05	268	34	⌈X	318	03	3	
219	69	OP	269	01	1	319	03	3	
220	00	00	270	00	0	320	04	4	

Program 9 Listing continued

321	03	3	371	76	LBL	421	55	÷
322	03	3	372	45	Yˣ	422	43	RCL
323	05	5	373	43	RCL	423	46	46
324	69	OP	374	47	47	424	95	=
325	04	04	375	55	÷	425	45	Yˣ
326	73	RC*	376	43	RCL	426	03	3
327	09	09	377	46	46	427	65	×
328	69	OP	378	65	×	428	73	RC*
329	06	06	379	73	RC*	429	09	09
330	98	ADV	380	07	07	430	95	=
331	69	OP	381	95	=	431	72	ST*
332	27	27	382	72	ST*	432	05	05
333	69	OP	383	03	03	433	69	OP
334	28	28	384	73	RC*	434	27	27
335	69	OP	385	08	08	435	69	OP
336	29	29	386	55	÷	436	28	28
337	97	DSZ	387	43	RCL	437	69	OP
338	06	06	388	43	43	438	29	29
339	33	X²	389	95	=	439	69	OP
340	71	SBR	390	45	Yˣ	440	23	23
341	34	ГX	391	43	RCL	441	69	OP
342	98	ADV	392	42	42	442	24	24
343	98	ADV	393	75	-	443	69	OP
344	92	RTN	394	01	1	444	25	25
345	76	LBL	395	95	=	445	97	DSZ
346	42	STO	396	65	×	446	06	06
347	02	2	397	53	(	447	45	Yˣ
348	07	7	398	43	RCL	448	71	SBR
349	93	.	399	47	47	449	34	ГX
350	07	7	400	55	÷	450	43	RCL
351	02	2	401	43	RCL	451	45	45
352	22	INV	402	46	46	452	42	STO
353	64	PD*	403	54	)	453	06	06
354	08	08	404	33	X²	454	92	RTN
355	43	RCL	405	85	+	455	76	LBL
356	41	41	406	01	1	456	43	RCL
357	74	SM*	407	95	=	457	43	RCL
358	08	08	408	45	Yˣ	458	41	41
359	69	OP	409	43	RCL	459	22	INV
360	28	28	410	42	42	460	74	SM*
361	97	DSZ	411	35	1/X	461	08	08
362	06	06	412	95	=	462	22	INV
363	42	STO	413	65	×	463	74	SM*
364	43	RCL	414	43	RCL	464	04	04
365	45	45	415	43	43	465	02	2
366	42	STO	416	95	=	466	07	7
367	06	06	417	72	ST*	467	93	.
368	71	SBR	418	04	04	468	07	7
369	34	ГX	419	43	RCL	469	02	2
370	92	RTN	420	47	47	470	64	PD*

(continued on next page)

Program 9 Listing continued

471	08	08	500	69	OP	529	05	05
472	64	PD*	501	06	06	530	58	FIX
473	04	04	502	22	INV	531	00	00
474	69	OP	503	58	FIX	532	69	OP
475	28	28	504	02	2	533	06	06
476	69	OP	505	03	3	534	22	INV
477	24	24	506	00	0	535	58	FIX
478	97	DSZ	507	03	3	536	69	OP
479	06	06	508	03	3	537	23	23
480	43	RCL	509	02	2	538	69	OP
481	71	SBR	510	69	OP	539	24	24
482	34	ΓX	511	04	04	540	69	OP
483	43	RCL	512	73	RC*	541	25	25
484	45	45	513	04	04	542	98	ADV
485	42	STO	514	58	FIX	543	97	DSZ
486	06	06	515	01	01	544	06	06
487	92	RTN	516	69	OP	545	35	1/X
488	76	LBL	517	06	06	546	98	ADV
489	35	1/X	518	22	INV	547	98	ADV
490	03	3	519	58	FIX	548	69	OP
491	04	4	520	03	3	549	00	00
492	00	0	521	03	3	550	92	RTN
493	02	2	522	04	4	551	00	0
494	69	OP	523	03	3	552	00	0
495	04	04	524	03	3	553	00	0
496	73	RC*	525	05	5	554	00	0
497	03	03	526	69	OP	555	00	0
498	58	FIX	527	04	04	556	00	0
499	00	00	528	73	RC*	557	00	0

Program 10

Suction Throttling
for the Pressure Curve (psi)

Background

Programs 7, 8, and 9 presented performance-curve programs for variable-speed driven centrifugal compressors. Often centrifugal compressors are powered by constant-speed drivers such as motors or motor-gear combinations. Since the speed is constant for these applications, the performance curve can be varied only by throttling across a valve placed upstream of the compressor inlet. (Discharge throttling is sometimes used, but it is not as efficient as suction throttling; therefore, it will not be considered here.)

The effect of suction throttling is to drop the inlet pressure at the compressor inlet flange, resulting in a corresponding drop in discharge pressure. The volume flow upstream of the throttle valve decreases also, resulting in a corresponding drop in power requirement.

To gain appreciation for this, consider the flow-head curve discussed in Program 7. Since the speed is constant, the compressor flow-head curve will not change when the compressor is throttled. Thus, the compressor defined by Figure 7-1 will produce 42,100 ft-lbf/lbm of polytropic head at a compressor inlet flow of 45,000 ICFM, regardless of the actual compressor inlet pressure. (Note that the compressor inlet pressure for the purpose of this discussion is defined as the pressure occurring at the compressor inlet flange and is therefore downstream of the suction throttle valve.) Since if the compressor is throttled, the pressure at the compressor inlet flange is lower than the process inlet pressure upstream of the valve, the upstream volume flow will be less than the compressor inlet volume flow:

$$(Q_1)_{us} = \frac{P_1}{(P_1)_{bc}} (Q_1)_{bc} \qquad (10\text{-}1)$$

where:

$(Q_1)_{us}$ = volume flow measured upstream of the valve

P_1 = actual compressor inlet pressure downstream of the valve

$(P_1)_{bc}$ = process inlet pressure upstream of the valve (it is assumed here that the process inlet pressure is identical to that on the manufacturer-supplied base curve; thus the subscript *bc*.)

$(Q_1)_{bc}$ = volume flow measured downstream of the valve, and represents the inlet volume flow values on the manufacturer-supplied base curve

If it is assumed that all process values (i.e., temperature, pressure, etc. upstream of the valve) remain constant and equal to those used for the base curve, the mass-flow throughput corresponding to a specific inlet volume flow will differ by the same pressure ratio as that used in Equation 10-1. Therefore:

$$m = \frac{P_1}{(P_1)_{bc}} (m)_{bc} \tag{10-2}$$

Since the power requirement is directly proportional to the head and mass flow and inversely proportional to the efficiency, and since the head and efficiency curves are not affected by suction throttling:

$$PWR = \frac{P_1}{(P_1)_{bc}} (PWR)_{bc} \tag{10-3}$$

Note that Equation 10-3 is not entirely accurate if the plotted power is shaft horsepower. The mechanical losses are a function of speed and machine size, not inlet pressure. The losses will thus remain constant. Equation 10-3 will, however, provide sufficient accuracy for all cases unless the mechanical losses are a significant percentage of the total power requirement.

Now consider the head equation as presented in Equation 2-9:

$$H_p = Z_a RT_1 \left(\frac{n}{n-1}\right) [r_p^{(n-1)/n} - 1] \tag{2-9}$$

Since the compressibility, molecular weight, inlet temperature, and k-value remain constant, and since the polytropic head and polytropic efficiency curves are not affected by suction throttling (neither are the adiabatic head and efficiency curves, when they apply), the pressure ratio is not affected by suction throttling. Therefore:

$$P_2 = \left(\frac{P_2}{P_1}\right)_{bc} (P_1) \tag{10-4}$$

Table 10-1
Program 10: Printer Nomenclature

Program Term	Definition	Units
KA	average ratio of specific heats	dimensionless
P1BC	inlet pressure of base curve	psia or psig
P1	inlet pressure of interest	psia or psig
PBAR	barometric pressure	psia
PSI	discharge pressure—base curve	psia or psig
PSIA	discharge pressure	psia
PSIG	discharge pressure	psig
PWR	gas or shaft power requirement	hp
Q1	inlet volume flow downstream of throttle valve	ICFM
QUS	inlet volume flow upstream of throttle valve	ICFM

The effects of suction throttling can be analyzed by plotting the discharge pressure and power requirement versus either the compressor inlet volume flow or the volume flow upstream of the valve. The latter is normally preferred, since it provides more information regarding process effects.

Note that suction throttling will save horsepower. The power savings, however, are not as great as those that would result from a corresponding speed reduction.

Program 10 Description

Program 10, Suction Throttling for the Pressure Curve (psi), calculates and prints the results of Equations 10-1, 10-3, and 10-4 for up to five curve points from a manufacturer's performance curve.

In order to execute the program, the following must be known:

1. Inlet volume flow, $(Q_1)_{bc}$
2. Discharge pressure, $(P_2)_{bc}$, either absolute or gauge pressure
3. Power requirement, PWR_{bc}
4. Average k-value, k_a
5. Barometric pressure, P_{bar}
6. Inlet pressure from manufacturer's curve, $(P_1)_{bc}$, either absolute or gauge pressure, but consistant with $(P_2)_{bc}$
7. Inlet pressure of interest, P_1, consistant with the units of $(P_2)_{bc}$

After the manufacturer's curve is entered into the program, curves for any number of inlet pressures can be calculated simply by entering the new inlet pressure of interest. Reentry of the manufacturer's curve is not necessary.

Table 10-1 is the nomenclature printed by the program; Table 10-2 shows the data registers used by the program.

Table 10-2
Data Registers Used by Program 10

00	not used	16	⎫	32	⎫
01	not used	17	⎬ $(P_2)_{bc}$	33	⎬ P_2
02	not used	18	⎭	34	⎭
03	pointer, $(Q_1)_{us}$	19		35	⎫
04	pointer, P_2	20	⎫	36	⎪
05	pointer, PWR	21	⎪	37	⎬ PWR
06	counter, number of points	22	⎬ PWR_{bc}	38	⎪
07	pointer, $(Q_1)_{bc}$	23	⎪	39	⎭
08	pointer, $(P_2)_{bc}$	24	⎭	40	k_a
09	pointer, PWR_{bc}	25	⎫	41	P_{bar}
10	⎫	26	⎪	42	$(k-1)/k$
11	⎪	27	⎬ $(Q_1)_{us}$	43	not used
12	⎬ $(Q_1)_{bc}$	28	⎪	44	PSIA or PSIG (title)
13	⎪	29	⎭	45	number of points
14	⎭	30	⎫ P_2	46	$(P_1)_{bc}$
15	$(P_2)_{bc}$	31	⎭	47	P_1

Note that if the power entered is gas horsepower, the program calculates gas horsepower. If the power entered is shaft horsepower, the program calculates shaft horsepower.

Labels Used by Program 10

```
004   10 E'        109   19 D'        374   45 Y×
067   11  A        164   14  D        431   35 1∕×
076   12  B        191   15  E        508   42 STO
083   13  C        236   34 ⌈×        526   43 RCL
090   17 B'        263   33 ×²
104   18 C'        314   44 SUM
```

Program 10 Usage

Program 10 is executed by using the user-defined keys. The definitions of the user-defined keys can be found in Table 10-3.

After initializing, the program is executed by first entering the base performance curve. This is accomplished by entering the inlet volume flow and the corresponding discharge pressure (psia or psig) and power through user-defined keys A, B, and C, respectively. Up to five curve points can be entered in this way.

The average ratio of specific heats and the barometric pressure (psia) are entered through user-defined keys B′ and C′, respectively. Note that the

Table 10-3
Program 10: Definitions of User-Defined Keys

A	Q1		
B	P2 (PSIA or PSIG)	B′	KA
C	PWR	C′	PBAR
D	P1, Calculate—PSIA	D′	P1BC
E	P1, Calculate—PSIG	E′	Initialize

barometric pressure need not be entered for cases computed in psia, unless desired for record purposes.

The inlet pressure for the base curve is entered through user-defined key D′. If the discharge pressure values for the base curve are entered in psia, the inlet pressures—both base curve and inlet pressure of interest—must be also. If the discharge pressures are in psig, the inlet pressures must be also.

Note on the program printouts that the discharge pressures for the curve of interest are titled PSIA and PSIG to denote the units used. The discharge pressures for the base curve are titled PSI to indicate either psia or psig.

The program will calculate the performance curve for any number of inlet pressures simply by entering the inlet pressure of interest through D for curves in psia, or through E for curves in psig. There is no need to reenter the base performance curve between performance-curve calculations.

Note that the calculator must be repartitioned to 559.49 before loading or keying in the program.

Sample Problem 10-1

Given a base performance curve in psia from which the following can be extracted:

$(P_1)_{bc} = 14.0$ psia

$k_a = 1.4$

$P_{bar} = 14.2$ psia

$(Q_1)_{bc}$	$(P_2)_{bc}$	PWR_{bc}
35,000	45.0	4400
45,000	43.5	5000
50,000	41.0	5250
54,000	35.5	5450

calculate the performance curves for suction-throttled inlet pressures of 13 psia and 11 psia.

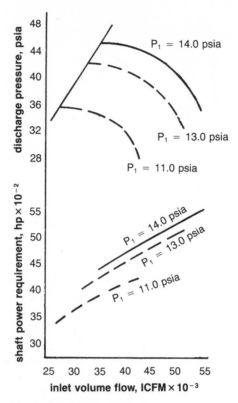

Figure 10-1. Inlet volume flow versus discharge pressure and power curve for Sample Problem 10-1. Inlet volume flow is plotted upstream of the throttle valve.

Figures 10-1 and 10-2 show the performance curves resulting from the calculations. The base curve is shown solid and the two calculated curves are dashed. Figure 10-1 shows discharge pressure and power requirement plotted against inlet volume flow upstream of the suction throttling valve. Figure 10-2 shows discharge pressure and power requirement plotted against inlet volume flow to the compressor—therefore, volume flow measured downstream of the throttle valve. Note that suction-throttled performance curves based on volume flow upstream of the valve resemble the performance curves resulting from variable-speed considerations.

Sample Problem 10-1 (psia): User Instructions

Step	Procedure	Enter	Press	Display
1.	Partition calculator.	5	2nd OP 17	559.49
2.	Load program.			

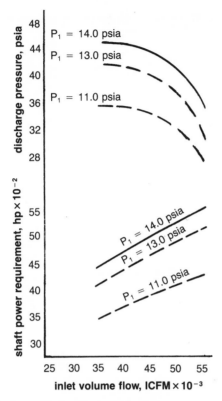

Figure 10-2. Inlet volume flow versus discharge pressure and power curve for Sample Problem 10-1. Inlet volume flow is plotted downstream of the throttle valve.

Sample Problem 10-1 (psia): User Instructions continued

Step	Procedure	Enter	Press	Display
3.	Initialize.		2nd E′	0
4.	Enter average k-value.	1.4	2nd B′	$.2857\ldots\left(\dfrac{k-1}{k}\right)$
5.	Enter barometric pressure.	14.2	2nd C′	14.2
6.	Enter base-curve inlet volume flow.	35000	A	35000
7.	Enter base-curve discharge pressure.	45.0	B	45

(continued on next page)

Sample Problem 10-1 (psia): User Instructions continued

Step	Procedure	Enter	Press	Display
8.	Enter base-curve power requirement.	4400	C	4400
9.	Repeat steps 6, 7, and 8 for up to five curve points.			
10.	Enter base-curve inlet pressure.	14.0	2nd D′	35
11.	Enter inlet pressure of interest and calculate.	13.0	D	
12.	For new inlet pressure, repeat step 11.	11.0	D	

Sample Problem 10-1: Program Printout

```
SUCTION THROTTLING **CURVE P1**        **CURVE P1**

    14.2      PBAR        11.      P1          13.      P1
     1.4      KA
                       35000.      Q1       35000.      Q1
    14.      P1BC      27500.      QUS      32500.      QUS
                          35.4     PSIA        41.8     PSIA
                        3457.      PWR       4086.      PWR
 35000.       Q1
    45.       PSI      45000.      Q1       45000.      Q1
  4400.       PWR      35357.      QUS      41786.      QUS
                          34.2     PSIA        40.4     PSIA
                        3929.      PWR       4643.      PWR
 45000.       Q1
    43.5      PSI      50000.      Q1       50000.      Q1
  5000.       PWR      39286.      QUS      46429.      QUS
                          32.2     PSIA        38.1     PSIA
                        4125.      PWR       4875.      PWR
 50000.       Q1
    41.       PSI
  5250.       PWR      54000.      Q1       54000.      Q1
                       42429.      QUS      50143.      QUS
 54000.       Q1          27.9     PSIA        33.0     PSIA
    35.5      PSI       4282.      PWR       5061.      PWR
  5450.       PWR
```

Sample Problem 10-2

Calculate the performance curves for Sample Problem 10-1 in psig. Plotting of the performance curves is left to the reader.

Sample Problem 10-2 (psig): User Instructions

Step	Procedure	Enter	Press	Display
1–10	Refer to Sample Problem 10-1, User Instructions, except that inlet and discharge pressures are entered in psig.			
11.	Enter inlet pressure of interest and calculate.	−1.2	E	
12.	For new inlet pressure, repeat step 11.	−3.2	E	

Sample Problem 10-2: Program Printout

```
SUCTION THROTTLING **CURVE P1**        **CURVE P1**

   14.2    PBAR
    1.4      KA      -1.2     P1       -3.2      P1


   -0.2    P1BC    35000.     Q1     35000.      Q1
                   32500.    QUS     27500.     QUS
                      27.6  PSIG        21.2   PSIG
 35000.      Q1     4086.    PWR      3457.     PWR
    30.8    PSI
  4400.     PWR    45000.     Q1     45000.      Q1
                   41786.    QUS     35357.     QUS
 45000.      Q1       26.2  PSIG        20.0   PSIG
    29.3    PSI     4643.    PWR      3929.     PWR
  5000.     PWR
                   50000.     Q1     50000.      Q1
                   46429.    QUS     39286.     QUS
 50000.      Q1       23.9  PSIG        18.0   PSIG
    26.8    PSI     4875.    PWR      4125.     PWR
  5250.     PWR
                   54000.     Q1     54000.      Q1
 54000.      Q1    50143.    QUS     42429.     QUS
    21.3    PSI       18.8  PSIG        13.7   PSIG
  5450.     PWR     5061.    PWR      4282.     PWR
```

Program 10 Listing

000	05	5	004	10	E'	008	03	3
001	69	OP	005	98	ADV	009	06	6
002	17	17	006	69	OP	010	04	4
003	76	LBL	007	00	00	011	01	1

(continued on next page)

Program 10 Listing continued

012	01	1	062	00	0	112	03	3
013	05	5	063	42	STO	113	03	3
014	03	3	064	06	06	114	01	1
015	07	7	065	91	R/S	115	04	4
016	69	OP	066	76	LBL	116	01	1
017	01	01	067	11	A	117	03	3
018	02	2	068	72	ST*	118	03	3
019	04	4	069	07	07	119	05	5
020	03	3	070	69	OP	120	69	OP
021	02	2	071	27	27	121	04	04
022	03	3	072	69	OP	122	43	RCL
023	01	1	073	26	26	123	41	41
024	00	0	074	91	R/S	124	69	OP
025	00	0	075	76	LBL	125	06	06
026	03	3	076	12	B	126	02	2
027	07	7	077	72	ST*	127	06	6
028	69	OP	078	08	08	128	01	1
029	02	02	079	69	OP	129	03	3
030	02	2	080	28	28	130	69	OP
031	03	3	081	91	R/S	131	04	04
032	03	3	082	76	LBL	132	43	RCL
033	05	5	083	13	C	133	40	40
034	03	3	084	72	ST*	134	69	OP
035	02	2	085	09	09	135	06	06
036	03	3	086	69	OP	136	98	ADV
037	07	7	087	29	29	137	98	ADV
038	03	3	088	91	R/S	138	03	3
039	07	7	089	76	LBL	139	03	3
040	69	OP	090	17	B'	140	00	0
041	03	03	091	42	STO	141	02	2
042	02	2	092	40	40	142	01	1
043	07	7	093	75	-	143	04	4
044	02	2	094	01	1	144	01	1
045	04	4	095	95	=	145	05	5
046	03	3	096	55	÷	146	69	OP
047	01	1	097	43	RCL	147	04	04
048	02	2	098	40	40	148	43	RCL
049	02	2	099	95	=	149	46	46
050	00	0	100	42	STO	150	69	OP
051	00	0	101	42	42	151	06	06
052	69	OP	102	91	R/S	152	98	ADV
053	04	04	103	76	LBL	153	98	ADV
054	69	OP	104	18	C'	154	43	RCL
055	05	05	105	42	STO	155	06	06
056	69	OP	106	41	41	156	42	STO
057	00	00	107	91	R/S	157	45	45
058	98	ADV	108	76	LBL	158	71	SBR
059	98	ADV	109	19	D'	159	34	ΓX
060	71	SBR	110	42	STO	160	71	SBR
061	34	ΓX	111	46	46	161	33	X²

Program 10 Listing continued

162	91	R/S	212	43	RCL	262	76	LBL
163	76	LBL	213	41	41	263	33	X²
164	14	D	214	44	SUM	264	03	3
165	42	STO	215	46	46	265	04	4
166	47	47	216	44	SUM	266	00	0
167	43	RCL	217	47	47	267	02	2
168	45	45	218	71	SBR	268	69	OP
169	42	STO	219	45	Yˣ	269	04	04
170	06	06	220	71	SBR	270	73	RC*
171	03	3	221	43	RCL	271	07	07
172	03	3	222	71	SBR	272	69	OP
173	03	3	223	35	1/X	273	06	06
174	06	6	224	71	SBR	274	03	3
175	02	2	225	34	⌐X	275	03	3
176	04	4	226	43	RCL	276	03	3
177	01	1	227	41	41	277	06	6
178	03	3	228	22	INV	278	02	2
179	42	STO	229	44	SUM	279	04	4
180	44	44	230	46	46	280	69	OP
181	71	SBR	231	22	INV	281	04	04
182	44	SUM	232	44	SUM	282	73	RC*
183	71	SBR	233	47	47	283	08	08
184	45	Yˣ	234	91	R/S	284	69	OP
185	71	SBR	235	76	LBL	285	06	06
186	35	1/X	236	34	⌐X	286	03	3
187	71	SBR	237	01	1	287	03	3
188	34	⌐X	238	00	0	288	04	4
189	91	R/S	239	42	STO	289	03	3
190	76	LBL	240	07	07	290	03	3
191	15	E	241	01	1	291	05	5
192	42	STO	242	05	5	292	69	OP
193	47	47	243	42	STO	293	04	04
194	43	RCL	244	08	08	294	73	RC*
195	45	45	245	02	2	295	09	09
196	42	STO	246	00	0	296	69	OP
197	06	06	247	42	STO	297	06	06
198	03	3	248	09	09	298	98	ADV
199	03	3	249	02	2	299	69	OP
200	03	3	250	05	5	300	27	27
201	06	6	251	42	STO	301	69	OP
202	02	2	252	03	03	302	28	28
203	04	4	253	03	3	303	69	OP
204	02	2	254	00	0	304	29	29
205	02	2	255	42	STO	305	97	DSZ
206	42	STO	256	04	04	306	06	06
207	44	44	257	03	3	307	33	X²
208	71	SBR	258	05	5	308	71	SBR
209	42	STO	259	42	STO	309	34	⌐X
210	71	SBR	260	05	05	310	98	ADV
211	44	SUM	261	92	RTN	311	98	ADV

(continued on next page)

Program 10 Listing continued

312	92	RTN	362	00	0	412	69	OP	
313	76	LBL	363	02	2	413	29	29	
314	44	SUM	364	69	OP	414	69	OP	
315	05	5	365	04	04	415	23	23	
316	01	1	366	43	RCL	416	69	OP	
317	69	OP	367	47	47	417	24	24	
318	01	01	368	69	OP	418	69	OP	
319	05	5	369	06	06	419	25	25	
320	01	1	370	98	ADV	420	97	DSZ	
321	01	1	371	98	ADV	421	06	06	
322	05	5	372	92	RTN	422	45	Y×	
323	04	4	373	76	LBL	423	71	SBR	
324	01	1	374	45	Y×	424	34	ГX	
325	03	3	375	43	RCL	425	43	RCL	
326	05	5	376	47	47	426	45	45	
327	04	4	377	55	÷	427	42	STD	
328	02	2	378	43	RCL	428	06	06	
329	69	OP	379	46	46	429	92	RTN	
330	02	02	380	65	×	430	76	LBL	
331	01	1	381	73	RC*	431	35	1/X	
332	07	7	382	07	07	432	03	3	
333	00	0	383	95	=	433	04	4	
334	00	0	384	72	ST*	434	00	0	
335	03	3	385	03	03	435	02	2	
336	03	3	386	43	RCL	436	69	OP	
337	00	0	387	47	47	437	04	04	
338	02	2	388	55	÷	438	73	RC*	
339	05	5	389	43	RCL	439	07	07	
340	01	1	390	46	46	440	58	FIX	
341	69	OP	391	65	×	441	00	00	
342	03	03	392	73	RC*	442	69	OP	
343	05	5	393	08	08	443	06	06	
344	01	1	394	95	=	444	22	INV	
345	00	0	395	72	ST*	445	58	FIX	
346	00	0	396	04	04	446	03	3	
347	00	0	397	43	RCL	447	04	4	
348	00	0	398	47	47	448	04	4	
349	00	0	399	55	÷	449	01	1	
350	00	0	400	43	RCL	450	03	3	
351	00	0	401	46	46	451	06	6	
352	00	0	402	65	×	452	69	OP	
353	69	OP	403	73	RC*	453	04	04	
354	04	04	404	09	09	454	73	RC*	
355	69	OP	405	95	=	455	03	03	
356	05	05	406	72	ST*	456	58	FIX	
357	69	OP	407	05	05	457	00	00	
358	00	00	408	69	OP	458	69	OP	
359	98	ADV	409	27	27	459	06	06	
360	03	3	410	69	OP	460	22	INV	
361	03	3	411	28	28	461	58	FIX	

Program 10 Listing continued

462	43	RCL	492	69	OP	522	71	SBR
463	44	44	493	24	24	523	34	ΓX
464	69	OP	494	69	OP	524	92	RTN
465	04	04	495	25	25	525	76	LBL
466	73	RC*	496	69	OP	526	43	RCL
467	04	04	497	27	27	527	43	RCL
468	58	FIX	498	98	ADV	528	41	41
469	01	01	499	97	DSZ	529	22	INV
470	69	OP	500	06	06	530	74	SM*
471	06	06	501	35	1/X	531	08	08
472	22	INV	502	98	ADV	532	22	INV
473	58	FIX	503	98	ADV	533	74	SM*
474	03	3	504	69	OP	534	04	04
475	03	3	505	00	00	535	69	OP
476	04	4	506	92	RTN	536	28	28
477	03	3	507	76	LBL	537	69	OP
478	03	3	508	42	STO	538	24	24
479	05	5	509	43	RCL	539	97	DSZ
480	69	OP	510	41	41	540	06	06
481	04	04	511	74	SM*	541	43	RCL
482	73	RC*	512	08	08	542	71	SBR
483	05	05	513	69	OP	543	34	ΓX
484	58	FIX	514	28	28	544	43	RCL
485	00	00	515	97	DSZ	545	45	45
486	69	OP	516	06	06	546	42	STO
487	06	06	517	42	STO	547	06	06
488	22	INV	518	43	RCL	548	92	RTN
489	58	FIX	519	45	45	549	00	0
490	69	OP	520	42	STO	550	00	0
491	23	23	521	06	06	551	00	0

Program 11

Head Rise to Surge

Background

A point of major concern when comparing proposals from compressor manufacturers is the slope of the performance curve from the rated operating point (or any of several operating points) to the surge point. Of equal importance is the percentage of rated inlet volume flow at the surge point. Both of these define the stability of the selected compressor when operating at other than the rated point and also the ability of the compressor to ride through a process upset.

There are many ways to express the slope of the performance curve:

1. Head rise to surge—the percentage increase in the polytropic or adiabatic head at the surge point when compared to the rated point.
2. Pressure-ratio rise to surge—the percentage increase in the pressure ratio across the compressor (or compression section) at the surge point when compared to the rated point.
3. Discharge-pressure rise to surge—the percentage increase in the absolute discharge pressure of the compressor (or compression section) at the surge point when compared to the rated point.
4. Differential-pressure rise to surge—the percentage increase in the differential pressure across the compressor (or compression section) at the surge point when compared to the rated point.

The truest indicator of the slope of the performance curve is the head rise to surge, because the heads produced at surge and at the rated point are functions of impeller geometry and rotational speed, not the inlet conditions to the compressor. The head rise to surge calculated from the manufacturer's performance curve would apply to the specific compressor even if it was subjected to entirely different inlet conditions. (This statement is not entirely true for multi-stage compressors where there is more than one impeller per section. The slope of the head curve and the flow stability will change with inlet conditions because of volume ratio effects—the effect one impeller's performance has on the other impellers. However, the statement is sufficiently accurate for normal excursions of inlet conditions.)

The other three expressions for the slope of the performance curve are not only functions of the slope of the head curve but functions of the inlet conditions and the shape of the efficiency curve (refer to Equations 2-9 and 2-10). For example, a compressor yielding a 10% head rise to surge may yield an 8%–9% pressure-ratio rise to surge on a 40-mole-weight gas and a 1% pressure-ratio rise to surge on a 2-mole-weight gas. For this reason, compressor manufacturers prefer to express the slope of the performance curve in terms of the head rise to surge.

However, these other three expressions for the performance-curve slope are important to the compressor user. In fact, they are probably more important than the actual value of the head rise to surge. For instance, the discharge pressure at surge may affect a relief-valve setting or the design criteria for piping, vessels, heat exchangers, etc. Perhaps the engineer is interested in knowing the percent rise in system resistance that the compressor can stably accept. Thus, all these expressions are useful in matching compressor selection to process requirements.

While the general philosophy regarding performance-curve slope is applicable to either polytropic or adiabatic head, the remainder of the discussion will consider only the polytropic head, since it finds the most use in industry. Should the reader have need for an adiabatic-head-rise-to-surge program, he can easily modify the one presented here by considering the following developments and the adiabatic head equation, Equation 1-11.

The four expressions for the slope of the performance curve are given by the following:

$$\%(H_p)_s = \left[\frac{(H_p)_s}{(H_p)_r} - 1\right](100) \tag{11-1}$$

$$\%(r_p)_s = \left[\frac{(r_p)_s}{(r_p)_r} - 1\right](100) \tag{11-2}$$

$$\%(P_2)_s = \left[\frac{(P_2)_s}{(P_2)_r} - 1\right](100) \tag{11-3}$$

$$\%(\Delta P)_s = \left[\frac{(P_2)_s - P_1}{(P_2)_r - P_1} - 1 \right](100) \tag{11-4}$$

where the subscript s represents the surge point, the subscript r represents the rated point, and:

$\%(H_p)_s$ = polytropic head rise to surge, %
$\%(r_p)_s$ = pressure ratio rise to surge, %
$\%(P_2)_s$ = discharge pressure rise to surge, %
$\%(\Delta P)_s$ = differential pressure rise to surge, %

If a polytropic head and power versus inlet volume flow curve is available, Equation 11-1 is directly solvable from information on the curve. In order to solve Equations 11-2, 11-3, and 11-4, the pressure ratio at surge must first be determined:

$$(r_p)_s = \left[\left(\frac{(H_p)_s}{(H_p)_r} \right) \left(\frac{n}{n-1} \right)_r \left(\frac{n-1}{n} \right)_s (r_p^{(n-1)/n} - 1)_r + 1 \right]^{[n/(n-1)]_s} \tag{11-5}$$

The derivation of Equation 11-5 is left to the reader. Note that in order to solve Equation 11-5, an n-value, and therefore a polytropic efficiency, at the surge point must first be estimated. The surge efficiency can be estimated from the performance curve and Equation 11-6:

$$(\eta_p)_s = (\eta_p)_r \left(\frac{(PWR)_r}{(PWR)_s} \right) \left(\frac{(H_p)_s}{(H_p)_r} \right) \left(\frac{(Q_1)_s}{(Q_1)_r} \right) \tag{11-6}$$

The percent inlet volume flow at surge is given by:

$$\%(Q_1)_s = \left[\frac{(Q_1)_s}{(Q_1)_r} \right](100) \tag{11-7}$$

where:
$\%(Q_1)_s$ = percent inlet volume flow at surge

If a pressure ratio and power versus inlet volume flow curve is available, Equations 11-2, 11-3, and 11-4 are directly solvable from information on the curve. With this curve, the ratio of surge head to rated head must be estimated. This ratio is given by Equation 11-8:

$$\frac{(H_p)_s}{(H_p)_r} = \left[\frac{\left(\dfrac{n}{n-1}\right)_s (r_p^{(n-1)/n} - 1)_s}{\left(\dfrac{n}{n-1}\right)_r (r_p^{(n-1)/n} - 1)_r} \right] \tag{11-8}$$

With a pressure ratio and power versus inlet volume flow curve, it is difficult to estimate a polytropic efficiency at surge. Note that it is required to solve Equation 11-8. The rigorous method would involve an estimate of surge efficiency, calculation of the polytropic head ratio from Equation 11-8, calculation of the surge efficiency from Equation 11-6, and continuous iteration until the change in efficiency is within the desired tolerance. The less-rigorous method is to realize that the efficiency at surge is normally 5–10 points lower than that at the rated point. Therefore, for a 78% efficiency at the rated point, the surge efficiency would normally be between 68% and 73%. Thus a very good estimation of the polytropic head rise to surge could be obtained by assuming that the polytropic efficiency at surge is, say, seven points less than that at the rated point.

The percent inlet volume flow at surge derives from Equation 11-7.

The expressions for the slope of the performance curve can also be obtained from either of the following curves by first converting them to pressure ratio:

1. Discharge pressure and power versus inlet volume flow.
2. Differential pressure and power versus inlet volume flow.

If the reader is interested in developing a program for adiabatic head, the following may be helpful. Equations 11-1, 11-2, 11-3, 11-4, 11-6, and 11-7 are all directly applicable. Equation 11-5 must be modified as follows:

$$(r_p)_s = \left[\left(\frac{(H_{ad})_s}{(H_{ad})_r} \right) ((r_p)_r^{(k-1)/k} - 1) + 1 \right]^{k/(k-1)} \tag{11-9}$$

Equation 11-8 must also be modified:

$$\frac{(H_{ad})_s}{(H_{ad})_r} = \left[\frac{(r_p)_s^{(k-1)/k} - 1}{(r_p)_r^{(k-1)/k} - 1} \right] \tag{11-10}$$

Program 11 Description

Program 11, Head Rise to Surge, calculates and prints the results of Equations 11-1, 11-2, 11-3, 11-4, and 11-7 from either a polytropic head and power versus inlet volume flow curve or from a pressure ratio and power versus inlet volume flow curve.

In order to execute the program, the following must be known:

1. Inlet volume flow at the rated point, $(Q_1)_r$
2. Inlet volume flow at the surge point, $(Q_1)_s$
3. One of the following sets of information:
   a. Polytropic head at the rated point, $(H_p)_r$
      Polytropic head at the surge point, $(H_p)_s$
   b. Pressure ratio at the rated point, $(r_p)_r$
      Pressure ratio at the surge point, $(r_p)_s$
4. Power requirement at the rated point, $(PWR)_r$
5. Power requirement at the surge point, $(PWR)_s$
6. Polytropic efficiency at the rated point, $(\eta_p)_r$
7. Average ratio of specific heats, k_a
8. Inlet pressure, P_1
9. Discharge pressure at the rated point, $(P_2)_r$

When using a polytropic head curve, the program uses Equations 11-5 and 11-6 to establish the pressure ratio at the surge point.

When using a pressure ratio curve, the program estimates the polytropic head ratio from Equation 11-8. The surge efficiency is estimated by subtracting seven points from the rated efficiency. This approach was used because the iteration procedure would add to the calculation time. Generally, the other three expressions for curve slope are of more value to the compressor user than the actual value of the head rise to surge, even though the head rise is the truest indicator of the performance curve slope. If the head rise to surge is of particular concern to the engineer for comparing compressor proposals, a polytropic head curve should be obtained from the manufacturer. This is the only way to be fair in bid evaluations. Note that the method selected to estimate the polytropic efficiency at surge, while not totally rigorous, will yield good approximations for the head rise to surge.

Table 11-1 is the nomenclature printed by the program; Table 11-2 shows the data registers used by the program.

Labels Used by Program 11

004	10	E'	096	14	D	128	18	C'
075	11	A	103	15	E	260	19	D'
082	12	B	108	16	A'	381	33	X²
089	13	C	123	17	B'	415	34	ΓX

Table 11-1
Program 11: Printer Nomenclature

Program Term	Definition	Units
DPRS	differential pressure rise to surge	percent
EFFR	polytropic efficiency at the rated point	dimensionless
EFFS	polytropic efficiency at the surge point	dimensionless
HDPR	polytropic head at the rated point	ft-lbf/lbm
HDPS	polytropic head at the surge point	ft-lbf/lbm
HRTS	head rise to surge	percent
KA	average ratio of specific heats	dimensionless
P1	inlet pressure	psia
P2R	discharge pressure at the rated point	psia
P2S	discharge pressure at the surge point	psia
PRTS	discharge pressure rise to surge	percent
PWRR	gas or shaft power requirement at the rated point	hp
PWSP	gas or shaft power requirement at the surge point	hp
%Q1S	percent of rated inlet volume flow at the surge point	percent
Q1R	inlet volume flow at the rated point	ICFM
Q1S	inlet volume flow at the surge point	ICFM
RPR	pressure ratio at the rated point	dimensionless
RPRS	pressure ratio rise to surge	percent
RPS	pressure ratio at the surge point	dimensionless

Table 11-2
Data Registers Used by Program 11

00	not used	10	$(Q_1)_r$	20	$[(n-1)/n]_s$		
01	not used	11	$(Q_1)_s$	21	P_1		
02	not used	12	$(H_p)_r$	22	$\%(H_p)_s$		
03	pointer, Q_1	13	$(H_p)_s$	23	$\%(r_p)_s$		
04	pointer, H_p	14	$(r_p)_r$	24	$\%(P_2)_s$		
05	pointer, r_p	15	$(r_p)_s$	25	$\%(\Delta P)_s$		
06	pointer, PWR	16	$(PWR)_r$	26	$\%(Q_1)_s$		
07	$(\eta_p)_r$	17	$(PWR)_s$	27	$(P_2)_r$		
08	k_a	18	$[(n-1)/n]_r$	28	$(P_2)_s$		
09	$k/(k-1)$	19	$(\eta_p)_s$				

Program 11 Usage

Program 11 is executed by using the user-defined keys. The definitions for the user-defined keys can be found in Table 11-3.

The values entered through user-defined keys A, B, and C must be entered in the order shown in Table 11-3, i.e. the rated values before the surge-point values.

Table 11-3
Program 11: Definitions of User-Defined Keys

A	Q1R, Q1S	A'	KA
B	HDPR, HDPS	B'	P1
C	RPR, RPS	C'	P2R, Calculate—Head given
D	PWRR, PWSP	D'	Calculate—Pressure ratio given
E	EFFP	E'	Intialize

When using a polytropic head curve, the head values are entered through user-defined key B. C is not used. After the remaining data required by user-defined keys A, D, E, A', and B' are entered, calculations are made by entering the rated discharge pressure through C'.

When using a pressure-ratio curve, the pressure ratios are entered through user-defined key C. B is not used. Calculations are made through D' after the remaining data required by user-defined keys A, D, E, A', and B' are entered.

Note that the calculator must be repartitioned to 719.29 before loading or keying in the program.

Sample Problem 11-1

Calculate all four curve slope expressions for the base performance curve of Figure 7-1 with the following rated data:

$(Q_1)_r = 45,000$ ICFM

$P_1 = 16$ psia

$(P_2)_r = 56$ psia

$k_a = 1.17$

$(\eta_p)_r = 78\%$

A review of Figure 7-1 yields the following:

$(Q_1)_s = 35,000$ ICFM
$(H_p)_s = 44,000$ ft-lbf/lbm
$(PWR)_s = 5050$ hp
$(H_p)_r = 42,100$ ft-lbf/lbm
$(PWR)_r = 5700$ hp

Sample Problem 11-1: User Instructions

Step	Procedure	Enter	Press	Display
1.	Partition calculator.	3	2nd OP 17	719.29
2.	Load program.			
3.	Initialize the program.		2nd E'	4135221700
4.	Enter rated-point inlet volume flow.	45000	A	45000
5.	Enter surge-point inlet volume flow.	35000	A	35000
6.	Enter rated-point polytropic head.	42100	B	42100
7.	Enter surge-point polytropic head.	44000	B	44000
8.	Enter rated-point power requirement.	5700	D	5700
9.	Enter surge-point power requirement.	5050	D	5050
10.	Enter rated-point polytropic efficiency.	0.78	E	0.78
11.	Enter average k-value.	1.17	2nd A'	$6.882\ldots\left(\dfrac{k}{k-1}\right)$
12.	Enter inlet pressure.	16	2nd B'	16
13.	Enter discharge pressure and calculate.	56	2nd C'	

Sample Problem 11-1: Program Printout

```
HEAD RISE TO SURGE

45000.     Q1R          77.8    %Q1S
35000.     Q1S           4.5    HRTS
42100.     HDPR          3.8    RPRS
44000.     HDPS          3.8    PRTS
 3.500     RPR           5.3    DPRS
 3.633     RPS
5700.      PWRR
5050.      PWSP
 0.78      EFFR
 0.716     EFFS
 1.17      KA
16.        P1
56.0       P2R
58.1       P2S
```

Sample Problem 11-2

Calculate all four curve slope expressions for the base performance curve of Figure 10-1 with the following rated data:

$(Q_1)_r = 45,000$ ICFM

$P_1 = 14$ psia

$(P_2)_r = 43.5$ psia

$k_a = 1.4$

$(\eta_p)_r = 78\%$

A review of Figure 10-1 yields the following:

$(Q_1)_s = 35,000$ ICFM
$(r_p)_s = 45/14 = 3.214$
$(PWR)_s = 4400$ hp
$(r_p)_r = 43.5/14 = 3.107$
$(PWR)_r = 5000$ hp

Note that since the program assumes a surge efficiency for this case, the power values do not have to be entered. If entered as done here, they will not be used in the calculations and will serve for record purposes only. With them, one can determine the surge efficiency as a comparison to that assumed by the program. Consider Equation 11-6, which can be rewritten as follows:

$$(\eta_p)_s = (\eta_p)_r \left(\frac{(PWR)_r}{(PWR)_s}\right) \left[1 + \frac{\%(H_p)_s}{100}\right] \left[\frac{\%(Q_1)_s}{100}\right] \qquad (11\text{-}11)$$

For Sample Problem 11-2:

$$(\eta_p)_s = (0.78)\left(\frac{5000}{4400}\right)(1.06)(0.778) = 0.731$$

which is higher than the assumed value of 0.710. The reader can verify that if a value of 0.731 was used for the surge efficiency, the resultant head rise to surge would have been 5.3%. The next iteration would yield a surge efficiency of 0.726 and a resultant head rise to surge of 5.5%, etc.

Sample Problem 11-2: User Instructions

Step	Procedure	Enter	Press	Display
1-5	Refer to Sample Problem 11-1, User Instructions.			
6.	Enter rated-point pressure ratio.	3.107	C	3.107
7.	Enter surge-point pressure ratio.	3.214	C	3.214
8.	Enter rated-point power requirement.	5000	D	5000
9.	Enter surge-point power requirement.	4400	D	4400
10.	Enter rated-point polytropic efficiency.	0.78	E	0.78
11.	Enter average k-value.	1.4	2nd A′	$3.5 \left(\dfrac{k}{k-1} \right)$
12.	Enter inlet pressure.	14	2nd B′	14
13.	Calculate.		2nd D′	

Sample Problem 11-2: Program Printout

```
HEAD RISE TO SURGE


    45000.      Q1R
    35000.      Q1S
        0.      HDPR
        0.      HDPS
     3.107      RPR
     3.214      RPS
     5000.      PWRR
     4400.      PWSP
      0.78      EFFR
      0.710     EFFS
       1.4      KA
      14.       P1
      43.5      P2R
      45.0      P2S

      77.8      %Q1S
       6.0      HRTS
       3.4      RPRS
       3.4      PRTS
       5.1      DPRS
```

Program 11 Listing

000	03	3	050	00	0	100	26	26
001	69	OP	051	03	3	101	91	R/S
002	17	17	052	06	6	102	76	LBL
003	76	LBL	053	69	OP	103	15	E
004	10	E'	054	03	03	104	42	STO
005	47	CMS	055	04	4	105	07	07
006	01	1	056	01	1	106	91	R/S
007	00	0	057	03	3	107	76	LBL
008	42	STO	058	05	5	108	16	A'
009	03	03	059	02	2	109	42	STO
010	01	1	060	02	2	110	08	08
011	02	2	061	01	1	111	75	-
012	42	STO	062	07	7	112	01	1
013	04	04	063	00	0	113	95	=
014	01	1	064	00	0	114	55	÷
015	04	4	065	69	OP	115	43	RCL
016	42	STO	066	04	04	116	08	08
017	05	05	067	69	OP	117	95	=
018	01	1	068	05	05	118	35	1/X
019	06	6	069	69	OP	119	42	STO
020	42	STO	070	00	00	120	09	09
021	06	06	071	98	ADV	121	91	R/S
022	69	OP	072	98	ADV	122	76	LBL
023	00	00	073	91	R/S	123	17	B'
024	98	ADV	074	76	LBL	124	42	STO
025	02	2	075	11	A	125	21	21
026	03	3	076	72	ST*	126	91	R/S
027	01	1	077	03	03	127	76	LBL
028	07	7	078	69	OP	128	18	C'
029	01	1	079	23	23	129	42	STO
030	03	3	080	91	R/S	130	27	27
031	01	1	081	76	LBL	131	43	RCL
032	06	6	082	12	B	132	13	13
033	69	OP	083	72	ST*	133	55	÷
034	01	01	084	04	04	134	43	RCL
035	03	3	085	69	OP	135	12	12
036	05	5	086	24	24	136	95	=
037	02	2	087	91	R/S	137	75	-
038	04	4	088	76	LBL	138	01	1
039	03	3	089	13	C	139	95	=
040	06	6	090	72	ST*	140	65	×
041	01	1	091	05	05	141	01	1
042	07	7	092	69	OP	142	00	0
043	69	OP	093	25	25	143	00	0
044	02	02	094	91	R/S	144	95	=
045	03	3	095	76	LBL	145	42	STO
046	07	7	096	14	D	146	22	22
047	03	3	097	72	ST*	147	43	RCL
048	02	2	098	06	06	148	11	11
049	00	0	099	69	OP	149	55	÷

Program 11 Listing continued

150	43	RCL	200	55	÷	250	42	STO
151	10	10	201	43	RCL	251	23	23
152	65	×	202	12	12	252	42	STO
153	01	1	203	65	×	253	24	24
154	00	0	204	43	RCL	254	71	SBR
155	00	0	205	18	18	255	33	X²
156	95	=	206	35	1/X	256	71	SBR
157	42	STO	207	65	×	257	34	√X
158	26	26	208	43	RCL	258	91	R/S
159	43	RCL	209	20	20	259	76	LBL
160	11	11	210	65	×	260	19	D'
161	55	÷	211	53	(	261	43	RCL
162	43	RCL	212	53	(	262	07	07
163	10	10	213	43	RCL	263	75	-
164	65	×	214	27	27	264	00	0
165	43	RCL	215	55	÷	265	93	.
166	13	13	216	43	RCL	266	00	0
167	55	÷	217	21	21	267	07	7
168	43	RCL	218	54	)	268	95	=
169	12	12	219	42	STO	269	42	STO
170	65	×	220	14	14	270	19	19
171	43	RCL	221	45	YX	271	43	RCL
172	16	16	222	43	RCL	272	11	11
173	55	÷	223	18	18	273	55	÷
174	43	RCL	224	75	-	274	43	RCL
175	17	17	225	01	1	275	10	10
176	65	×	226	54	)	276	65	×
177	43	RCL	227	95	=	277	01	1
178	07	07	228	85	+	278	00	0
179	95	=	229	01	1	279	00	0
180	42	STO	230	95	=	280	95	=
181	19	19	231	45	YX	281	42	STO
182	65	×	232	43	RCL	282	26	26
183	43	RCL	233	20	20	283	43	RCL
184	09	09	234	35	1/X	284	15	15
185	95	=	235	95	=	285	55	÷
186	35	1/X	236	42	STO	286	43	RCL
187	42	STO	237	15	15	287	14	14
188	20	20	238	55	÷	288	95	=
189	43	RCL	239	43	RCL	289	75	-
190	09	09	240	14	14	290	01	1
191	65	×	241	95	=	291	95	=
192	43	RCL	242	75	-	292	65	×
193	07	07	243	01	1	293	01	1
194	95	=	244	95	=	294	00	0
195	35	1/X	245	65	×	295	00	0
196	42	STO	246	01	1	296	95	=
197	18	18	247	00	0	297	42	STO
198	43	RCL	248	00	0	298	23	23
199	13	13	249	95	=	299	42	STO

(continued on next page)

Program 11 Listing continued

300	24	24	350	14	14	400	21	21
301	43	RCL	351	45	Yˣ	401	54	)
302	14	14	352	43	RCL	402	95	=
303	65	×	353	18	18	403	75	-
304	43	RCL	354	54	)	404	01	1
305	21	21	355	75	-	405	95	=
306	95	=	356	01	1	406	65	×
307	42	STO	357	54	)	407	01	1
308	27	27	358	65	×	408	00	0
309	43	RCL	359	43	RCL	409	00	0
310	14	14	360	20	20	410	95	=
311	65	×	361	35	1/X	411	42	STO
312	43	RCL	362	55	÷	412	25	25
313	21	21	363	43	RCL	413	92	RTN
314	95	=	364	18	18	414	76	LBL
315	42	STO	365	35	1/X	415	34	√X
316	27	27	366	95	=	416	03	3
317	71	SBR	367	75	-	417	04	4
318	33	X²	368	01	1	418	00	0
319	43	RCL	369	95	=	419	02	2
320	09	09	370	65	×	420	03	3
321	65	×	371	01	1	421	05	5
322	43	RCL	372	00	0	422	69	OP
323	07	07	373	00	0	423	04	04
324	95	=	374	95	=	424	43	RCL
325	35	1/X	375	42	STO	425	10	10
326	42	STO	376	22	22	426	69	OP
327	18	18	377	71	SBR	427	06	06
328	43	RCL	378	34	√X	428	03	3
329	19	19	379	91	R/S	429	04	4
330	65	×	380	76	LBL	430	00	0
331	43	RCL	381	33	X²	431	02	2
332	09	09	382	43	RCL	432	03	3
333	95	=	383	15	15	433	06	6
334	35	1/X	384	65	×	434	69	OP
335	42	STO	385	43	RCL	435	04	04
336	20	20	386	21	21	436	43	RCL
337	43	RCL	387	95	=	437	11	11
338	15	15	388	42	STO	438	69	OP
339	45	Yˣ	389	28	28	439	06	06
340	43	RCL	390	75	-	440	02	2
341	20	20	391	43	RCL	441	03	3
342	95	=	392	21	21	442	01	1
343	75	-	393	95	=	443	06	6
344	01	1	394	55	÷	444	03	3
345	95	=	395	53	(	445	03	3
346	55	÷	396	43	RCL	446	03	3
347	53	(	397	27	27	447	05	5
348	53	(	398	75	-	448	69	OP
349	43	RCL	399	43	RCL	449	04	04

Program 11 Listing continued

450	43	RCL	500	43	RCL	550	01	1
451	12	12	501	15	15	551	07	7
452	58	FIX	502	58	FIX	552	02	2
453	00	00	503	03	03	553	01	1
454	69	OP	504	69	OP	554	02	2
455	06	06	505	06	06	555	01	1
456	22	INV	506	22	INV	556	03	3
457	58	FIX	507	58	FIX	557	06	6
458	02	2	508	03	3	558	69	OP
459	03	3	509	03	3	559	04	04
460	01	1	510	04	4	560	43	RCL
461	06	6	511	03	3	561	19	19
462	03	3	512	03	3	562	58	FIX
463	03	3	513	05	5	563	03	03
464	03	3	514	03	3	564	69	OP
465	06	6	515	05	5	565	06	06
466	69	OP	516	69	OP	566	22	INV
467	04	04	517	04	04	567	58	FIX
468	43	RCL	518	43	RCL	568	02	2
469	13	13	519	16	16	569	06	6
470	58	FIX	520	69	OP	570	01	1
471	00	00	521	06	06	571	03	3
472	69	OP	522	03	3	572	69	OP
473	06	06	523	03	3	573	04	04
474	22	INV	524	04	4	574	43	RCL
475	58	FIX	525	03	3	575	08	08
476	03	3	526	03	3	576	69	OP
477	05	5	527	06	6	577	06	06
478	03	3	528	03	3	578	03	3
479	03	3	529	03	3	579	03	3
480	03	3	530	69	OP	580	00	0
481	05	5	531	04	04	581	02	2
482	69	OP	532	43	RCL	582	69	OP
483	04	04	533	17	17	583	04	04
484	43	RCL	534	69	OP	584	43	RCL
485	14	14	535	06	06	585	21	21
486	58	FIX	536	01	1	586	69	OP
487	03	03	537	07	7	587	06	06
488	69	OP	538	02	2	588	03	3
489	06	06	539	01	1	589	03	3
490	22	INV	540	02	2	590	00	0
491	58	FIX	541	01	1	591	03	3
492	03	3	542	03	3	592	03	3
493	05	5	543	05	5	593	05	5
494	03	3	544	69	OP	594	69	OP
495	03	3	545	04	04	595	04	04
496	03	3	546	43	RCL	596	43	RCL
497	06	6	547	07	07	597	27	27
498	69	OP	548	69	OP	598	58	FIX
499	04	04	549	06	06	599	01	01

(continued on next page)

Program 11 Listing continued

600	69	ΠP	639	02	2	678	05	5
601	06	06	640	03	3	679	03	3
602	22	INV	641	03	3	680	07	7
603	58	FIX	642	05	5	681	03	3
604	03	3	643	03	3	682	06	6
605	03	3	644	07	7	683	69	ΠP
606	00	0	645	03	3	684	04	04
607	03	3	646	06	6	685	43	RCL
608	03	3	647	69	ΠP	686	24	24
609	06	6	648	04	04	687	58	FIX
610	69	ΠP	649	43	RCL	688	01	01
611	04	04	650	22	22	689	69	ΠP
612	43	RCL	651	58	FIX	690	06	06
613	28	28	652	01	01	691	22	INV
614	58	FIX	653	69	ΠP	692	58	FIX
615	01	01	654	06	06	693	01	1
616	69	ΠP	655	22	INV	694	06	6
617	06	06	656	58	FIX	695	03	3
618	22	INV	657	03	3	696	03	3
619	58	FIX	658	05	5	697	03	3
620	98	ADV	659	03	3	698	05	5
621	06	6	660	03	3	699	03	3
622	01	1	661	03	3	700	06	6
623	03	3	662	05	5	701	69	ΠP
624	04	4	663	03	3	702	04	04
625	00	0	664	06	6	703	43	RCL
626	02	2	665	69	ΠP	704	25	25
627	03	3	666	04	04	705	58	FIX
628	06	6	667	43	RCL	706	01	01
629	69	ΠP	668	23	23	707	69	ΠP
630	04	04	669	58	FIX	708	06	06
631	43	RCL	670	01	01	709	22	INV
632	26	26	671	69	ΠP	710	58	FIX
633	58	FIX	672	06	06	711	69	ΠP
634	01	01	673	22	INV	712	00	00
635	69	ΠP	674	58	FIX	713	92	RTN
636	06	06	675	03	3	714	00	0
637	22	INV	676	03	3	715	00	0
638	58	FIX	677	03	3	716	00	0

Program 12

Constructing a Quadrant Curve

Background

It is possible to construct a nomograph that will convert polytropic head to discharge pressure for variations in inlet pressure, inlet temperature, and molecular weight. The nomograph can also be extended to convert power requirement to a power constant for variations in the same parameters. Such a nomograph is called a quadrant curve.

Consider the polytropic head equation:

$$H_p = Z_a R T_1 \left(\frac{n}{n - 1} \right) [r_p^{(n-1)/n} - 1] \qquad (2\text{-}9)$$

which can be rewritten as follows:

$$H_p = Z_a \left(\frac{1545}{MW} \right) T_1 \left(\frac{n}{n - 1} \right) [r_p^{(n-1)/n} - 1]$$

This equation can be transposed to solve for r_p as a function of H_p and (T_1/MW):

$$r_p = \left[\frac{H_p}{1545(Z_a)(T_1/MW)[n/(n - 1)]} + 1 \right]^{n/(n-1)} \qquad (12\text{-}1)$$

For quadrant-curve construction, the average compressibility and the average k-value are normally considered constant. (It is possible to construct

133

a quadrant curve for variable Z-value. This would be done by changing the term T_1/MW to Z_aT_1/MW. This program allows for the modification.) The efficiency can be considered variable if an efficiency curve exists or if the efficiency is back calculated from the power curve. Note, however, that considering the efficiency constant across the curve yields useful results from Equation 12-1.

The discharge pressure comes from Equation 12-2:

$$P_2 = P_1 r_p \tag{12-2}$$

The power curve can be made to include variations in the inlet pressure, inlet temperature, and molecular weight by defining a power constant, as in Equation 12-3:

$$C_{pwr} = \frac{(PWR)(T_1)}{(P_1)(MW)} \tag{12-3}$$

Note that C_{pwr} varies with inlet volume flow and speed, just as the power curve does. (If the compressibility is considered a variable, as discussed previously, a corresponding modification would have to be made to Equation 12–3, i.e. T_1/MW would have to be changed to Z_aT_1/MW. This program allows for the modification.)

A note on efficiency: It was stated previously that useful results can be obtained from Equation 12-1 by considering constant efficiency across the performance curve. The interested reader may wish to vary the efficiency and thereby gain more accuracy. This is easy when an efficiency curve is available. However, without one the efficiency can be back calculated from the head and power for each point on the curve by the following equation:

$$\eta_p = (\eta_p)_r \left(\frac{Q_1}{(Q_1)_r}\right)\left(\frac{H_p}{(H_p)_r}\right)\left(\frac{PWR_r}{PWR}\right) \tag{12-4}$$

where the subscript r stands for the rated conditions, or the inlet volume flow, polytropic head, power point where the efficiency is known.

Program 12 Description

Program 12, Constructing a Quadrant Curve, calculates and prints the results of Equations 12-1, 12-2, and 12-3 for each polytropic head and power point entered into the program.

Table 12-1
Program 12: Printer Nomenclature

Program Term	Definition	Units
CPWR	power constant	(hp) (°F)/(psia) (lbm/lbm-mol)
EFF	polytropic efficiency	dimensionless
HEAD	polytropic head	ft-lbf/lbm
KA	average ratio of specific heats	dimensionless
P1	inlet pressure	psia
P2	discharge pressure	psia
PWR	gas or shaft power requirement	hp
RP	pressure ratio	dimensionless
T/MW	inlet temperature divided by molecular weight	°F/(lbm/lbm-mol)
ZA	average compressibility	dimensionless

Table 12-2
Data Registers Used by Program 12

00	not used	05	T_1/MW	10	H_p
01	not used	06	k_a	11	$n/(n-1)$
02	not used	07	Z_a	12	PWR
03	η_p	08	r_p	13	C_{pwr}
04	P_1	09	P_2		

In order to execute the program, an inlet volume flow versus polytropic head and power curve must be available, and the following must be known:

1. Inlet pressure, P_1
2. Inlet temperature divided by molecular weight (T_1/MW),—rated, with a range of values to be considered
3. Average k-value, k_a
4. Average Z-value, Z_a
5. Polytropic efficiency, η_p
6. Polytropic head, H_p, for several points on the curve
7. Power requirement, PWR, for several points on the curve

The range of T_1/MW evolves from dividing the minimum inlet temperature by the maximum molecular weight and dividing the maximum inlet temperature by the minimum molecular weight.

The program is set up for continuous usage, without the need for complete data reentry. Therefore, the operator need only change the desired parameters prior to succeeding calculations.

Table 12-1 is the nomenclature printed by the program; Table 12-2 shows the data registers used by the program.

Labels Used by Program 12

```
001    10 E'          065    17 B'          080    13  C
055    11  A          070    18 C'          128    12  B
060    16 A'          075    19 D'          255    14  D
```

Table 12-3
Program 12: Definitions of User-Defined Keys

A	EFF	A'	P1
B	HEAD, Calculate RP	B'	T/MW
C	RP, Calculate P2	C'	KA
D	PWR, Calculate CPWR	D'	ZA
		E'	Initialize

Program 12 Usage

Program 12 is executed by using the user-defined keys. The definitions for the user-defined keys can be found in Table 12-3.

After initializing and entering the data required by user-defined keys A, A', B', C', and D', the program is executed by using B to convert the entered value of polytropic head to pressure ratio, C to convert the entered value of pressure ratio to discharge pressure, and D to convert the entered value of power requirement (either gas or shaft horsepower) to the power constant. Subsequent calculations can be made simply by changing only the desired parameters.

Note that if a quadrant curve with variable Z-value is required, the value of $Z_a T_1 / MW$ is entered through user-defined key B' instead of T_1 / MW. The program printout for the variable would still be titled T/MW. The operator would have to remember the substitution.

Sample Problem

Given a compressor whose performance curve is the base curve of Figure 7-1 and the following rated data:

$$P_1 = 16 \text{ psia}$$

$$Z_a = 0.985$$

$$k_a = 1.17$$

$$\eta_p = 78\%$$

$$T_1 / MW = \frac{100 + 460}{29} = 19.3$$

where:

$T_1 = 100°F$
$MW = 29$

$(Q_1)_{bc}$	$(H_p)_{bc}$	PWR_{bc}
35,000	44,000	5050
45,000	42,100	5700
54,000	34,000	6200

draw a quadrant curve for variations in inlet pressure from 15 psia to 17 psia and for variations in T_1/MW from 18 to 20.

Assume a constant polytropic efficiency for the quadrant curve. Figure 12-2 is the result.

Note that the C_{pwr} curve was developed from the rated values of inlet pressure and T_1/MW. This has to be the case, since each power value from the curve was based on a specific mass flow which produced the inlet volume flow tabulated. If the rated values were changed, the inlet volume flows would remain the same, but the mass flows would vary, resulting in different power values. This can be deduced from the following:

$$Q_1 = m_1 \left(\frac{Z_1 R T_1}{144\ P_1} \right)$$

The resulting C_{pwr} curve is good, however, for variations in pressure, temperature, and molecular weight.

Note also that the efficiency has been varied for the head and power curves, since these came from the manufacturer. However, the efficiency was held constant at the rated value for the rest of the quadrant curve.

Sample Problem 12-1: User Instructions

Step	Procedure	Enter	Press	Display
1.	Load program.			
2.	Initialize.		2nd E'	4217000000
3.	Enter polytropic efficiency.	0.78	A	0.78
4.	Enter average *k*-value.	1.17	2nd C'	1.17
5.	Enter average Z-value.	0.985	2nd D'	0.985
6.	Enter inlet pressure.	16	2nd A'	16

(continued on page 139)

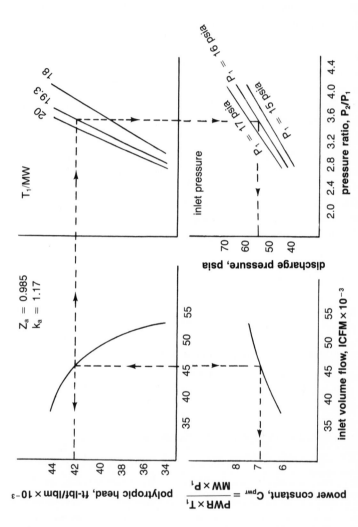

Figure 12-1. Quadrant curve for variations in inlet pressure, inlet temperature, and molecular weight for Sample Problem 12-1.

Sample Problem 12-1: User Instructions continued

Step	Procedure	Enter	Press	Display
7.	Enter T_1/MW.	19.3	2nd B'	19.3
8.	Enter polytropic head and calculate pressure ratio.	44000	B	
9.	Repeat step 8 for each value of polytropic head.			
10.	Enter power and calculate power constant.	5050	D	
11.	Repeat step 10 for each value of power.			
12.	Enter new value for T_1/MW.	18	2nd B'	18
13.	Repeat steps 8 and 9.			
14.	Repeat steps 12 and 13 for each value of T_1/MW.			
15.	Enter minimum pressure ratio from previous calculations and calculate discharge pressure.	2.759	C	
16.	Enter maximum pressure ratio from previous calculations and calculate discharge pressure.	4.076	C	
17.	Enter new value for inlet pressure.	15	2nd A'	15
18.	Repeat steps 15 and 16.			
19.	Repeat steps 17 and 18 for each value of inlet pressure.			

Sample Problem 12-1: Program Printout

```
QUADRANT CURVE

    1.17    KA          1.17    KA          1.17    KA
   0.985    ZA         0.985    ZA         0.985    ZA
    0.78    EFF         0.78    EFF         0.78    EFF
   19.3     T/MW       19.3     T/MW       19.3     T/MW
 44000.     HEAD     42100.     HEAD     34000.     HEAD
    3.748   RP          3.562   RP          2.853   RP
```

Sample Problem 21-1: Program Printout continued

```
   16.        P1         1.17       KA         16.        P1
   19.3       T/MW       0.985      ZA         2.759      RP
 5050.        PWR        0.78       EFF        44.1       P2
 6.092 03     CPWR      18.0        T/MW
                        34000.      HEAD       16.        P1
   16.        P1         3.054      RP         4.076      RP
   19.3       T/MW                             65.2       P2
 5700.        PWR        1.17       KA
 6.876 03     CPWR       0.985      ZA
                         0.78       EFF        15.        P1
   16.        P1        20.0        T/MW       2.759      RP
   19.3       T/MW      44000.      HEAD       41.4       P2
 6200.        PWR        3.597      RP
 7.479 03     CPWR                             15.        P1
                         1.17       KA         4.076      RP
                         0.985      ZA         61.1       P2
   1.17       KA         0.78       EFF
   0.985      ZA        20.0        T/MW
   0.78       EFF      42100.       HEAD       17.        P1
  18.0        T/MW       3.424      RP         2.759      RP
44000.        HEAD                             46.9       P2
   4.076      RP
                         1.17       KA         17.        P1
                         0.985      ZA         4.076      RP
   1.17       KA         0.78       EFF        69.3       P2
   0.985      ZA        20.0        T/MW
   0.78       EFF      34000.       HEAD
  18.0        T/MW       2.759      RP
42100.        HEAD
   3.863      RP
```

Program 12 Listing

000	76	LBL	016	05	5	032	05	5
001	10	E'	017	01	1	033	69	OP
002	69	OP	018	03	3	034	03	03
003	00	00	019	03	3	035	04	4
004	98	ADV	020	01	1	036	02	2
005	03	3	021	69	OP	037	01	1
006	04	4	022	02	02	038	07	7
007	04	4	023	03	3	039	00	0
008	01	1	024	07	7	040	00	0
009	69	OP	025	00	0	041	00	0
010	01	01	026	00	0	042	00	0
011	01	1	027	01	1	043	00	0
012	03	3	028	05	5	044	00	0
013	01	1	029	04	4	045	69	OP
014	06	6	030	01	1	046	04	04
015	03	3	031	03	3	047	69	OP

Program 12 Listing continued

048	05	05	098	06	06	148	43	RCL
049	69	OP	099	03	3	149	05	05
050	00	00	100	05	5	150	65	×
051	98	ADV	101	03	3	151	43	RCL
052	98	ADV	102	03	3	152	07	07
053	91	R/S	103	69	OP	153	65	×
054	76	LBL	104	04	04	154	01	1
055	11	A	105	43	RCL	155	05	5
056	42	STO	106	08	08	156	04	4
057	03	03	107	69	OP	157	05	5
058	91	R/S	108	06	06	158	55	÷
059	76	LBL	109	03	3	159	43	RCL
060	16	A'	110	03	3	160	10	10
061	42	STO	111	00	0	161	95	=
062	04	04	112	03	3	162	35	1/X
063	91	R/S	113	69	OP	163	85	+
064	76	LBL	114	04	04	164	01	1
065	17	B'	115	43	RCL	165	95	=
066	42	STO	116	09	09	166	45	Y×
067	05	05	117	58	FIX	167	43	RCL
068	91	R/S	118	01	01	168	11	11
069	76	LBL	119	69	OP	169	95	=
070	18	C'	120	06	06	170	42	STO
071	42	STO	121	22	INV	171	08	08
072	06	06	122	58	FIX	172	02	2
073	91	R/S	123	69	OP	173	06	6
074	76	LBL	124	00	00	174	01	1
075	19	D'	125	98	ADV	175	03	3
076	42	STO	126	91	R/S	176	69	OP
077	07	07	127	76	LBL	177	04	04
078	91	R/S	128	12	B	178	43	RCL
079	76	LBL	129	42	STO	179	06	06
080	13	C	130	10	10	180	69	OP
081	42	STO	131	43	RCL	181	06	06
082	08	08	132	06	06	182	04	4
083	65	×	133	75	-	183	06	6
084	43	RCL	134	01	1	184	01	1
085	04	04	135	95	=	185	03	3
086	95	=	136	55	÷	186	69	OP
087	42	STO	137	43	RCL	187	04	04
088	09	09	138	06	06	188	43	RCL
089	03	3	139	95	=	189	07	07
090	03	3	140	35	1/X	190	69	OP
091	00	0	141	65	×	191	06	06
092	02	2	142	43	RCL	192	01	1
093	69	OP	143	03	03	193	07	7
094	04	04	144	95	=	194	02	2
095	43	RCL	145	42	STO	195	01	1
096	04	04	146	11	11	196	02	2
097	69	OP	147	65	×	197	01	1

(continued on next page)

Program 12 Listing continued

198	69	OP	243	08	08	288	05	05
199	04	04	244	58	FIX	289	58	FIX
200	43	RCL	245	03	03	290	01	01
201	03	03	246	69	OP	291	69	OP
202	69	OP	247	06	06	292	06	06
203	06	06	248	22	INV	293	22	INV
204	03	3	249	58	FIX	294	58	FIX
205	07	7	250	69	OP	295	03	3
206	06	6	251	00	00	296	03	3
207	03	3	252	98	ADV	297	04	4
208	03	3	253	91	R/S	298	03	3
209	00	0	254	76	LBL	299	03	3
210	04	4	255	14	D	300	05	5
211	03	3	256	42	STO	301	69	OP
212	69	OP	257	12	12	302	04	04
213	04	04	258	55	÷	303	43	RCL
214	43	RCL	259	43	RCL	304	12	12
215	05	05	260	04	04	305	69	OP
216	58	FIX	261	65	×	306	06	06
217	01	01	262	43	RCL	307	01	1
218	69	OP	263	05	05	308	05	5
219	06	06	264	95	=	309	03	3
220	22	INV	265	42	STO	310	03	3
221	58	FIX	266	13	13	311	04	4
222	02	2	267	03	3	312	03	3
223	03	3	268	03	3	313	03	3
224	01	1	269	00	0	314	05	5
225	07	7	270	02	2	315	69	OP
226	01	1	271	69	OP	316	04	04
227	03	3	272	04	04	317	43	RCL
228	01	1	273	43	RCL	318	13	13
229	06	6	274	04	04	319	57	ENG
230	69	OP	275	69	OP	320	58	FIX
231	04	04	276	06	06	321	03	03
232	43	RCL	277	03	3	322	69	OP
233	10	10	278	07	7	323	06	06
234	69	OP	279	06	6	324	22	INV
235	06	06	280	03	3	325	57	ENG
236	03	3	281	03	3	326	22	INV
237	05	5	282	00	0	327	58	FIX
238	03	3	283	04	4	328	69	OP
239	03	3	284	03	3	329	00	00
240	69	OP	285	69	OP	330	98	ADV
241	04	04	286	04	04	331	91	R/S
242	43	RCL	287	43	RCL	332	00	0

Program 13

Varying Inlet Pressure for Constant Discharge Pressure

Background

Centrifugal compressors often operate in processes having a constant discharge pressure. One such process is refrigeration, where the discharge pressure is set by the high pressure level heat exchanger. With the discharge pressure constant, if the speed is also fixed at a constant speed, the inlet pressure must vary with inlet volume flow to satisfy the variation in polytropic head.

With this type of process, it is necessary to be able to evaluate the variation in inlet pressure with inlet volume flow. This requires a different type of curve than those discussed in previous programs, since the discharge pressure is constant and the inlet pressure varies.

For the polytropic process, the equation for the inlet pressure is Equation 13-1:

$$P_1 = P_2 \left[\frac{H_p}{Z_a R T_1 \left[n/(n-1) \right]} + 1 \right]^{-n/(n-1)} \tag{13-1}$$

Equation 13-1 derives directly from the polytropic head equation, Equation 2-9.

The developments here are for the construction of a variable inlet pressure curve from a polytropic head curve. The resulting program can be modified for use with an adiabatic head curve or a discharge pressure curve.

If a program for the adiabatic head curve is desired, Equation 13-1 must be modified by substituting the k-value for the n-value.

If a program for the discharge pressure curve is desired, the reader should realize that the pressure ratio at each point remains the same. Therefore, the inlet pressure comes from Equation 13-2:

$$P_1 = \frac{P_2}{(P_2/P_1)_{bc}} \qquad (13\text{-}2)$$

Program 13 Description

Program 13, Varying Inlet Pressure for Constant Discharge Pressure, calculates and prints the results of Equation 13-1 for any number of head values from a polytropic head versus inlet volume flow curve. In order to execute the program, the following must be known:

1. Discharge pressure (to be held constant), P_2
2. Inlet temperature, T_1
3. Molecular weight, MW
4. Average k-value, k_a
5. Average Z-value, Z_a
6. Polytropic efficiency, η_p
7. Polytropic head, H_p
8. Inlet volume flow, Q_1

The inlet volume flow corresponding to each head value is entered merely for recording purposes.

The program is most accurate when polytropic efficiency is varied along with polytropic head. The best way to obtain the required polytropic efficiency values is to request an efficiency versus inlet volume flow curve from the manufacturer. As a second choice, an approximate curve can be constructed from the polytropic head and power versus inlet volume flow curve and Equation 12-4:

$$\eta_p = (\eta_p)_r \left[\left(\frac{PWR_r}{PWR} \right) \left(\frac{H_p}{(H_p)_r} \right) \left(\frac{Q_1}{(Q_1)_r} \right) \right] \qquad (12\text{-}4)$$

Depending on the accuracy required, a constant efficiency value could be used for all points considered. This approach will yield a useful curve of inlet pressure variation, although the prudent user may wish to reduce the rated-point efficiency by two or three points (i.e. if the rated efficiency is 78%, use 76% or 75%) to reduce the error.

Table 13-1
Program 13: Printer Nomenclature

Program Term	Definition	Units
EFF	polytropic efficiency	dimensionless
HEAD	polytropic head	ft-lbf/lbm
KA	average ratio of specific heats	dimensionless
MW	molecular weight	lbm/lbm-mol
P1	inlet pressure	psia
P2	discharge pressure	psia
Q1	inlet volume flow	ICFM
T1	inlet temperature	°F
ZA	average compressibility	dimensionless

Table 13-2
Data Registers Used by Program 13

00	not used	05	η_p	10	P_1
01	not used	06	MW	11	$(H_p MW)/(1545 Z_a T_1)$
02	not used	07	k_a	12	$n/(n-1)$
03	P_2	08	Z_a	13	Q_1
04	T_1	09	H_p		

This program is set up for continuous usage, without the need for complete data reentry. Therefore, only the desired parameters need to be changed before rerunning the program.

An interesting note: Since there are no power calculations in this program, it can be used with adiabatic head by entering 100%, or 1.0, for the polytropic efficiency. The only disadvantage would be a printout with $\eta_p = 1.0$.

Table 13-1 is the nomenclature printed by the program; Table 13-2 shows the data registers used by the program.

Labels Used by Program 13

001	12	B	021	16	A'	036	19	D'
006	13	C	026	17	B'	041	10	E'
016	14	D	031	18	C'	132	15	E

Program 13 Usage

Program 13 is executed by using the user-defined keys. The definitions for the user-defined keys can be found in Table 13-3.

Table 13-3
Program 13: Definitions of User-Defined Keys

		A'	MW
B	P2	B'	KA
C	T1	C'	ZA
D	Q1	D'	EFF
E	HEAD, Calculate P1	E'	Initiate the program

E' is used to initiate the program after the discharge pressure, inlet temperature, molecular weight, average k-value, and average Z-value are entered. The inlet volume flow and polytropic efficiency values should be changed for each polytropic head value. The flow and efficiency are entered first; then the polytropic head is entered and the inlet pressure calculated through user defined key E.

After all the head values are converted to inlet pressure, a new curve for different conditions can be calculated simply by changing only the desired parameters and reinitiating the program through E'.

Sample Problem 13-1

Given a compressor whose performance curve is the base curve of figure 10-1 and the following rated data:

$T_1 = 100°F$

$MW = 29$

$Z_a = 0.985$

$k_a = 1.17$

$(Q_1)_r = 45,000$ ICFM

$(P_1)_r = 16$ psia

$(P_2)_r = 57$ psia

$(\eta_p)_r = 78\%$

$(Q_1)_{bc}$	$(H_p)_{bc}$
35,000	44,000
45,000	42,100
54,000	34,000

calculate the inlet pressure variation curve for a constant discharge pressure of 57 psia. For simplicity, assume the efficiency is 76% and constant across the curve. Figure 13-1 is the resulting curve.

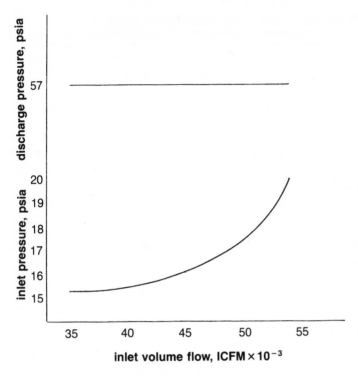

Figure 13-1. Inlet volume flow versus inlet pressure curve for constant discharge pressure and constant speed for Sample Problem 13-1.

Note that the inlet pressure for 45,000 ICFM is slightly higher than the rated value of 16 psia. This is due to the use of 76% as the polytropic efficiency value, while the actual polytropic efficiency was 78%.

Sample Problem 13-1: User Instructions

Step	Procedure	Enter	Press	Display
1.	Load program.			
2.	Enter molecular weight.	29	2nd A′	29
3.	Enter average k-value.	1.17	2nd B′	1.17
4.	Enter average Z-value.	0.985	2nd C′	0.985
5.	Enter discharge pressure.	57	B	57
6.	Enter inlet temperature.	100(°F)	C	560(°R)
7.	Initiate the program.		2nd E′	57 (P_2)

(continued on next page)

Sample Problem 13-1: User Instructions continued

Step	Procedure	Enter	Press	Display
8.	Enter polytropic efficiency.	0.76	2nd D'	0.76
9.	Enter inlet volume flow.	35000	D	35000
10.	Enter polytropic head and calculate inlet pressure.	44000	E	
11.	Repeat steps 8, 9, and 10 for all desired points.			

Sample Problem 13-1: Program Printout

```
P1 FROM P2               0.76      EFF        0.76      EFF
                      44000.      HEAD     34000.      HEAD
                      35000.      Q1       54000.      Q1
        100.     T1      15.28     P1       20.04     P1
         29.     MW
        1.17     KA       0.76      EFF
       0.985     ZA    42100.      HEAD
                       45000.      Q1
         57.     P2      16.07     P1
```

Program 13 Listing

000	76	LBL	020	76	LBL	040	76	LBL
001	12	B	021	16	A'	041	10	E'
002	42	STO	022	42	STO	042	69	OP
003	03	03	023	06	06	043	00	00
004	91	R/S	024	91	R/S	044	03	3
005	76	LBL	025	76	LBL	045	03	3
006	13	C	026	17	B'	046	00	0
007	85	+	027	42	STO	047	02	2
008	04	4	028	07	07	048	00	0
009	06	6	029	91	R/S	049	00	0
010	00	0	030	76	LBL	050	02	2
011	95	=	031	18	C'	051	01	1
012	42	STO	032	42	STO	052	03	3
013	04	04	033	08	08	053	05	5
014	91	R/S	034	91	R/S	054	69	OP
015	76	LBL	035	76	LBL	055	02	02
016	14	D	036	19	D'	056	03	3
017	42	STO	037	42	STO	057	02	2
018	13	13	038	05	05	058	03	3
019	91	R/S	039	91	R/S	059	00	0

Program 13 Listing continued

060	00	0	110	03	3	160	95	=
061	00	0	111	69	OP	161	35	1/X
062	03	3	112	04	04	162	65	×
063	03	3	113	43	RCL	163	43	RCL
064	00	0	114	08	08	164	05	05
065	03	3	115	69	OP	165	95	=
066	69	OP	116	06	06	166	42	STO
067	03	03	117	98	ADV	167	12	12
068	69	OP	118	03	3	168	35	1/X
069	05	05	119	03	3	169	65	×
070	98	ADV	120	00	0	170	43	RCL
071	98	ADV	121	03	3	171	11	11
072	03	3	122	69	OP	172	85	+
073	07	7	123	04	04	173	01	1
074	00	0	124	43	RCL	174	95	=
075	02	2	125	03	03	175	45	YX
076	69	OP	126	69	OP	176	43	RCL
077	04	04	127	06	06	177	12	12
078	43	RCL	128	98	ADV	178	95	=
079	04	04	129	98	ADV	179	35	1/X
080	75	-	130	91	R/S	180	65	×
081	04	4	131	76	LBL	181	43	RCL
082	06	6	132	15	E	182	03	03
083	00	0	133	42	STO	183	95	=
084	95	=	134	09	09	184	42	STO
085	69	OP	135	65	×	185	10	10
086	06	06	136	43	RCL	186	01	1
087	03	3	137	06	06	187	07	7
088	00	0	138	55	÷	188	02	2
089	04	4	139	01	1	189	01	1
090	03	3	140	05	5	190	02	2
091	69	OP	141	04	4	191	01	1
092	04	04	142	05	5	192	69	OP
093	43	RCL	143	55	÷	193	04	04
094	06	06	144	43	RCL	194	43	RCL
095	69	OP	145	08	08	195	05	05
096	06	06	146	55	÷	196	69	OP
097	02	2	147	43	RCL	197	06	06
098	06	6	148	04	04	198	02	2
099	01	1	149	95	=	199	03	3
100	03	3	150	42	STO	200	01	1
101	69	OP	151	11	11	201	07	7
102	04	04	152	43	RCL	202	01	1
103	43	RCL	153	07	07	203	03	3
104	07	07	154	75	-	204	01	1
105	69	OP	155	01	1	205	06	6
106	06	06	156	95	=	206	69	OP
107	04	4	157	55	÷	207	04	04
108	06	6	158	43	RCL	208	43	RCL
109	01	1	159	07	07	209	09	09

(continued on next page)

Program 13 Listing continued

210	69	OP	220	69	OP	230	58	FIX
211	06	06	221	06	06	231	02	02
212	03	3	222	03	3	232	69	OP
213	04	4	223	03	3	233	06	06
214	00	0	224	00	0	234	22	INV
215	02	2	225	02	2	235	58	FIX
216	69	OP	226	69	OP	236	69	OP
217	04	04	227	04	04	237	00	00
218	43	RCL	228	43	RCL	238	98	ADV
219	13	13	229	10	10	239	91	R/S

Part III

Centrifugal Compressor Testing

Program 14

Mass Flow from an ASME Flow Nozzle or Venturi Meter

Background

When flow measurements are obtained from either a long-radius ASME flow nozzle or a Herschel-type venturi meter, the mass flow is given by Equation 14-1. Refer to ASME PTC 10-1965 for the test arrangements.

$$m = 31.501 \ C_d F_a d^2 Y_N \ \sqrt{\frac{P_1 - P_2}{v_1}} \qquad (14\text{-}1)$$

where:
  m = mass flow, lbm/min
  C_d = coefficient of discharge
  F_a = thermal expansion factor for the fluid meter
  d = throat diameter of the fluid meter, inches
  Y_N = expansion factor for flow nozzles and venturi meters
  v_1 = specific volume upstream of the fluid meter, ft^3/lbm
  P_1 = pressure upstream of the fluid meter, psia
  P_2 = pressure downstream of the fluid meter, psia

The expansion factor in Equation 14-1 is given by Equation 14-2:

$$Y_N = \left[\left(\frac{k}{k-1} \right) r_p^{2/k} \left(\frac{1 - r_p^{(k-1)/k}}{1 - r_p} \right) \right]^{1/2} \left[\frac{1}{1 - r_p^{2/k} \beta^4} \right]^{1/2} \qquad (14\text{-}2)$$

where:

r_p = pressure ratio across the meter, P_2/P_1
k = ratio of specific heats upstream of the fluid meter
β = diameter ratio for the fluid meter, d/D, where D is the upstream pipe diameter

The specific volume in Equation 14-1 is measured upstream of the fluid meter and is therefore as given in Equation 14-3:

$$v_1 = 10.729 \; \frac{Z_1 T_1}{(MW)(P_1)}$$

(14-3)

where:

Z_1 = compressibility upstream of the fluid meter
T_1 = temperature upstream of the fluid meter, °R
MW = molecular weight of gas, lbm/lbm-mol

The coefficient of discharge for a flow nozzle or venturi meter is a function of the diameter ratio of the meter, β, and the Reynolds number for the upstream pipe conditions. The Reynolds number is given by:

$$\text{Re}_1 = \frac{m}{3.927 \; D\mu_1}$$

(14-4)

where:

Re_1 = Reynolds number upstream of the fluid meter
D = pipe diameter upstream of the fluid meter, inches
μ_1 = absolute viscosity upstream of the fluid meter, lbm/ft-sec

Values for C_d for flow nozzles can be found in ASME PTC 10-1965. Values for C_d for Herschel-type venturi meters can be found in ASME PTC 19.5;4-1959.

Program 14 Description

Program 14, Mass Flow From an ASME Flow Nozzle or Venturi Meter, calculates and prints the results of Equations 14-1 and 14-4.
In order to execute the program, the following must be known:

1. Pressure upstream of fluid meter, P_1
2. Pressure downstream of fluid meter, P_2
3. Temperature upstream of fluid meter, T_1
4. Molecular weight of gas, MW

5. k-value upstream of fluid meter, k_1
6. Z-value upstream of fluid meter, Z_1
7. Pipe diameter upstream of fluid meter, D
8. Throat diameter of fluid meter, d
9. Coefficient of discharge, C_d
10. Thermal expansion factor for the fluid meter, F_a
11. Absolute viscosity upstream of fluid meter, μ_1

For Reynolds numbers in excess of about 200,000 and β ratios between 0.3 and 0.75, the value of C_d is approximately 0.99. After the program calculates the mass flow, an option to calculate the Reynolds number exists. It is therefore suggested that an initial guess of $C_d = 0.99$ be made. After the Reynolds number is calculated, the value of C_d can be further refined. (The Reynolds number for the upstream pipe diameter is calculated from Equation 14-4. The program also calculates an approximate Reynolds number at the throat by ratioing the diameters, i.e. $Re_t = Re_1 (D/d)$, where Re_t = Reynolds number at the throat.)

Entering the molecular weight sets the value of F_a to 1.0 automatically. If F_a is not equal to 1.0, it must be calculated and entered manually.

The program is set up for continuous usage, without the need for complete data reentry unless the molecular weight is revised. Reentering the molecular weight will reset F_a to 1.0. If F_a is other than 1.0, it will have to be reentered. Otherwise, only the parameters of interest need to be changed.

Table 14-1 is the nomenclature printed by the program; Table 14-2 shows the data registers used by the program.

Labels Used by Program 14

001	11	A	026	16	A'	058	10	E'
006	12	B	034	17	B'	063	15	E
011	13	C	048	18	C'			
021	14	D	053	19	D'			

Program 14 Usage

Program 14 is executed by using the user-defined keys and the R/S key. The definitions of the user-defined and R/S keys can be found in Table 14-3.

When the molecular weight is entered through user-defined key A', the thermal expansion factor, F_a, is automatically set at 1.0. If the value of F_a is other than 1.0, it must be manually calculated, entered, and stored in data-register 12 after the molecular weight is entered.

Once all the data are entered, program execution is initiated through user-defined key E. The program calculates the mass flow and stops. The operator can opt to calculate the Reynolds number by entering the absolute

Table 14-1
Program 14: Printer Nomenclature

Program Term	Definition	Units
BETA	diameter ratio $= d/D$	dimensionless
CD	coefficient of discharge	dimensionless
D1	upstream pipe diameter	inches
DT	throat diameter	inches
FA	thermal expansion factor	dimensionless
K1	ratio of specific heats upstream of fluid meter	dimensionless
M	mass flow	lbm/min
MU	absolute viscosity upstream of fluid meter	lbm/ft-sec
MW	molecular weight	lbm/lbm-mol
P1	pressure upstream of fluid meter	psia
P2	pressure downstream of fluid meter	psia
RE1	Reynolds number based on upstream conditions and upstream pipe diameter	dimensionless
RET	approximate Reynolds number at throat of fluid meter, based on upstream conditions and throat diameter	dimensionless
T1	temperature upstream of fluid meter	°F
Z1	compressibility upstream of fluid meter	dimensionless

Table 14-2
Data Registers Used by Program 14

00	not used	07	MW	14	β
01	not used	08	k_1	15	Y_N
02	not used	09	Z_1	16	r_p
03	P_1	10	d	17	m
04	P_2	11	C_d	18	μ_1
05	T_1	12	F_a	19	Re_1
06	D	13	$(k-1)/k$	20	Re_t

Table 14-3
Program 14: Definitions of User-Defined and R/S Keys

A	P1	A'	MW	
B	P2	B'	K1	
C	T1	C'	Z1	
D	D1	D'	DT	
E	Calculate	E'	CD	
		R/S	MU, Continue execution	

viscosity and pressing the R/S key as prompted by the program. Once the Reynolds number is known, the operator can modify the coefficient of discharge, if necessary, and reexecute the program through E.

Subsequent calculations can be made by changing only the parameters desired, unless the molecular weight is revised. Revising the molecular weight resets the thermal expansion factor to 1.0. If necessary, F_a must be reentered and stored in data-register 12 after the new molecular weight is entered.

Sample Problem 14-1

A test arrangement is set up with an ASME flow nozzle to determine the mass flow during a compressor performance test. The following is recorded:

$$P_1 = 14.7 \text{ psia}$$
$$P_2 = 14.1 \text{ psia}$$
$$T_1 = 100°F$$
$$MW = 28.0$$
$$k_1 = 1.4$$
$$Z_1 = 1.0$$
$$D = 15.25 \text{ inches (16-inch pipe)}$$
$$d = 10 \text{ inches}$$
$$F_a = 1.0$$
$$C_d = 0.99$$
$$\mu_1 = 12.8 \times 10^{-6} \text{ lbm/ft-sec}$$

Calculate the mass flow through the flow nozzle.

Sample Problem 14-1: User Instructions

Step	Procedure	Enter	Press	Display
1.	Load program.			
2.	Enter pressure upstream of flow nozzle.	14.7	A	14.7
3.	Enter pressure downstream of flow nozzle.	14.1	B	14.1
4.	Enter temperature upstream of flow nozzle.	100(°F)	C	560(°R)
5.	Enter molecular weight.	28.0	2nd A'	1 (F_a)
6.	Enter k-value upstream of flow nozzle.	1.4	2nd B'	$.2857\dots\left(\dfrac{k-1}{k}\right)$

(continued on next page)

Sample Problem 14-1: User Instructions continued

Step	Procedure	Enter	Press	Display
7.	Enter Z-value upstream of flow nozzle.	1.0	2nd C′	1
8.	Enter pipe diameter upstream of flow nozzle.	15.25	D	15.25
9.	Enter throat diameter of flow nozzle.	10	2nd D′	10
10.	Enter coefficient of discharge.	0.99	2nd E′	0.99
11.	Calculate mass flow.		E	
12.	Enter absolute viscosity; calculate Reynolds number.	12.8 EE-6	R/S	

Sample Problem 14-1: Program Printout

```
FLOW  NOZZLE          15.25       D1        ENTER MU, R/S
                      10.         DT
14.7         P1        1.         FA              1.28-05     MU
14.1         P2       0.99        CD         887591.         RE1
100.         T1                              1353576.        RET
 28.         MW
  1.4        K1       0.656       BETA
  1.         Z1      680.4          M
```

Program 14 Listing

000	76	LBL		016	95	=		032	91	R/S	
001	11	A		017	42	STO		033	76	LBL	
002	42	STO		018	05	05		034	17	B′	
003	03	03		019	91	R/S		035	42	STO	
004	91	R/S		020	76	LBL		036	08	08	
005	76	LBL		021	14	D		037	75	-	
006	12	B		022	42	STO		038	01	1	
007	42	STO		023	06	06		039	95	=	
008	04	04		024	91	R/S		040	55	÷	
009	91	R/S		025	76	LBL		041	43	RCL	
010	76	LBL		026	16	A′		042	08	08	
011	13	C		027	42	STO		043	95	=	
012	85	+		028	07	07		044	42	STO	
013	04	4		029	01	1		045	13	13	
014	06	6		030	42	STO		046	91	R/S	
015	00	0		031	12	12		047	76	LBL	

Program 14 Listing continued

048	18	C'	098	00	00	148	55	÷
049	42	STO	099	98	ADV	149	53	(
050	09	09	100	98	ADV	150	01	1
051	91	R/S	101	43	RCL	151	75	-
052	76	LBL	102	04	04	152	43	RCL
053	19	D'	103	55	÷	153	16	16
054	42	STO	104	43	RCL	154	54	)
055	10	10	105	03	03	155	65	×
056	91	R/S	106	95	=	156	43	RCL
057	76	LBL	107	42	STO	157	16	16
058	10	E'	108	16	16	158	45	Yˣ
059	42	STO	109	43	RCL	159	53	(
060	11	11	110	10	10	160	02	2
061	91	R/S	111	55	÷	161	55	÷
062	76	LBL	112	43	RCL	162	43	RCL
063	15	E	113	06	06	163	08	08
064	69	OP	114	95	=	164	54	)
065	00	00	115	42	STO	165	65	×
066	98	ADV	116	14	14	166	43	RCL
067	02	2	117	45	Yˣ	167	13	13
068	01	1	118	04	4	168	35	1/X
069	69	OP	119	65	×	169	95	=
070	01	01	120	43	RCL	170	34	ΓX
071	02	2	121	16	16	171	65	×
072	07	7	122	45	Yˣ	172	43	RCL
073	03	3	123	53	(	173	15	15
074	02	2	124	02	2	174	95	=
075	04	4	125	55	÷	175	42	STO
076	03	3	126	43	RCL	176	15	15
077	00	0	127	08	08	177	01	1
078	00	0	128	54	)	178	00	0
079	03	3	129	95	=	179	93	.
080	01	1	130	94	+/-	180	07	7
081	69	OP	131	85	+	181	02	2
082	02	02	132	01	1	182	09	9
083	03	3	133	95	=	183	65	×
084	02	2	134	35	1/X	184	43	RCL
085	04	4	135	34	ΓX	185	09	09
086	06	6	136	42	STO	186	65	×
087	04	4	137	15	15	187	43	RCL
088	06	6	138	43	RCL	188	05	05
089	02	2	139	16	16	189	55	÷
090	07	7	140	45	Yˣ	190	43	RCL
091	01	1	141	43	RCL	191	03	03
092	07	7	142	13	13	192	55	÷
093	69	OP	143	95	=	193	43	RCL
094	03	03	144	94	+/-	194	07	07
095	69	OP	145	85	+	195	95	=
096	05	05	146	01	1	196	35	1/X
097	69	OP	147	95	=	197	65	×

(continued on next page)

Program 14 Listing continued

198	53	(	248	69	□P	298	00	0
199	43	RCL	249	06	06	299	02	2
200	03	03	250	03	3	300	69	□P
201	75	-	251	07	7	301	04	04
202	43	RCL	252	00	0	302	43	RCL
203	04	04	253	02	2	303	06	06
204	54	)	254	69	□P	304	69	□P
205	95	=	255	04	04	305	06	06
206	34	┌X	256	43	RCL	306	01	1
207	65	×	257	05	05	307	06	6
208	43	RCL	258	75	-	308	03	3
209	15	15	259	04	4	309	07	7
210	65	×	260	06	6	310	69	□P
211	43	RCL	261	00	0	311	04	04
212	10	10	262	95	=	312	43	RCL
213	33	X²	263	69	□P	313	10	10
214	65	×	264	06	06	314	69	□P
215	43	RCL	265	03	3	315	06	06
216	12	12	266	00	0	316	02	2
217	65	×	267	04	4	317	01	1
218	43	RCL	268	03	3	318	01	1
219	11	11	269	69	□P	319	03	3
220	65	×	270	04	04	320	69	□P
221	03	3	271	43	RCL	321	04	04
222	01	1	272	07	07	322	43	RCL
223	93	.	273	69	□P	323	12	12
224	05	5	274	06	06	324	69	□P
225	00	0	275	02	2	325	06	06
226	01	1	276	06	6	326	01	1
227	95	=	277	00	0	327	05	5
228	42	STO	278	02	2	328	01	1
229	17	17	279	69	□P	329	06	6
230	03	3	280	04	04	330	69	□P
231	03	3	281	43	RCL	331	04	04
232	00	0	282	08	08	332	43	RCL
233	02	2	283	69	□P	333	11	11
234	69	□P	284	06	06	334	69	□P
235	04	04	285	04	4	335	06	06
236	43	RCL	286	06	6	336	98	ADV
237	03	03	287	00	0	337	01	1
238	69	□P	288	02	2	338	04	4
239	06	06	289	69	□P	339	01	1
240	03	3	290	04	04	340	07	7
241	03	3	291	43	RCL	341	03	3
242	00	0	292	09	09	342	07	7
243	03	3	293	69	□P	343	01	1
244	69	□P	294	06	06	344	03	3
245	04	04	295	98	ADV	345	69	□P
246	43	RCL	296	01	1	346	04	04
247	04	04	297	06	6	347	43	RCL

Program 14 Listing continued

348	14	14	391	02	02	434	20	20
349	58	FIX	392	03	3	435	03	3
350	03	03	393	05	5	436	00	0
351	69	OP	394	06	6	437	04	4
352	06	06	395	03	3	438	01	1
353	22	INV	396	03	3	439	69	OP
354	58	FIX	397	06	6	440	04	04
355	03	3	398	00	0	441	43	RCL
356	00	0	399	00	0	442	18	18
357	69	OP	400	00	0	443	69	OP
358	04	04	401	00	0	444	06	06
359	43	RCL	402	69	OP	445	22	INV
360	17	17	403	03	03	446	52	EE
361	58	FIX	404	69	OP	447	03	3
362	01	01	405	05	05	448	05	5
363	69	OP	406	69	OP	449	01	1
364	06	06	407	00	00	450	07	7
365	22	INV	408	98	ADV	451	00	0
366	58	FIX	409	91	R/S	452	02	2
367	98	ADV	410	42	STO	453	69	OP
368	69	OP	411	18	18	454	04	04
369	00	00	412	35	1/X	455	43	RCL
370	01	1	413	65	X	456	19	19
371	07	7	414	43	RCL	457	59	INT
372	03	3	415	17	17	458	69	OP
373	01	1	416	55	÷	459	06	06
374	03	3	417	03	3	460	03	3
375	07	7	418	93	.	461	05	5
376	01	1	419	09	9	462	01	1
377	07	7	420	02	2	463	07	7
378	03	3	421	07	7	464	03	3
379	05	5	422	55	÷	465	07	7
380	69	OP	423	43	RCL	466	69	OP
381	01	01	424	06	06	467	04	04
382	03	3	425	95	=	468	43	RCL
383	00	0	426	42	STO	469	20	20
384	04	4	427	19	19	470	59	INT
385	01	1	428	65	X	471	69	OP
386	05	5	429	43	RCL	472	06	06
387	07	7	430	14	14	473	69	OP
388	00	0	431	35	1/X	474	00	00
389	00	0	432	95	=	475	91	R/S
390	69	OP	433	42	STO	476	00	0

Program 15

Mass Flow from an Orifice

Background

When flow measurements are obtained from a square-edge orifice, the mass flow is given by Equation 15-1. Refer to ASME PTC 10-1965 for the test arrangements.

$$m = 31.501 \, K_{fc} F_a d^2 Y_O \sqrt{\frac{P_1 - P_2}{v_1}} \tag{15-1}$$

where:

m = mass flow, lbm/min
K_{fc} = flow coefficient
F_a = thermal expansion factor for the fluid meter
d = throat diameter of the fluid meter, inches
Y_O = expansion factor for orifices
v_1 = specific volume upstream of the fluid meter, ft³/lbm
P_1 = pressure upstream of the fluid meter, psia
P_2 = pressure downstream of the fluid meter, psia

The expansion factor in Equation 15-1 is given by Equation 15-2:

$$Y_O = 1 - \left[(0.41 + 0.35 \, \beta^4) \left(\frac{P_1 - P_2}{P_1 k} \right) \right] \tag{15-2}$$

where:

    k = ratio of specific heats upstream of the fluid meter

    β = diameter ratio for the fluid meter, d/D, where D is the upstream pipe diameter

The specific volume in Equation 15-1 is measured upstream of the fluid meter and is therefore as given in Equation 14-3, presented here for convenience:

$$v_1 = 10.729 \frac{Z_1 T_1}{(MW)(P_1)} \tag{14-3}$$

The flow coefficient in Equation 15-1 is related to the coefficient of discharge, C_d, by the following:

$$K_{fc} = \frac{C_d}{\sqrt{1 - \beta^4}} \tag{15-3}$$

where:

    C_d = coefficient of discharge

The flow coefficient and the coefficient of discharge are functions of the diameter ratio of the orifice, β, the upstream pipe diameter, and the Reynolds number for the upstream pipe conditions. The Reynolds number is given by Equation 14-4 and presented here for convenience:

$$\mathrm{Re}_1 = \frac{m}{3.927 \, D\mu_1} \tag{14-4}$$

Values for K_{fc} can be found in ASME PTC 19.5;4-1959; Values for C_d can be found elsewhere in the literature.

Program 15 Description

Program 15, Mass Flow From an Orifice, calculates and prints the results of Equations 15-1, 15-3, and 14-4.

In order to execute the program, the following must be known:

1. Pressure upstream of orifice, P_1
2. Pressure downstream of orifice, P_2

3. Temperature upstream of orifice, T_1
4. Molecular weight of gas, MW
5. k-value upstream of orifice, k_1
6. Z-value upstream of orifice, Z_1
7. Pipe diameter upstream of orifice, D
8. Throat diameter of orifice, d
9. Either the flow coefficient, K_{fc}, or the coefficient of discharge, C_d
10. Thermal expansion factor for the orifice, F_a
11. Absolute viscosity upstream of orifice, μ_1

The program contains the option to calculate the mass flow from either the coefficient of discharge or the flow coefficient. The coefficient of discharge for square-edge orifices is approximately 0.61. After the program calculates the mass flow, an option to calculate the Reynolds number exists. It is therefore suggested that an initial guess of $C_d = 0.61$ be made. After the Reynolds number is calculated, the value of either K_{fc} or C_d can be further refined, based on the data available. (The Reynolds number for the upstream pipe diameter is calculated from Equation 14-4. The program also calculates an approximate Reynolds number at the throat by ratioing the diameters, i.e. $Re_t = Re_1 (D/d)$, where Re_t = Reynolds number at the throat.)

Entering the molecular weight sets the value of F_a to 1.0 automatically. If F_a is not equal to 1.0, it must be calculated and entered manually.

The program is set up for continuous usage, without the need for complete data reentry unless the molecular weight is revised. Reentering the molecular weight will reset F_a to 1.0. If F_a is other than 1.0, it will have to be reentered. Otherwise, only the parameters of interest need to be changed.

Table 15-1 is the nomenclature printed by the program; Table 15-2 shows the data registers used by the program.

Labels Used by Program 15

001	11	A	026	16	A'	058	10	E'
006	12	B	034	17	B'	070	15	E
011	13	C	048	18	C'	458	33	X²
021	14	D	053	19	D'			

Program 15 Usage

Program 15 is executed by using the user-defined keys and the R/S key. The definitions of the user-defined and R/S keys can be found in Table 15-3.

When the molecular weight is entered through user-defined key A', the thermal expansion factor, F_a, is automatically set at 1.0. If the value of F_a

Table 15-1
Program 15: Printer Nomenclature

Program Term	Definition	Units
BETA	diameter ratio, d/D	dimensionless
CD	coefficient of discharge	dimensionless
D1	upstream pipe diameter	inches
DT	throat diameter	inches
FA	thermal expansion factor	dimensionless
KFC	flow coefficient	dimensionless
K1	ratio of specific heats upstream of orifice	dimensionless
M	mass flow	lbm/min
MU	absolute viscosity upstream of orifice	lbm/ft-sec
MW	molecular weight	lbm/lbm-mol
P1	pressure upstream of orifice	psia
P2	pressure downstream of orifice	psia
RE1	Reynolds number based on upstream conditions and upstream pipe diameter	dimensionless
RET	approximate Reynolds number at throat of orifice, based on upstream conditions and throat diameter	dimensionless
T1	temperature upstream of orifice	°R
Z1	compressibility upstream of orifice	dimensionless

Table 15-2
Data Registers Used by Program 15

00	not used	08	k_1	16	not used
01	not used	09	Z_1	17	m
02	not used	10	d	18	μ_1
03	P_1	11	K_{fc}	19	Re_1
04	P_2	12	F_a	20	Re_t
05	T_1	13	$(k-1)/k$	21	C_d
06	D	14	β	22	$1/\sqrt{1-\beta^4}$
07	MW	15	Y_0		

Table 15-3
Program 15: Definitions of User-Defined and R/S Keys

A	P1	A'	MW
B	P2	B'	K1
C	T1	C'	Z1
D	D1	D'	DT
E	KFC, Calculate	E'	CD, Calculate
		R/S	MU, Continue execution

is other than 1.0, it must be manually calculated, entered, and stored in data register 12 after the molecular weight is entered.

Once all other data are entered, program execution is initiated either by entering the flow coefficient, K_{fc}, through user-defined key E, or by entering the coefficient of discharge, C_d, through E'. The program calculates the mass flow and stops. The operator can opt to calculate the Reynolds number by entering the absolute viscosity and pressing the R/S key as prompted by the program. Once the Reynolds number is known, the operator can modify either the flow coefficient or the coefficient of discharge, if necessary, and reexecute the program through E or E', respectively.

Subsequent calculations can be made by changing only the parameters desired, unless the molecular weight is revised. Revising the molecular weight resets the thermal expansion factor to 1.0. If necessary, F_a must be reentered and stored in data-register 12 after the new molecular weight is entered.

Sample Problem 15-1

A test arrangement is set up with an orifice to determine the mass flow during a compressor performance test. The following is recorded:

$$P_1 = 14.7 \text{ psia}$$
$$P_2 = 13.3 \text{ psia}$$
$$T_1 = 100°F$$
$$MW = 28.0$$
$$k_1 = 1.4$$
$$Z_1 = 1.0$$
$$D = 15.25 \text{ inches (16-inch pipe)}$$
$$d = 10 \text{ inches}$$
$$F_a = 1.0$$
$$C_d = 0.61$$
$$\mu_1 = 12.8 \times 10^{-6} \text{ lbm/ft-sec}$$

Calculate the mass flow through the orifice.

Sample Problem 15-1: User Instructions

Step	Procedure	Enter	Press	Display
1.	Load program.			
2.	Enter pressure upstream of orifice.	14.7	A	14.7
3.	Enter pressure down-stream of orifice.	13.3	B	13.3

Sample Problem 15-1: User Instructions continued

Step	Procedure	Enter	Press	Display
4.	Enter temperature upstream of orifice.	100(°F)	C	560(°R)
5.	Enter molecular weight.	28.0	2nd A′	$1 (F_a)$
6.	Enter k-value upstream of orifice.	1.4	2nd B′	$.2857... \left(\dfrac{k-1}{k} \right)$
7.	EnterZ-value upstream of orifice.	1.0	2nd C′	1
8.	Enter pipe diameter upstream of orifice.	15.25	D	15.25
9.	Enter throat diameter of orifice.	10	2nd D′	10
10.	Enter coefficient of discharge and calculate.	0.61	2nd E′	
11.	Enter absolute viscosity; calculate Reynolds number.	12.8 EE-6	R/S	

Sample Problem 15-1: Program Printout

```
ORIFICE              15.25      D1      ENTER  MU,  R/S
14.7       P1         10.        DT
13.3       P2          1.        FA           1.28-05    MU
100.       T1        0.676       KFC       832104.       RE1
28.        MW       ·0.610       CD       1268959.       RET
1.4        K1        0.656       BETA
1.         Z1       637.9        M
```

Sample Problem 15-2

Using the same data as in Sample Problem 15-1, calculate the mass flow through an orifice with $K_{fc} = 0.68$.

Sample Problem 15-2: User Instructions

Step	Procedure	Enter	Press	Display
1–9	Refer to Sample Problem 15-1, User Instructions			

(continued on next page)

Sample Problem 15-2: User Instructions continued

Step	Procedure	Enter	Press	Display
10.	Enter flow coefficient and calculate.	0.68	E	
11.	Refer to Sample Problem 15-1, User Instructions			

Sample Problem 15-2: Program Printout

```
ORIFICE                   15.25     D1       ENTER   MU,   R/S
 14.7          P1          10.      DT
 13.3          P2           1.      FA                1.28-05    MU
100.           T1          0.680    KFC          837460.        RE1
 28.           MW          0.614    CD          1277127.        RET
  1.4          K1          0.656    BETA
  1.           Z1         642.0     M
```

Program 15 Listing

000	76	LBL	025	76	LBL	050	09	09
001	11	A	026	16	A'	051	91	R/S
002	42	STO	027	42	STO	052	76	LBL
003	03	03	028	07	07	053	19	D'
004	91	R/S	029	01	1	054	42	STO
005	76	LBL	030	42	STO	055	10	10
006	12	B	031	12	12	056	91	R/S
007	42	STO	032	91	R/S	057	76	LBL
008	04	04	033	76	LBL	058	10	E'
009	91	R/S	034	17	B'	059	42	STO
010	76	LBL	035	42	STO	060	21	21
011	13	C	036	08	08	061	71	SBR
012	85	+	037	75	-	062	33	X²
013	04	4	038	01	1	063	65	×
014	06	6	039	95	=	064	43	RCL
015	00	0	040	55	÷	065	21	21
016	95	=	041	43	RCL	066	95	=
017	42	STO	042	08	08	067	15	E
018	05	05	043	95	=	068	91	R/S
019	91	R/S	044	42	STO	069	76	LBL
020	76	LBL	045	13	13	070	15	E
021	14	D	046	91	R/S	071	42	STO
022	42	STO	047	76	LBL	072	11	11
023	06	06	048	18	C'	073	69	OP
024	91	R/S	049	42	STO	074	00	00

Program 15 Listing continued

075	98	ADV	125	53	(	175	43	RCL	
076	03	3	126	43	RCL	176	15	15
077	02	2	127	03	03	177	65	×
078	03	3	128	75	-	178	43	RCL
079	05	5	129	43	RCL	179	10	10
080	02	2	130	04	04	180	33	X²
081	04	4	131	54	)	181	65	×
082	69	OP	132	55	÷	182	43	RCL
083	02	02	133	43	RCL	183	12	12
084	02	2	134	03	03	184	65	×
085	01	1	135	55	÷	185	43	RCL
086	02	2	136	43	RCL	186	11	11
087	04	4	137	08	08	187	65	×
088	01	1	138	94	+/-	188	03	3
089	05	5	139	85	+	189	01	1
090	01	1	140	01	1	190	93	.
091	07	7	141	95	=	191	05	5
092	00	0	142	42	STO	192	00	0
093	00	0	143	15	15	193	01	1
094	69	OP	144	01	1	194	95	=
095	03	03	145	00	0	195	42	STO
096	69	OP	146	93	.	196	17	17
097	05	05	147	07	7	197	03	3
098	69	OP	148	02	2	198	03	3
099	00	00	149	09	9	199	00	0
100	98	ADV	150	65	×	200	02	2
101	98	ADV	151	43	RCL	201	69	OP
102	71	SBR	152	09	09	202	04	04
103	33	X²	153	65	×	203	43	RCL
104	35	1/X	154	43	RCL	204	03	03
105	65	×	155	05	05	205	69	OP
106	43	RCL	156	55	÷	206	06	06
107	11	11	157	43	RCL	207	03	3
108	95	=	158	03	03	208	03	3
109	42	STO	159	55	÷	209	00	0
110	21	21	160	43	RCL	210	03	3
111	43	RCL	161	07	07	211	69	OP
112	14	14	162	95	=	212	04	04
113	45	Yˣ	163	35	1/X	213	43	RCL
114	04	4	164	65	×	214	04	04
115	65	×	165	53	(	215	69	OP
116	93	.	166	43	RCL	216	06	06
117	03	3	167	03	03	217	03	3
118	05	5	168	75	-	218	07	7
119	85	+	169	43	RCL	219	00	0
120	93	.	170	04	04	220	02	2
121	04	4	171	54	)	221	69	OP
122	01	1	172	95	=	222	04	04
123	95	=	173	34	√X	223	43	RCL
124	65	×	174	65	×	224	05	05

(continued on next page)

Program 15 Listing continued

225	75	–	275	03	3	325	04	4
226	04	4	276	07	7	326	01	1
227	06	6	277	69	□P	327	07	7
228	00	0	278	04	04	328	03	3
229	95	=	279	43	RCL	329	07	7
230	69	□P	280	10	10	330	01	1
231	06	06	281	69	□P	331	03	3
232	03	3	282	06	06	332	69	□P
233	00	0	283	02	2	333	04	04
234	04	4	284	01	1	334	43	RCL
235	03	3	285	01	1	335	14	14
236	69	□P	286	03	3	336	58	FIX
237	04	04	287	69	□P	337	03	03
238	43	RCL	288	04	04	338	69	□P
239	07	07	289	43	RCL	339	06	06
240	69	□P	290	12	12	340	22	INV
241	06	06	291	69	□P	341	58	FIX
242	02	2	292	06	06	342	03	3
243	06	6	293	02	2	343	00	0
244	00	0	294	06	6	344	69	□P
245	02	2	295	02	2	345	04	04
246	69	□P	296	01	1	346	43	RCL
247	04	04	297	01	1	347	17	17
248	43	RCL	298	05	5	348	58	FIX
249	08	08	299	69	□P	349	01	01
250	69	□P	300	04	04	350	69	□P
251	06	06	301	43	RCL	351	06	06
252	04	4	302	11	11	352	22	INV
253	06	6	303	58	FIX	353	58	FIX
254	00	0	304	03	03	354	98	ADV
255	02	2	305	69	□P	355	69	□P
256	69	□P	306	06	06	356	00	00
257	04	04	307	22	INV	357	01	1
258	43	RCL	308	58	FIX	358	07	7
259	09	09	309	01	1	359	03	3
260	69	□P	310	05	5	360	01	1
261	06	06	311	01	1	361	03	3
262	98	ADV	312	06	6	362	07	7
263	01	1	313	69	□P	363	01	1
264	06	6	314	04	04	364	07	7
265	00	0	315	43	RCL	365	03	3
266	02	2	316	21	21	366	05	5
267	69	□P	317	58	FIX	367	69	□P
268	04	04	318	03	03	368	01	01
269	43	RCL	319	69	□P	369	03	3
270	06	06	320	06	06	370	00	0
271	69	□P	321	22	INV	371	04	4
272	06	06	322	58	FIX	372	01	1
273	01	1	323	98	ADV	373	05	5
274	06	6	324	01	1	374	07	7

Program 15 Listing continued

375	69	OP		410	43	RCL		445	03	3
376	02	02		411	14	14		446	07	7
377	03	3		412	35	1/X		447	69	OP
378	05	5		413	95	=		448	04	04
379	06	6		414	42	STO		449	43	RCL
380	03	3		415	20	20		450	20	20
381	03	3		416	03	3		451	59	INT
382	06	6		417	00	0		452	69	OP
383	69	OP		418	04	4		453	06	06
384	03	03		419	01	1		454	69	OP
385	69	OP		420	69	OP		455	00	00
386	05	05		421	04	04		456	91	R/S
387	69	OP		422	43	RCL		457	76	LBL
388	00	00		423	18	18		458	33	X²
389	98	ADV		424	69	OP		459	43	RCL
390	91	R/S		425	06	06		460	10	10
391	42	STO		426	22	INV		461	55	÷
392	18	18		427	52	EE		462	43	RCL
393	35	1/X		428	03	3		463	06	06
394	65	×		429	05	5		464	95	=
395	43	RCL		430	01	1		465	42	STO
396	17	17		431	07	7		466	14	14
397	55	÷		432	00	0		467	45	Y^X
398	03	3		433	02	2		468	04	4
399	93	.		434	69	OP		469	95	=
400	09	9		435	04	04		470	94	+/-
401	02	2		436	43	RCL		471	85	+
402	07	7		437	19	19		472	01	1
403	55	÷		438	59	INT		473	95	=
404	43	RCL		439	69	OP		474	34	ΓX
405	06	06		440	06	06		475	35	1/X
406	95	=		441	03	3		476	42	STO
407	42	STO		442	05	5		477	22	22
408	19	19		443	01	1		478	92	RTN
409	65	×		444	07	7		479	00	0

Program 16

Centrifugal Compressor Performance Test

Background

ASME PTC 10-1965 suggests Equation 16-1 for the determination of the polytropic head from test data for real gases:

$$H_p = 144\left(\frac{n}{n-1}\right) f P_1 v_1 \left[\left(\frac{P_2}{P_1}\right)^{(n-1)/n} - 1\right] \tag{16-1}$$

The term f is referred to as the polytropic work factor. It compensates for the value of n not being constant during compression. The value of f is normally very near 1.0 and can be set at 1.0 within the accuracy that one might expect when testing with field-installed gauges. Furthermore, in order to employ the effects of f, the inlet and discharge enthalpies must be known (refer to ASME PTC 10-1965). The purpose here is to develop a program for checking centrifugal compressor performance with relative accuracy while employing readily available thermodynamic data.

Thus, Equation 16-1 can be revised as shown in Equation 16-2:

$$H_p = 144\left(\frac{n}{n-1}\right) P_1 v_1 \left[\left(\frac{P_2}{P_1}\right)^{(n-1)/n} - 1\right] \tag{16-2}$$

The n-value in Equation 16-2 can be determined from test data as shown by the following:

$$n = \frac{\log_e(P_2/P_1)}{\log_e(v_1/v_2)} \tag{16-3}$$

In turn, the inlet and discharge specific volumes can be respectively calculated from the following, if actual thermodynamic data are not readily available:

$$v_1 = 10.729 \frac{Z_1 T_1}{(MW)(P_1)} \tag{14-3}$$

$$v_2 = 10.729 \frac{Z_2 T_2}{(MW)(P_2)} \tag{16-4}$$

Note that Equation 16-2 is based on the product $P_1 v_1$. If the compressibility is used to calculate the specific volume in the absence of actual thermodynamic data, the polytropic head expressed in Equation 16-2 would be based on the inlet compressibility. As discussed in Program 2, since the polytropic head is based on the inlet compressibility to each stage (impeller), the average compressibility tends to yield a more accurate compromise in calculating the polytropic head for multi-stage compressors, especially as the number of stages between cooling points increases. Since compressibilities are generally more readily available than actual thermodynamic data, the specific volumes will be calculated here from the compressibilities. It is therefore suggested that the reader look at the ratio of the average compressibility to the inlet compressibility as a possible correction on the results of Equation 16-2. (It would be easy to modify these developments to allow for entry of the actual specific volumes. However, if the actual thermodynamic data are available, the reader should consider calculating the polytropic head from the enthalpies, as this approach is more accurate. Refer to ASME PTC 10-1965.)

With the value of n known from Equation 16-3, the polytropic efficiency can be calculated from Equation 16-5:

$$\eta_p = \frac{\dfrac{n}{n-1}}{\dfrac{k}{k-1}} \tag{16-5}$$

The polytropic efficiency thus calculated is somewhat approximate, because for many gases it is difficult to determine a representative k-value for use in Equation 16-5. The suggested approach is to use the average k-value based on inlet and discharge conditions.

ASME PTC 10-1965 suggests calculating the polytropic efficiency from the following:

$$\eta_p = \frac{H_p}{h_2 - h_1} \tag{16-6}$$

where:

h_2 = discharge enthalpy, Btu/lbm
h_1 = inlet enthalpy, Btu/lbm

However, this equation requires access to actual thermodynamic data, which may not be readily available.

Thus, for these developments it will be assumed that Equation 16-5 is sufficiently accurate. (The resulting program can be easily modified to incorporate the enthalpies.)

Once the specific volume, polytropic head, and polytropic efficiency are known, the gas power requirement can be calculated from:

$$PWR_g = \frac{mH_p}{33,000\ \eta_p} \qquad (2\text{-}15)$$

and the inlet and discharge volume flows from:

$$Q_1 = mv_1 \qquad (16\text{-}7)$$

$$Q_2 = mv_2 \qquad (16\text{-}8)$$

Program 16 Description

Program 16, Centrifugal Compressor Performance Test, uses the results of Equations 16-3, 14-3, and 16-4 to calculate and print the results of Equations 16-2, 16-5, 2-15, 16-7, and 16-8.

In order to execute the program, the following must be known:

1. Inlet pressure, P_1
2. Discharge pressure, P_2
3. Inlet temperature, T_1
4. Discharge temperature, T_2
5. Molecular weight, MW
6. Average k-value, k_a
7. Inlet Z-value, Z_1
8. Discharge Z-value, Z_2
9. Mass flow, m

This program uses inlet and discharge compressibilities to calculate the inlet and discharge specific volumes. It is therefore not as accurate as a program based on actual thermodynamic data. However, this approach is more universally useful.

Table 16-1
Program 16: Printer Nomenclature

Program Term	Definition	Units
EFF	polytropic efficiency	dimensionless
HEAD	polytropic head	ft-lbf/lbm
KA	average ratio of specific heats	dimensionless
M	mass flow	lbm/min
MW	molecular weight	lbm/lbm-mol
P1	inlet pressure	psia
P2	discharge pressure	psia
PWRG	gas power requirement	hp
Q1	inlet volume flow	ICFM
Q2	discharge volume flow	CFM
T1	inlet temperature	°F
T2	discharge temperature	°F
Z1	inlet compressibility	dimensionless
Z2	discharge compressibility	dimensionless

Table 16-2
Data Registers Used by Program 16

00	not used	07	MW	14	n
01	not used	08	k_a	15	$n/(n-1)$
02	not used	09	Z_1	16	H_p
03	P_1	10	Z_2	17	η_p
04	P_2	11	m	18	PWR_g
05	T_1	12	v_1	19	Q_1
06	T_2	13	v_2	20	Q_2

The polytropic efficiency is based on the average k-value. Some error is anticipated, depending on the type of compressed gas, since for some gases the average k-value may not be a good representative k-value for use in Equation 16-5.

The program is set up for continuous usage, without the need for complete data reentry. Therefore, only the parameters of interest need to be changed before program reexecution.

Table 16-1 is the nomenclature printed by the program; Table 16-2 shows the data registers used by the program.

Labels Used by Program 16

001	11	A	031	16	A'	051	10	E'
006	12	B	036	17	B'	056	15	E
011	13	C	041	18	C'			
021	14	D	046	19	D'			

Table 16-3
Program 16: Definitions of User-Defined Keys

A	P1	A′	MW
B	P2	B′	KA
C	T1	C′	Z1
D	T2	D′	Z2
E	Calculate	E′	M

Program 16 Usage

Program 16 is executed by using the user-defined keys. The definitions of the user-defined keys can be found in Table 16-3.

After entering all the data, program execution is initiated through user-defined key E. Subsequent calculations can be made by changing only those terms desired.

Sample Problem 16-1

A compressor performance test is conducted and the following data are recorded:

$$P_1 = 17 \text{ psia}$$
$$T_1 = 100°F$$
$$P_2 = 75 \text{ psia}$$
$$T_2 = 275°F$$
$$MW = 30$$
$$k_a = 1.16$$
$$Z_1 = 0.99$$
$$Z_2 = 0.987$$
$$m = 2500 \text{ lbm/min}$$

Calculate the polytropic head, polytropic efficiency, gas power requirement, inlet volume flow, and discharge volume flow.

Sample Problem 16-1: User Instructions

Step	Procedure	Enter	Press	Display
1.	Load program.			
2.	Enter inlet pressure.	17	A	17

Sample Problem 16-1: User Instructions continued

Step	Procedure	Enter	Press	Display
3.	Enter discharge pressure.	75	B	75
4.	Enter inlet temperature.	100(°F)	C	560(°R)
5.	Enter discharge temperature.	275(°F)	D	735(°R)
6.	Enter molecular weight.	30	2nd A'	30
7.	Enter average k-value.	1.16	2nd B'	1.16
8.	Enter inlet Z-value.	0.99	2nd C'	0.99
9.	Enter discharge Z-value.	0.987	2nd D'	0.987
10.	Enter mass flow.	2500	2nd E'	2500
11.	Calculate		E	

Sample Problem 16-1: Program Printout

```
COMPRESSOR TEST

   17.        P1        0.987       Z2
   75.        P2        2500.        M
  100.        T1       29158.       Q1
  275.        T2        8648.       Q2
   30.        MW       48622.      HEAD
  1.16        KA        0.761       EFF
  0.99        Z1        4838.      PWRG
```

Program 16 Listing

000	76	LBL	017	42	STD	034	91	R/S
001	11	A	018	05	05	035	76	LBL
002	42	STD	019	91	R/S	036	17	B'
003	03	03	020	76	LBL	037	42	STD
004	91	R/S	021	14	D	038	08	08
005	76	LBL	022	85	+	039	91	R/S
006	12	B	023	04	4	040	76	LBL
007	42	STD	024	06	6	041	18	C'
008	04	04	025	00	0	042	42	STD
009	91	R/S	026	95	=	043	09	09
010	76	LBL	027	42	STD	044	91	R/S
011	13	C	028	06	06	045	76	LBL
012	85	+	029	91	R/S	046	19	D'
013	04	4	030	76	LBL	047	42	STD
014	06	6	031	16	A'	048	10	10
015	00	0	032	42	STD	049	91	R/S
016	95	=	033	07	07	050	76	LBL

(continued on next page)

Program 16 Listing continued

051	10	E'	101	04	04	151	04	04
052	42	STO	102	69	OP	152	55	÷
053	11	11	103	05	05	153	43	RCL
054	91	R/S	104	69	OP	154	03	03
055	76	LBL	105	00	00	155	95	=
056	15	E	106	98	ADV	156	23	LNX
057	98	ADV	107	98	ADV	157	55	÷
058	69	OP	108	01	1	158	53	(
059	00	00	109	00	0	159	43	RCL
060	01	1	110	93	.	160	12	12
061	05	5	111	07	7	161	55	÷
062	03	3	112	02	2	162	43	RCL
063	02	2	113	09	9	163	13	13
064	69	OP	114	65	×	164	54	)
065	01	01	115	43	RCL	165	23	LNX
066	03	3	116	09	09	166	95	=
067	00	0	117	65	×	167	42	STO
068	03	3	118	43	RCL	168	14	14
069	03	3	119	05	05	169	55	÷
070	03	3	120	55	÷	170	53	(
071	05	5	121	43	RCL	171	43	RCL
072	01	1	122	07	07	172	14	14
073	07	7	123	55	÷	173	75	-
074	03	3	124	43	RCL	174	01	1
075	06	6	125	03	03	175	54	)
076	69	OP	126	95	=	176	95	=
077	02	02	127	42	STO	177	42	STO
078	03	3	128	12	12	178	15	15
079	06	6	129	01	1	179	43	RCL
080	03	3	130	00	0	180	04	04
081	02	2	131	93	.	181	55	÷
082	03	3	132	07	7	182	43	RCL
083	05	5	133	02	2	183	03	03
084	00	0	134	09	9	184	95	=
085	00	0	135	65	×	185	45	Y×
086	03	3	136	43	RCL	186	43	RCL
087	07	7	137	10	10	187	15	15
088	69	OP	138	65	×	188	35	1/X
089	03	03	139	43	RCL	189	75	-
090	01	1	140	06	06	190	01	1
091	07	7	141	55	÷	191	95	=
092	03	3	142	43	RCL	192	65	×
093	06	6	143	07	07	193	43	RCL
094	03	3	144	55	÷	194	12	12
095	07	7	145	43	RCL	195	65	×
096	00	0	146	04	04	196	43	RCL
097	00	0	147	95	=	197	03	03
098	00	0	148	42	STO	198	65	×
099	00	0	149	13	13	199	43	RCL
100	69	OP	150	43	RCL	200	15	15

Program 16 Listing continued

201	65	✕	251	95	=	301	95	=
202	01	1	252	42	STO	302	69	OP
203	04	4	253	20	20	303	06	06
204	04	4	254	03	3	304	03	3
205	95	=	255	03	3	305	00	0
206	42	STO	256	00	0	306	04	4
207	16	16	257	02	2	307	03	3
208	43	RCL	258	69	OP	308	69	OP
209	08	08	259	04	04	309	04	04
210	75	-	260	43	RCL	310	43	RCL
211	01	1	261	03	03	311	07	07
212	95	=	262	69	OP	312	69	OP
213	55	÷	263	06	06	313	06	06
214	43	RCL	264	03	3	314	02	2
215	08	08	265	03	3	315	06	6
216	65	✕	266	00	0	316	01	1
217	43	RCL	267	03	3	317	03	3
218	15	15	268	69	OP	318	69	OP
219	95	=	269	04	04	319	04	04
220	42	STO	270	43	RCL	320	43	RCL
221	17	17	271	04	04	321	08	08
222	35	1/X	272	69	OP	322	69	OP
223	65	✕	273	06	06	323	06	06
224	43	RCL	274	03	3	324	04	4
225	11	11	275	07	7	325	06	6
226	65	✕	276	00	0	326	00	0
227	43	RCL	277	02	2	327	02	2
228	16	16	278	69	OP	328	69	OP
229	55	÷	279	04	04	329	04	04
230	03	3	280	43	RCL	330	43	RCL
231	03	3	281	05	05	331	09	09
232	00	0	282	75	-	332	69	OP
233	00	0	283	04	4	333	06	06
234	00	0	284	06	6	334	04	4
235	95	=	285	00	0	335	06	6
236	42	STO	286	95	=	336	00	0
237	18	18	287	69	OP	337	03	3
238	43	RCL	288	06	06	338	69	OP
239	11	11	289	03	3	339	04	04
240	65	✕	290	07	7	340	43	RCL
241	43	RCL	291	00	0	341	10	10
242	12	12	292	03	3	342	69	OP
243	95	=	293	69	OP	343	06	06
244	42	STO	294	04	04	344	03	3
245	19	19	295	43	RCL	345	00	0
246	43	RCL	296	06	06	346	69	OP
247	11	11	297	75	-	347	04	04
248	65	✕	298	04	4	348	43	RCL
249	43	RCL	299	06	6	349	11	11
250	13	13	300	00	0	350	69	OP

(continued on next page)

Program 16 Listing continued

351	06	06	381	02	2	411	69	□P
352	98	ADV	382	03	3	412	06	06
353	03	3	383	01	1	413	22	INV
354	04	4	384	07	7	414	58	FIX
355	00	0	385	01	1	415	03	3
356	02	2	386	03	3	416	03	3
357	69	□P	387	01	1	417	04	4
358	04	04	388	06	6	418	03	3
359	43	RCL	389	69	□P	419	03	3
360	19	19	390	04	04	420	05	5
361	58	FIX	391	43	RCL	421	02	2
362	00	00	392	16	16	422	02	2
363	69	□P	393	58	FIX	423	69	□P
364	06	06	394	00	00	424	04	04
365	22	INV	395	69	□P	425	43	RCL
366	58	FIX	396	06	06	426	18	18
367	03	3	397	22	INV	427	58	FIX
368	04	4	398	58	FIX	428	00	00
369	00	0	399	01	1	429	69	□P
370	03	3	400	07	7	430	06	06
371	69	□P	401	02	2	431	22	INV
372	04	04	402	01	1	432	58	FIX
373	43	RCL	403	02	2	433	98	ADV
374	20	20	404	01	1	434	98	ADV
375	58	FIX	405	69	□P	435	69	□P
376	00	00	406	04	04	436	00	00
377	69	□P	407	43	RCL	437	91	R/S
378	06	06	408	17	17	438	00	0
379	22	INV	409	58	FIX	439	00	0
380	58	FIX	410	03	03	440	00	0

Part IV

Gas Properties

Program 17

Gas Calculations
(Mols to Mol Fraction)

Background

In many cases, gas analyses are given in terms of the number of mols per time element of each constituent in the gas mixture. In order to determine the mixture molecular weight and mixture properties, it is necessary to convert mols per time element of each constituent to the mol fraction of that constituent.

The mol fraction of any constituent is the number of mols per time element of that constituent divided by the total number of mols per time element of the mixture, as given by Equation 17-1:

$$x_i = \frac{\text{mols/time element}_i}{\text{total mols/time element}} \qquad (17\text{-}1)$$

where:
    i = the ith constituent
    x = mol fraction

Progam 17 Description

Program 17, Gas Calculations (Mols to Mol Fraction) calculates and prints the results of Equation 17-1 for up to 51 gases.

In order to execute the program, the mols/time element for each constituent must be known. The program must be reinitialized for each new gas analysis.

Table 17-1
Program 17: Printer Nomenclature

Program Term	Definition	Units
GAS	numerical listing of entered gas	dimensionless
MOLS	mols per time element of constituent	lbm-mol/time
MOLT	total mols of mixture per time element	lbm-mol/time
MF	mol fraction of constituent	dimensionless

Table 17-2
Data Registers Used by Program 17

00	not used	05	total mols
01	not used	06	gas number
02	not used	07	output register, mol fraction
03	counter, number of gases	08	counter, number of gases
		09	
04	pointer, mols/time element	to	mols/time element
		59	

Table 17-1 is the nomenclature printed by the program; Table 17-2 shows the data registers used by the program

Labels Used by Program 17

```
001  10 E'        121  33 X²
072  11  A        158  34 ΓX
110  15  E
```

Program 17 Usage

Program 17 is executed by using the user-defined keys. The definitions of the user-defined keys can be found in Table 17-3.

After initializing, the program is executed by entering the mols per time element of each constituent through user-defined key A. After all gases have

Table 17-3
Program 17: Definitions of User-Defined Keys

A	MOLS		
E	Calculate	E'	Initialize

been entered, the mol fractions of all constituents are calculated by depressing E.

In order to run a new gas analysis, the program must be reinitialized.

Sample Problem 17-1

Given the following gas analysis:

4800 mols/hr propane
 900 mols/hr butane
 400 mols/hr ethane

Calculate the mol fraction of each constituent.

Sample Problem 17-1: User Instructions

Step	Procedure	Enter	Press	Display
1.	Load program.			
2.	Initialize.		2nd E′	9
3.	Enter mols/time element of gas constituent.	4800	A	4800
4.	Repeat step 3 for all gas constituents.			
5.	Calculate.		E	

Sample Problem 17-1: Program Printout

```
  GAS CALC              1.      GAS
  MOLS - MF         0.7869      MF


                         2.      GAS
     1.      GAS     0.1475      MF
  4800.      MOLS

                         3.      GAS
     2.      GAS     0.0656      MF
   900.      MOLS

     3.      GAS
   400.      MOLS


  6100.      MOLT
```

Program 17 Listing

000	76	LBL	050	00	0	100	06	06
001	10	E'	051	00	0	101	69	□P
002	47	CMS	052	69	□P	102	23	23
003	98	ADV	053	03	03	103	69	□P
004	69	□P	054	69	□P	104	24	24
005	00	00	055	05	05	105	69	□P
006	02	2	056	69	□P	106	28	28
007	02	2	057	00	00	107	98	ADV
008	01	1	058	01	1	108	91	R/S
009	03	3	059	42	STO	109	76	LBL
010	03	3	060	06	06	110	15	E
011	06	6	061	42	STO	111	98	ADV
012	00	0	062	08	08	112	69	□P
013	00	0	063	42	STO	113	33	33
014	69	□P	064	03	03	114	69	□P
015	02	02	065	09	9	115	34	34
016	01	1	066	42	STO	116	00	0
017	05	5	067	04	04	117	71	SBR
018	01	1	068	98	ADV	118	33	X²
019	03	3	069	98	ADV	119	91	R/S
020	02	2	070	91	R/S	120	76	LBL
021	07	7	071	76	LBL	121	33	X²
022	01	1	072	11	A	122	85	+
023	05	5	073	72	ST*	123	73	RC*
024	00	0	074	04	04	124	04	04
025	00	0	075	02	2	125	69	□P
026	69	□P	076	02	2	126	34	34
027	03	03	077	01	1	127	97	DSZ
028	69	□P	078	03	3	128	03	03
029	05	05	079	03	3	129	33	X²
030	03	3	080	06	6	130	95	=
031	00	0	081	69	□P	131	42	STO
032	03	3	082	04	04	132	05	05
033	02	2	083	43	RCL	133	03	3
034	02	2	084	03	03	134	00	0
035	07	7	085	69	□P	135	03	3
036	03	3	086	06	06	136	02	2
037	06	6	087	03	3	137	02	2
038	00	0	088	00	0	138	07	7
039	00	0	089	03	3	139	03	3
040	69	□P	090	02	2	140	07	7
041	02	02	091	02	2	141	69	□P
042	02	2	092	07	7	142	04	04
043	00	0	093	03	3	143	43	RCL
044	00	0	094	06	6	144	05	05
045	00	0	095	69	□P	145	69	□P
046	03	3	096	04	04	146	06	06
047	00	0	097	73	RC*	147	98	ADV
048	02	2	098	04	04	148	98	ADV
049	01	1	099	69	□P	149	69	□P

Program 17 Listing continued

150	38	38	168	02	2	186	07	07
151	09	9	169	01	1	187	58	FIX
152	42	STO	170	03	3	188	04	04
153	04	04	171	03	3	189	69	OP
154	71	SBR	172	06	6	190	06	06
155	34	ΓX	173	69	OP	191	22	INV
156	92	RTN	174	04	04	192	58	FIX
157	76	LBL	175	43	RCL	193	98	ADV
158	34	ΓX	176	06	06	194	69	OP
159	73	RC*	177	69	OP	195	24	24
160	04	04	178	06	06	196	69	OP
161	55	÷	179	03	3	197	26	26
162	43	RCL	180	00	0	198	97	DSZ
163	05	05	181	02	2	199	08	08
164	95	=	182	01	1	200	34	ΓX
165	42	STO	183	69	OP	201	69	OP
166	07	07	184	04	04	202	00	00
167	02	2	185	43	RCL	203	92	RTN

Program 18

Gas Properties Calculations

Background

In order to estimate compressor performance it is necessary to obtain the molecular weight, ratio of specific heats, and compressibility of the gas mixture.

The molecular weight of the mixture is given by Equation 18-1:

$$MW_{mix} = \sum_{i=1}^{a} x_i MW_i \qquad (18\text{-}1)$$

where:

i = the ith constituent
a = number of constituents
x = mol fraction of the constituents
MW_{mix} = mixture molecular weight, lbm/lbm-mol

The ratio of specific heats is derived from the specific heat at constant pressure, c_p. The c_p of the mixture can be calculated from Equation 18-2:

$$c_{p_{mix}} = \sum_{i=1}^{a} x_i (c_p)_i \qquad (18\text{-}2)$$

where:

c_p = specific heat at constant pressure, Btu/lbm-mol-°R
$c_{p_{mix}}$ = mixture specific heat at constant pressure, Btu/lbm-mol-°R

The ratio of specific heats is then:

$$k = \frac{c_{p_{\text{mix}}}}{c_{p_{\text{mix}}} - 1.986}$$ (18-3)

where:
k = ratio of specific heats

The compressibility can be obtained from a compressibility chart once the reduced pressure, P_r, and reduced temperature, T_r, are known. In order to calculate P_r and T_r, the mixture critical pressure and critical temperature must first be determined:

$$P_{c_{\text{mix}}} = \sum_{i=1}^{a} x_i (P_c)_i$$ (18-4)

$$T_{c_{\text{mix}}} = \sum_{i=1}^{a} x_i (T_c)_i$$ (18-5)

where:
P_c = critical pressure, psia
T_c = critical temperature, °R
$P_{c_{\text{mix}}}$ = mixture critical pressure, psia
$T_{c_{\text{mix}}}$ = mixture critical temperature, °R

The reduced pressure and temperature are then given by:

$$P_r = \frac{P}{P_{c_{\text{mix}}}}$$ (18-6)

$$T_r = \frac{T}{T_{c_{\text{mix}}}}$$ (18-7)

where:
P_r = reduced pressure, psia
T_r = reduced temperature, °R
P = pressure of interest, psia
T = temperature of interest, °R

Progam 18 Description

This Gas Properties Calculation, Program 18, calculates and prints the results of Equations 18-1, 18-2, 18-3, 18-4, and 18-5 for as many gas constituents as desired.

In order to execute the program, the following must be known:

1. Mol fraction of each constituent, x_i
2. Molecular weight of each constituent, MW_i
3. Specific heat at constant pressure for each constituent, $(c_p)_i$
4. Critical pressure of each constituent, $(P_c)_i$
5. Critical temperature of each constituent, $(T_c)_i$

The molecular weight, critical pressure, and critical temperature for each constituent can be determined from Table 18-1. The specific heat at constant pressure for each constituent can be estimated from Figures 18-1 and 18-2.

The critical pressure and critical temperature of the mixture are constant. Therefore, they can be used to determine the compressibility at any point of the compression process. The value of c_p, and therefore the k-value, varies with temperature, however. Thus there is an option in the program to calculate c_p and the k-value only, when the values for these are desired at a specific temperature. In order to use this option, the following must be known:

1. Mol fraction of each constituent.
2. Specific heat at constant pressure for each constituent.

The program must be reinitialized for each new gas analysis.

Table 18-2 is the nomenclature printed by the program; Table 18-3 shows the data registers used by the program.

Labels Used by Program 18

001	10	E'	072	13	C	136	18 C'
036	11	A	093	14	D	186	19 D'
051	12	B	114	15	E		

Program 18 Usage

Program 18 is executed by using the user-defined keys. The definitions for the user-defined keys can be found in Table 18-4.

After initializing, the program is executed by entering the mol fraction, molecular weight, specific heat at constant pressure, critical pressure, and

(continued on page 194)

Table 18-1
Gas Properties*

Compound	Formula	Hydrocarbon Reference Symbol	Molecular Weight	Critical Constants				Specific Heat, c_p	
				English		Metric		English	Metric
				Pressure, psia	Temperature, °R	Pressure, kPa	Temperature, K	Btu/lbm-mol-°R @ 60°F, 14.696 psia	kJ/kmol·K @ 15°C, 101.325 kPa
Methane	CH_4	C_1	16.04	668	343	4,604	191	8.45	35.35
Ethane	C_2H_6	C_2	30.07	708	550	4,880	305	12.27	51.30
Propane	C_3H_8	C_3	44.10	616	666	4,249	370	17.14	71.66
n-Butane	C_4H_{10}	nC_4	58.12	551	765	3,797	425	22.96	96.01
Isobutane	C_4H_{10}	iC_4	58.12	529	735	3,648	408	22.48	93.92
n-Pentane	C_5H_{12}	nC_5	72.15	489	845	3,369	470	27.99	117.03
Isopentane	C_5H_{12}	iC_5	72.15	490	829	3,381	460	27.63	115.44
n-Hexane	C_6H_{14}	nC_6	86.18	437	913	3,012	507	33.24	139.01
n-Heptane	C_7H_{16}	nC_7	100.20	397	972	2,736	540	38.50	160.92
n-Octane	C_8H_{18}	nC_8	114.23	361	1,024	2,486	569	43.76	182.88
n-Nonane	C_9H_{20}	nC_9	128.26	332	1,070	2,288	595	49.02	204.96
n-Decane	$C_{10}H_{22}$	nC_{10}	142.29	304	1,111	2,099	617	54.30	226.95
Ethylene	C_2H_4	C_2^-	28.05	731	508	5,041	282	10.16	42.47
Propylene (Propene)	C_3H_6	C_3^-	42.08	667	657	4,600	365	14.90	62.28
Butylene (1-Butene)	C_4H_8	nC_4^-	56.11	584	755	4,023	420	19.91	83.21
Cis-2-Butene	C_4H_8		56.11	612	784	4,220	436	18.34	76.65
Trans-2-Butene	C_4H_8		56.11	587	771	4,047	429	20.50	85.74
Isobutylene (Isobutene)	C_4H_8	iC_4^-	56.11	580	752	3,999	418	20.77	86.80
Pentylene (1-Pentene)	C_5H_{10}	C_5^-	70.14	512	837	3,529	465	25.50	106.54
1, 2 Butadiene	C_4H_6		54.09	653	800	4,502	444	18.70	78.21
1, 3 Butadiene	C_4H_6		54.09	628	765	4,330	425	18.46	77.13

*Values derived by permission from Gas Processors Suppliers Association *Engineering Data Book*. Ninth Edition, 1972, 5th Revision, 1981, and *SI Engineering Data Book*. 1980.

Table 18-1 (continued)

Compound	Formula	Hydrocarbon Reference Symbol	Molecular Weight	Critical Constants				Specific Heat, c_p	
				English		Metric		English	Metric
				Pressure, psia	Temperature, °R	Pressure, kPa	Temperature, K	Btu/lbm-mol·°R @ 60°F, 14.696 psia	kJ/kmol·K @ 15°C, 101.325 kPa
Isoprene	C_5H_8		68.12	558	872	3,850	484	24.32	101.64
Acetylene	C_2H_2	$C_2^=$	26.04	890	555	6,139	308	10.33	43.20
Benzene	C_6H_6		78.11	710	1,012	4,898	562	18.92	79.20
Toluene	C_7H_8		92.14	596	1,065	4,106	592	23.94	99.97
o-Xylene	C_8H_{10}		106.17	542	1,135	3,734	630	30.94	129.32
m-Xylene	C_8H_{10}		106.17	513	1,111	3,536	617	29.54	123.48
p-Xylene	C_8H_{10}		106.17	509	1,109	3,511	616	29.40	122.84
Styrene	C_8H_8		104.15	580	1,166	3,999	648	28.18	118.00
Methyl alcohol	CH_4O		32.04	1,174	923	8,096	513	10.35	43.32
Ethyl alcohol	C_2H_6O		46.07	926	925	6,383	514	15.29	63.99
Carbon monoxide	CO		28.01	508	239	3,499	133	6.96	29.13
Carbon dioxide	CO_2		44.01	1,071	547	7,382	304	8.76	36.66
Hydrogen sulfide	H_2S		34.08	1,036	672	9,005	374	8.11	33.94
Sulfur dioxide	SO_2		64.06	1,145	775	7,894	431	9.28	38.83
Ammonia	NH_3		17.03	1,636	730	11,280	406	8.46	35.41
Air	$N_2 + O_2$		28.96	547	238	3,771	132	6.95	29.10
Hydrogen	H_2		2.02	188	60	1,297	33	6.87	28.76
Oxygen	O_2		32.00	737	278	5,081	155	7.00	29.33
Nitrogen	N_2		28.01	493	227	3,399	126	6.96	29.13
Chlorine	Cl_2		70.91	1,118	751	7,711	417	8.06	33.75
Water	H_2O		18.02	3,208	1,165	22,118	647	8.01	33.55
Helium	He		4.00	33	9	228	5	4.96	20.77
Hydrogen chloride	HCl		36.46	1,205	584	8,309	325	6.96	29.14

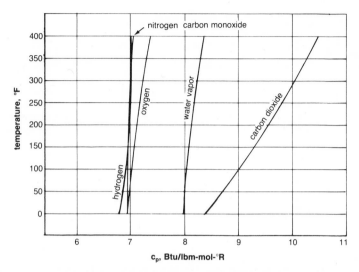

Figure 18-1. Molal specific heat as a function of temperature for several nonhydro-carbon gases. (Reference data were developed and published by the Thermodynamics Research Center of Texas A&M University.)

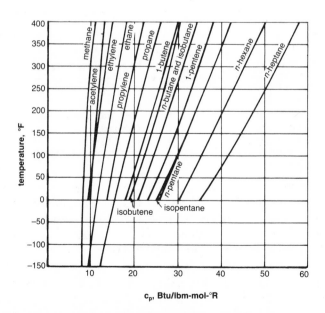

Figure 18-2. Molal specific heat as a function of temperature for several hydrocarbon gases. (Reference data were developed and published by the Thermodynamics Research Center of Texas A&M University.)

Table 18-2
Program 18: Printer Nomenclature

Program Term	Definition	Units
CP	specific heat at constant pressure of constituent	Btu/lbm-mol-°R
CPM	specific heat at constant pressure of mixture	Btu/lbm-mol-°R
K	ratio of specific heats of mixture	dimensionless
MF	mol fraction of constituent	dimensionless
MW	molecular weight of constituent	lbm/lbm-mol
MWM	molecular weight of mixture	lbm/lbm-mol
PC	critical pressure of constituent	psia
PCM	critical pressure of mixture	psia
TC	critical temperture of constituent	°R
TCM	critical temperature of mixture	°R

Table 18-3
Data Registers Used by Program 18

00	not used	05	$(c_p)_i$	10	$\Sigma x_i(P_c)_i$
01	not used	06	$(P_c)_i$	11	$\Sigma x_i(T_c)_i$
02	not used	07	$(T_c)_i$	12	k
03	x_i	08	$\Sigma x_i MW_i$		
04	MW_i	09	$\Sigma x_i(c_p)_i$		

Table 18-4
Program 18: Definitions of User-Defined Keys

A	MF		
B	MW		
C	CP	C'	Calculate, c_p and k only
D	PC	D'	Calculate
E	TC	E'	Initialize

critical temperature of each constituent through their respective user-defined keys. The mol fraction must be entered first and the critical temperature last. The other three parameters can be entered in any order, although consistency will yield a more readable output. After all gas constituents are entered, the mixture properties are calculated through D'.

There is an option for calculating only the mixture specific heat at constant pressure and the ratio of specific heats, should these terms be desired for different temperatures. In order to use the option, only the mol fraction and specific heat at constant pressure for each constituent need be entered, the mol fraction first. The mixture c_p and k-values are then obtained through C'.

Sample Problem 18-1

Given the gas analysis of Sample Problem 17-1, calculate the mixture properties at 100°F and the *k*-value at 200°F.

The molecular weight, critical pressure, and critical temperature come from Table 18-1. The specific heat at constant pressure at 100°F and 200°F can be estimated from Figure 18-2.

Gas	x	MW	P_c	T_c	$(c_p)_{100}$	$(c_p)_{200}$
propane	0.7869	44.10	616	666	18	21
butane	0.1475	58.12	551	765	24	28
ethane	0.0656	30.07	708	550	13	15

Sample Problem 18-1: User Instructions

Step	Procedure	Enter	Press	Display
1.	Load program.			
2.	Initialize.		2nd E′	1513271500
3.	Enter mol fraction of first constituent.	0.7869	A	0.7869
4.	Enter molecular weight of first constituent.	44.10	B	44.1
5.	Enter specific heat at constant pressure of first constituent.	18	C	18
6.	Enter critical pressure of first constituent.	616	D	616
7.	Enter critical temperature of first constituent.	666	E	666
8.	Repeat steps 3 thru 7 for each constituent.			
9.	Calculate.		2nd D′	
10.	Initialize.		2nd E′	1513271500
11.	Enter mol fraction of first constituent.	0.7869	A	0.7869
12.	Enter specific heat at constant pressure of first constituent.	21	C	21
13.	Repeat steps 11 and 12 for each constituent.			
14.	Calculate.		2nd C′	

Sample Problem 18-1: Program Printout

```
GAS CALC              0.0656    MF      GAS CALC
   0.7869    MF         30.07    MW
     44.1    MW            13.   CP
      18.    CP          708.    PC
     616.    PC          550.    TC       0.7869        MF
     666.    TC                             21.         CP
                                          0.1475        MF
                                            28.         CP
   0.1475    MF         18.56    CPM       0.0656        MF
    58.12    MW          1.120     K         15.         CP
      24.    CP         45.25    MWM
     551.    PC          612.    PCM
     765.    TC          673.    TCM       21.64        CPM
                                            1.101         K
```

Program 18 Listing

000	76	LBL	033	98	ADV	066	43	RCL	
001	10	E'	034	91	R/S	067	04	04	
002	47	CMS	035	76	LBL	068	69	OP	
003	98	ADV	036	11	A	069	06	06	
004	69	OP	037	42	STO	070	91	R/S	
005	00	00	038	03	03	071	76	LBL	
006	02	2	039	03	3	072	13	C	
007	02	2	040	00	0	073	42	STO	
008	01	1	041	02	2	074	05	05	
009	03	3	042	01	1	075	65	x	
010	03	3	043	69	OP	076	43	RCL	
011	06	6	044	04	04	077	03	03	
012	00	0	045	43	RCL	078	95	=	
013	00	0	046	03	03	079	44	SUM	
014	69	OP	047	69	OP	080	09	09	
015	02	02	048	06	06	081	01	1	
016	01	1	049	91	R/S	082	05	5	
017	05	5	050	76	LBL	083	03	3	
018	01	1	051	12	B	084	03	3	
019	03	3	052	42	STO	085	69	OP	
020	02	2	053	04	04	086	04	04	
021	07	7	054	65	x	087	43	RCL	
022	01	1	055	43	RCL	088	05	05	
023	05	5	056	03	03	089	69	OP	
024	00	0	057	95	=	090	06	06	
025	00	0	058	44	SUM	091	91	R/S	
026	69	OP	059	08	08	092	76	LBL	
027	03	03	060	03	3	093	14	D	
028	69	OP	061	00	0	094	42	STO	
029	05	05	062	04	4	095	06	06	
030	69	OP	063	03	3	096	65	x	
031	00	00	064	69	OP	097	43	RCL	
032	98	ADV	065	04	04	098	03	03	

Program 18 Listing continued

099	95	=		146	43	RCL		193	00	0
100	44	SUM		147	09	09		194	69	⊡P
101	10	10		148	58	FIX		195	04	04
102	03	3		149	02	02		196	43	RCL
103	03	3		150	69	⊡P		197	08	08
104	01	1		151	06	06		198	58	FIX
105	05	5		152	22	INV		199	02	02
106	69	⊡P		153	58	FIX		200	69	⊡P
107	04	04		154	43	RCL		201	06	06
108	43	RCL		155	09	09		202	22	INV
109	06	06		156	75	–		203	58	FIX
110	69	⊡P		157	01	1		204	03	3
111	06	06		158	93	.		205	03	3
112	91	R/S		159	09	9		206	01	1
113	76	LBL		160	08	8		207	05	5
114	15	E		161	06	6		208	03	3
115	42	STD		162	95	=		209	00	0
116	07	07		163	35	1/X		210	69	⊡P
117	65	×		164	65	×		211	04	04
118	43	RCL		165	43	RCL		212	43	RCL
119	03	03		166	09	09		213	10	10
120	95	=		167	95	=		214	58	FIX
121	44	SUM		168	42	STD		215	00	00
122	11	11		169	12	12		216	69	⊡P
123	03	3		170	02	2		217	06	06
124	07	7		171	06	6		218	22	INV
125	01	1		172	69	⊡P		219	58	FIX
126	05	5		173	04	04		220	03	3
127	69	⊡P		174	43	RCL		221	07	7
128	04	04		175	12	12		222	01	1
129	43	RCL		176	58	FIX		223	05	5
130	07	07		177	03	03		224	03	3
131	69	⊡P		178	69	⊡P		225	00	0
132	06	06		179	06	06		226	69	⊡P
133	98	ADV		180	22	INV		227	04	04
134	91	R/S		181	58	FIX		228	43	RCL
135	76	LBL		182	69	⊡P		229	11	11
136	18	C'		183	00	00		230	58	FIX
137	98	ADV		184	92	RTN		231	00	00
138	01	1		185	76	LBL		232	69	⊡P
139	05	5		186	19	D'		233	06	06
140	03	3		187	18	C'		234	22	INV
141	03	3		188	03	3		235	58	FIX
142	03	3		189	00	0		236	69	⊡P
143	00	0		190	04	4		237	00	00
144	69	⊡P		191	03	3		238	91	R/S
145	04	04		192	03	3		239	00	0

Program 19

Air/Water Vapor

Background

When the process gas is air, the gas analysis in terms of mol-fraction air and mol-fraction water vapor is not normally available. Rather, an air-gas analysis is specified in terms of dry-bulb and wet-bulb temperatures, or dry-bulb temperature and relative humidity. It thus becomes necessary to determine the molecular weight from the information given.

Dry-bulb and wet-bulb temperatures, or dry-bulb temperature and relative humidity, can be converted to specific humidity (the number of pounds of water per pound of dry air) by using a psychometric chart, as shown in Figure 19-1.

Once the specific humidity is known, the partial pressure of the water vapor can be determined from Equation 19-1:

$$P_w = \frac{28.96(SH)(P)}{18.02 + 28.96(SH)} \tag{19-1}$$

where:

P_w = partial pressure of water vapor, psia
SH = specific humidity
P = pressure at which the gas is measured, psia

The value 18.02 in Equation 19-1 is the molecular weight of water vapor; 28.96 is the molecular weight of dry air. The derivation of Equation 19-1 is left to the reader.

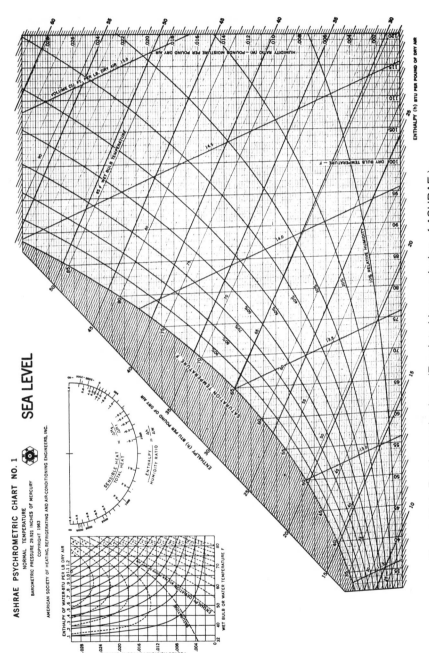

Figure 19-1. Psychometric chart. (Reprinted by permission of ASHRAE.)

As long as the partial pressure of water vapor calculated from Equation 19-1 is less than the saturation pressure of water vapor at the specified dry-bulb temperature, the calculated P_w is the water-vapor pressure existing in the gas. If the saturation pressure is less than the calculated P_w, the saturation pressure exists and becomes the actual value of P_w. (Under these circumstances the wrong value of specific humidity was used. Note that the psychometric chart is an atmospheric chart based at sea level, and that the ability of air to hold water decreases with increasing pressure.) The saturation pressures are tabulated in the Keenan *et al* 1969 *Steam Tables*.

If the saturation pressure is lower than the calculated P_w, the specific humidity determined from the psychometric chart is too high and must be recalculated from Equation 19-2:

$$SH = 0.622\left(\frac{P_w}{P - P_w}\right) \tag{19-2}$$

where:
> $0.622 = MW_w/MW_a = 18.02/28.96$ and where the subcript w represents water vapor and the subscript a represents air.

Note: In Equation 19-2, P_w is a tabulated value for the saturation pressure.

With the partial pressure of water vapor known, the mol fractions of water vapor and air can be calculated from Equations 19-3 and 19-4:

$$x_w = \frac{P_w}{P} \tag{19-3}$$

$$x_a = 1 - x_w \tag{19-4}$$

where:
> x_w = mol fraction of water vapor
> x_a = mol fraction of air

The molecular weight is then:

$$MW_{mix} = x_w MW_w + x_a MW_a$$

$$MW_{mix} = 18.02x_w + 28.96x_a \tag{19-5}$$

If the required dry mass flow is known, the mass flow corrected for water-vapor content can be determined from Equation 19-6:

$$m = m_a(1 + SH) \tag{19-6}$$

where:

m_a = mass flow of dry air

m = corrected, or total, mass flow

Program 19 Description

Program 19, Air/Water Vapor, calculates and prints the results of Equations 19-1, 19-3, 19-4, 19-5, and 19-6. If the calculated partial pressure of water vapor is higher than the saturation pressure read from the Keenan *et al* 1969 *Steam Tables*, it will calculate and print the result of Equation 19-2 and use it in Equations 19-3, 19-4, 19-5, and 19-6.

In order to execute the program, the following must be known:

1. Mixture pressure of interest, P
2. Dry-air mass flow, m_a
3. Specific humidity, SH

The user will need a psychometric chart to determine the specific humidity. In addition, he should also have the Keenan *et al* 1969 *Steam Tables* available to compare the calculated partial pressure of water vapor to the saturation pressure of water vapor at the temperature of interest.

After the pressure, dry-air mass flow, and specific humidity are entered, the program calculates the partial pressure of water vapor and stops. The user then compares it to the saturation pressure and enters the saturation pressure if lower. If the saturation pressure is entered, the program prints the statement REL. HUM. = 100%. The program then continues to solve Equations 19–3, 19–4, 19–5, and 19–6.

The program is set up for continuous usage without the need for complete data reentry. Therefore, only the parameters of interest need be changed.

Table 19-1 is the nomenclature printed by the program; Tables 19-2 shows the data registers used by the program.

Labels Used by Program 19

001	11	A	011	13	C	089	34	ΓX
006	12	B	016	15	E	243	33	X²

Program 19 Usage

Program 19 is executed by using the user-defined keys and the R/S key. The definitions of the user-defined and R/S keys can be found in Table 19-3.

Table 19-1
Program 19: Printer Nomenclature

Program Term	Definition	Units
M	corrected mass flow	lbm/min
MA	mass flow of dry air	lbm/min
MFA	mol fraction of air	dimensionless
MFW	mol fraction of water vapor	dimensionless
MW	molecular weight of mixture	lbm/lbm-mol
P	mixture pressure of interest	psia
PW	partial pressure of water vapor	psia
SH	specific humidity	dimensionless

Table 19-2
Data Registers Used by Program 19

00	not used	04	m_a	08	x_a
01	not used	05	SH	09	MW
02	not used	06	P_w	10	m
03	P	07	x_w		

Table 19-3
Program 19: Definitions of User-Defined and R/S Keys

A	P	E	Calculate
B	MA	R/S	Continue program execution
C	SH		

After the pressure, dry-air mass flow, and specific humidity are entered, program execution is started by pressing user-defined key E. The program stops after calculating the partial pressure of water vapor, which is displayed in the calculator. If this value is lower than the saturation pressure, press R/S to continue program execution. If the calculated value of the partial pressure of water vapor is higher than the saturation pressure, enter the saturation pressure and then press R/S.

This program is especially useful for calculating molecular weights and corrected mass flows for intercooled compressors. The first-section inlet specific humidity can be obtained from the psychometric chart (Figure 19-1). The value of P_w calculated by the program for the first section should be lower than the saturation pressure unless the inlet relative humidity is 100%. For the second section, however, the inlet pressure is much higher. Some of the water vapor from the first section may drop out as liquid after cooling, leaving the second section with a relative humidity of 100%. For this case, reenter the specific humidity used in the first section. The value of P_w calculated by the program may be higher than the saturation pressure. If so, enter the saturation pressure and depress the R/S key. In this way, not only will the new molecular weight be correct but so will the corrected mass flow. Comparing the mass flows for the first and second sections results in the mass of water knocked out as a result of cooling.

Sample Problem 19-1

Given air at 14.7 psia, 90°F, and 80% relative humidity, find the molecular weight and corrected mass flow for 1500 lbm/min of dry air.

Reference to the psychometric chart, Figure 19-1, will show that the specific humidity is 0.0247. Note that since the relative humidity is less than 100%, the partial pressure of water vapor will be lower than the saturation pressure.

Sample Problem 19-1: User Instructions

Step	Procedure	Enter	Press	Display
1.	Load program.			
2.	Enter mixture pressure.	14.7	A	14.7
3.	Enter dry-air mass flow.	1500	B	1500
4.	Enter specific humidity from Figure 19-1.	0.0247	C	0.0247
5.	Calculate.		E	0.5612
6.	Continue execution.		R/S	

Sample Problem 19-1: Program Printout

```
AIR/H2O

   14.7        P
  1500.        MA
  0.0247       SH

  0.5612       PW
  0.0382       MFW
  0.9618       MFA

  1537.1       M
   28.54       MW
```

Sample Problem 19-2

Given the same air sample in Sample Problem 19-1, assume the air was compressed in the first section of an intercooled compressor to 45 psia and cooled to 100°F in an intercooler. What is the molecular weight and corrected mass flow for the second compression section?

Note that the calculated value for P_w was 1.7181 (not shown on the printout but in the display), which is higher than the saturation pressure of 0.9492 at 100°F (refer to the Keenan *et al* 1969 *Steam Tables*).

Comparing the mass flows from the two sample problems shows that 17 lbm/min (1537.1–1520.1) of water was knocked out as liquid because of intercooling.

Sample Problem 19-2: User Instructions

Step	Procedure	Enter	Press	Display
1.	Load program.			
2.	Enter mixture pressure.	45	A	45
3.	Enter dry-air mass flow.	1500	B	1500
4.	Enter specific humidity from Sample Problem 19-1.	0.0247	C	0.0247
5.	Calculate.		E	1.7181
6.	Enter saturation pressure and continue execution	0.9492	R/S	

Sample Problem 19-2: Program Printout

```
AIR/H2O

**REL. HUM. = 100%**

        45.        P
      1500.        MA
     0.0134        SH

     0.9492        PW
     0.0211        MFW
     0.9789        MFA

     1520.1        M
      28.73        MW
```

Program 19 Listing

000	76	LBL	050	06	6	100	01	1
001	11	A	051	65	×	101	95	=
002	42	STO	052	43	RCL	102	42	STO
003	03	03	053	05	05	103	08	08
004	91	R/S	054	65	×	104	65	×
005	76	LBL	055	43	RCL	105	02	2
006	12	B	056	03	03	106	08	8
007	42	STO	057	55	÷	107	93	.
008	04	04	058	53	(	108	09	9
009	91	R/S	059	01	1	109	06	6
010	76	LBL	060	08	8	110	85	+
011	13	C	061	93	.	111	43	RCL
012	42	STO	062	00	0	112	07	07
013	05	05	063	02	2	113	65	×
014	91	R/S	064	85	+	114	01	1
015	76	LBL	065	02	2	115	08	8
016	15	E	066	08	8	116	93	.
017	98	ADV	067	93	.	117	00	0
018	69	OP	068	09	9	118	02	2
019	00	00	069	06	6	119	95	=
020	01	1	070	65	×	120	42	STO
021	03	3	071	43	RCL	121	09	09
022	02	2	072	05	05	122	43	RCL
023	04	4	073	54	)	123	05	05
024	03	3	074	95	=	124	85	+
025	05	5	075	42	STO	125	01	1
026	69	OP	076	06	06	126	95	=
027	02	02	077	32	X:T	127	65	×
028	06	6	078	43	RCL	128	43	RCL
029	03	3	079	06	06	129	04	04
030	02	2	080	58	FIX	130	95	=
031	03	3	081	04	04	131	42	STO
032	00	0	082	91	R/S	132	10	10
033	03	3	083	22	INV	133	03	3
034	03	3	084	77	GE	134	03	3
035	02	2	085	33	X²	135	69	OP
036	00	0	086	22	INV	136	04	04
037	00	0	087	58	FIX	137	43	RCL
038	69	OP	088	76	LBL	138	03	03
039	03	03	089	34	ΓX	139	69	OP
040	69	OP	090	43	RCL	140	06	06
041	05	05	091	06	06	141	03	3
042	69	OP	092	55	÷	142	00	0
043	00	00	093	43	RCL	143	01	1
044	98	ADV	094	03	03	144	03	3
045	98	ADV	095	95	=	145	69	OP
046	02	2	096	42	STO	146	04	04
047	08	8	097	07	07	147	43	RCL
048	93	.	098	94	+/-	148	04	04
049	09	9	099	85	+	149	69	OP

(continued on next page)

Program 19 Listing continued

150	06	06	200	01	1	250	03	03
151	03	3	201	03	3	251	95	=
152	06	6	202	69	OP	252	94	+/-
153	02	2	203	04	04	253	55	÷
154	03	3	204	43	RCL	254	43	RCL
155	69	OP	205	08	08	255	06	06
156	04	04	206	58	FIX	256	95	=
157	43	RCL	207	04	04	257	35	1/X
158	05	05	208	69	OP	258	65	×
159	58	FIX	209	06	06	259	93	.
160	04	04	210	22	INV	260	06	6
161	69	OP	211	58	FIX	261	02	2
162	06	06	212	98	ADV	262	02	2
163	22	INV	213	03	3	263	95	=
164	58	FIX	214	00	0	264	42	STO
165	98	ADV	215	69	OP	265	05	05
166	03	3	216	04	04	266	05	5
167	03	3	217	43	RCL	267	01	1
168	04	4	218	10	10	268	05	5
169	03	3	219	58	FIX	269	01	1
170	69	OP	220	01	01	270	03	3
171	04	04	221	69	OP	271	05	5
172	43	RCL	222	06	06	272	01	1
173	06	06	223	22	INV	273	07	7
174	58	FIX	224	58	FIX	274	02	2
175	04	04	225	03	3	275	07	7
176	69	OP	226	00	0	276	69	OP
177	06	06	227	04	4	277	01	01
178	22	INV	228	03	3	278	04	4
179	58	FIX	229	69	OP	279	00	0
180	03	3	230	04	04	280	00	0
181	00	0	231	43	RCL	281	00	0
182	02	2	232	09	09	282	02	2
183	01	1	233	58	FIX	283	03	3
184	04	4	234	02	02	284	04	4
185	03	3	235	69	OP	285	01	1
186	69	OP	236	06	06	286	03	3
187	04	04	237	22	INV	287	00	0
188	43	RCL	238	58	FIX	288	69	OP
189	07	07	239	69	OP	289	02	02
190	58	FIX	240	00	00	290	04	4
191	04	04	241	91	R/S	291	00	0
192	69	OP	242	76	LBL	292	00	0
193	06	06	243	33	X²	293	00	0
194	22	INV	244	22	INV	294	06	6
195	58	FIX	245	58	FIX	295	04	4
196	03	3	246	42	STO	296	00	0
197	00	0	247	06	06	297	00	0
198	02	2	248	75	-	298	00	0
199	01	1	249	43	RCL	299	02	2

Program 19 Listing continued

300	69	⍙P		308	05	5		316	69	⍙P
301	03	03		309	01	1		317	00	00
302	00	0		310	05	5		318	98	ADV
303	01	1		311	01	1		319	71	SBR
304	00	0		312	69	⍙P		320	34	⌠X
305	01	1		313	04	04		321	92	RTN
306	06	6		314	69	⍙P		322	00	0
307	01	1		315	05	05		323	00	0

Part V

Centrifugal Compressor Drivers

Program 20

Steam Turbine Estimates

Background

There is an apparent need in the industry for a good means of estimating the efficiency that might reasonably be expected from a steam turbine. Certainly a reasonable approach to estimating steam-turbine efficiency would be valuable to the process engineer in the process development stage. To date, steam-turbine efficiency estimates conducted without the assistance of a turbine manufacturer have been more a matter of art than science, the engineer hoping to find a similar application in the past to refer to. Without knowing the amount of steam that will be required by each turbine, the steam balance may very well become an exercise in futility. This discussion attempts to bridge the gap between art and science, presenting a program that should yield steam rates within ±10% of actual machinery.

There are two types of staging used commonly in steam turbines: the single-row, or Rateau, stage and the two-row, or Curtiss, stage. The Rateau stage has the advantage of higher efficiency; the Curtiss stage has the advantage of removing more energy from the steam, resulting in less stages and, therefore, a smaller (lengthwise) turbine.

The single-stage turbine in common use for general-purpose requirements nearly always contains a single Curtiss stage. Multi-stage turbines will generally be composed of Rateau staging. However, when the energy in the steam between inlet and exhaust conditions is too high for a reasonable number of Rateau stages, one or two Curtiss stages are often used in the front end of the turbine to remove enough energy to keep turbine length within reason.

The remainder of this discussion will assume that in all cases, turbines are composed of the following staging:

Single stage—one Curtiss stage
Multi-stage—all Rateau staging

The basic efficiency of a steam-turbine stage is a function of the velocity ratio, as shown in Figure 20-1. The "2-row impulse wheel" is the Curtiss stage; the "1-row impulse wheel" is the Rateau stage. The velocity ratio is defined by Equation 20-1:

$$V_{rat} = u/C \tag{20-1}$$

where:
V_{rat} = velocity ratio
u = blade velocity, ft/sec
C = theoretical steam velocity, ft/sec

The blade velocity is given by Equation 20-2:

$$u = \frac{N\pi d_w}{720} \tag{20-2}$$

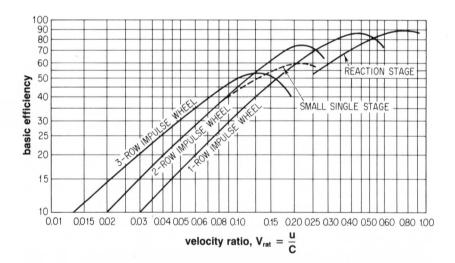

Figure 20-1. Basic efficiency for steam turbine stages not corrected for steam-path losses. (From *DeLaval Engineering Handbook,* Third Edition, edited by Hans Gartmann. Copyright 1970 by Transamerica Delaval Inc. Used with the permission of McGraw-Hill Book Company.)

where:

N = rotational speed, rpm

π = mathematical pi, 3.14159

d_w = outside diameter of wheel (stage), inches

The theoretical steam velocity is a function of the available isentropic enthalpy difference and the number of stages. The isentropic enthalpy difference is defined as the enthalpy at the inlet pressure and temperature of the steam less the enthalpy at the exhaust pressure and inlet entropy:

$$\Delta h_s = h_1 - h_{2s} \qquad (20\text{-}3)$$

where:

Δh_s = isentropic enthalpy difference, Btu/lbm

h_1 = inlet enthalpy, Btu/lbm

h_{2s} = isentropic exhaust enthalpy determined by following a constant entropy line from the inlet state point to the exhaust pressure, Btu/lbm

The theoretical steam velocity is then:

$$C = 224 \sqrt{\Delta h_s / \text{stage}} \qquad (20\text{-}4)$$

where:

$\Delta h_s / \text{stage} = \Delta h_s / \text{number of stages}$

Equations 20-3 and 20-4 will be altered slightly after considering the pressure drop across the governor valve.

Usually, the main difference, and perhaps the only difference, between single-valve and multi-valve turbines is the pressure drop across the governor valve. A pressure drop is a loss of useful energy. A multi-valve governor has a lower pressure drop than a single valve governor; thus there is more energy to convert to useful power. Due to the Joule-Thompson effect, the enthalpy downstream of the governor valve is the same as that upstream, but the pressure downstream is less. Examination of the steam Mollier chart in Figure 20-2 reveals that since the exhaust pressure is fixed, the isentropic enthalpy difference starting with the lower pressure downstream of the valve is less than would be available starting with the pressure upstream of the valve. Furthermore, the higher the pressure drop across the valve, the lower the isentropic enthalpy difference available for useful work.

Now define the isentropic exhaust enthalpy resulting from the pressure downstream of the governor valve h'_{2s}, and modify Equations 20-3 and 20-4 as follows:

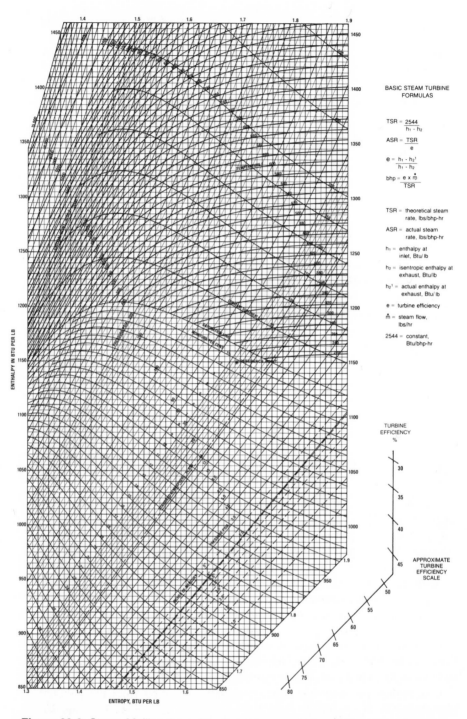

BASIC STEAM TURBINE FORMULAS

$$TSR = \frac{2544}{h_1 - h_2}$$

$$ASR = \frac{TSR}{e}$$

$$e = \frac{h_1 - h_2^1}{h_1 - h_2}$$

$$bhp = \frac{e \times \dot{m}}{TSR}$$

TSR = theoretical steam rate, lbs/bhp-hr

ASR = actual steam rate, lbs/bhp-hr

h_1 = enthalpy at inlet, Btu/lb

h_2 = isentropic enthalpy at exhaust, Btu/lb

h_2^1 = actual enthalpy at exhaust, Btu/lb

e = turbine efficiency

$\dot{m}$ = steam flow, lbs/hr

2544 = constant, Btu/bhp-hr

TURBINE EFFICIENCY %

APPROXIMATE TURBINE EFFICIENCY SCALE

Figure 20-2. Steam Mollier chart. (Reprinted by permission of The Trane Company, 1980. Adapted from the *ASME Steam Tables,* Fourth Edition, 1967.)

$$\Delta h_s' = h_1 - h_{2s}' \tag{20-5}$$

$$C = 224\sqrt{\Delta h_s'/\text{stage}} \tag{20-6}$$

where:

$\Delta h_s'$ = isentropic enthalpy difference downstream of governor valve, Btu/lbm

h_{2s}' = isentropic exhaust enthalpy based on the pressure downstream of the governor valve, determined by following a constant entropy line from the state point downstream of the governor valve to the exhaust pressure, Btu/lbm

Equation 20-6 is used to determine the velocity ratio.

In order to determine the pressure downstream of the governor valve, the governor-valve pressure drop must be known or assumed. The pressure drop for a multi-valve governor is on the order of five percent of the steam inlet pressure. The pressure drop for a single-valve governor, including the general-purpose single-stage turbine, is on the order of eight percent. These values will provide useful results.

Since the number of stages in a single-stage turbine is known, the theoretical steam velocity can immediately be determined, which leads directly to the velocity ratio and the basic efficiency from Figure 20-1.

For a multi-stage turbine, however, neither the number of stages nor the velocity ratio is known. For this case, a guess can be made at the velocity ratio and refined after the number of stages is estimated. Reference to Figure 20-1 shows that the Rateau stage experiences peak efficiency at a velocity ratio of approximately 0.45. Therefore, a good initial assumption is that the velocity ratio equals 0.45. With this velocity ratio, $\Delta h_s'/\text{stage}$ can be determined, and the number of stages can be estimated fom Equation 20-7:

$$\text{no. stages} = \frac{h_1 - h_{2s}'}{\Delta h_s'/\text{stage}} \tag{20-7}$$

The next step is to round down to the next lower whole number of stages. Why down? The most efficient turbine for off-design performance is one selected to the left of the highest efficiency point, referring to Figure 20-1. This is because as the turbine is throttled for lower horsepower, the velocity ratio increases. If the turbine is selected to the left of the highest efficiency point, the basic efficiency will increase with throttling. If the turbine is selected to the right of the highest efficiency point, the efficiency will rapidly decrease with throttling.

Once the number of stages is known, it is possible to calculate the actual velocity ratio and determine the basic efficiency from Figure 20-1.

The basic efficiency should be reduced some due to steam-path losses in the turbine. A good rule of thumb is to reduce the curve efficiency by 6% for all turbines except the multi-stage, back-pressure turbine, for which 12% is a better value. With the efficiency known, the discharge enthalpy can be determined from Equation 20-8:

$$h_2 = h_1 - \eta_c(h_1 - h'_{2s}) \qquad\qquad (20\text{-}8)$$

where:

h_2 = actual exhaust enthalpy, Btu/lbm

η_c = base efficiency from Figure 20-1, but corrected for steam path losses

The steam-turbine efficiency must be referenced to the actual inlet enthalpy upstream of the governor valve. Also, the steam-turbine efficiency should account for mechanical losses. The mechanical losses can be assumed to be on the order of two percent. Therefore:

$$\eta_{st} = 0.98 \left[\frac{h_1 - h_2}{h_1 - h_{2s}} \right] \qquad\qquad (20\text{-}9)$$

where:

η_{st} = steam-turbine efficiency

The steam rate is given by Equation 20-10:

$$SR = \frac{2545}{\eta_{st}(h_1 - h_{2s})} \qquad\qquad (20\text{-}10)$$

where:

SR = steam rate, lbm/hp-hr

The required steam flowrate is then:

$$G = (SR)(PWR) \qquad\qquad (20\text{-}11)$$

where:

G = required steam flowrate, lbm/hr

PWR = power required from the turbine, hp

Program 20 Description

Program 20, Steam-Turbine Estimates, considers single-stage and multi-stage turbines, condensing and back-pressure (i.e. exhaust pressures below and above atmospheric, respectively), and single-valve and multi-valve governors. The program contains curve fits for the Curtiss and Rateau basic-efficiency curves of Figure 20-1. It calculates the results of Equations 20-1, 20-2, 20-5, and 20-6 and uses them to calculate and print the results of Equations 20-7, 20-8, 20-9, 20-10, and 20-11.

In order to execute the program, the following must be known:

1. Inlet steam pressure, P_1
2. Inlet enthalpy, h_1
3. Isentropic exhaust enthalpy based on P_1, h_{2s}
4. Outside diameter of wheel, d_w
5. Rotational speed, N
6. Required power output, PWR
7. Type of turbine, TYPE

The inlet enthalpy, h_1, is obtained from the steam Mollier chart by plotting the turbine steam inlet pressure and inlet temperature.

The isentropic exhaust enthalpy based on P_1, (h_{2s}) is obtained by following a constant entropy line on the steam Mollier chart from the turbine inlet-pressure inlet-temperature point to the exhaust pressure.

The outside diameter of the wheel should be obtained from a turbine manufacturer. However, lacking manufacturer's data, it can be obtained from Table 20-1, noting that the speed will normally be fixed by the driven equipment unless a gear is employed. When selecting a diameter, use the closest tabulated speed in Table 20-1. This diameter is then used along with the actual speed, N, required by the driven equipment. Note that when using Table 20-1 for single-stage turbines and speeds in the 6000-rpm range, the 15-inch wheel should be considered for power requirements up to 200 hp; the 20-inch wheel should be considered when power requirements are in excess of 200 hp.

The type of turbine, TYPE, comes from Table 20-2.

After the operator enters the type of turbine, the program calculates the pressure downstream of the governor valve. This pressure, along with the inlet enthalpy, establishes the actual state point at the turbine nozzle ring. The actual isentropic exhaust enthalpy, h'_{2s}, is obtained by following a constant entropy line from this new state point to the exhaust pressure. Note that the inlet pressure, P_1, is listed by the program in psig as a matter of record, since steam conditions are given this way. However, the pressure downstream of the governor valve, P'_1, is listed in terms of psia, since the pressure needs to be in psia in order to use the steam Mollier chart.

Table 20-1
Typical Turbine Wheel Diameters and Nominal Speeds*

Single-Stage		Multi-Stage	
Speed (rpm)	Diameter (inches)	Speed (rpm)	Diameter (inches)
6000 ≤ 200 hp	15	12,000	15
6000	20	8500	20
5000	25	6800	25
4000	30	5700	30
		4800	35
		4250	40

*While this table is based on a survey of currently available equipment, the instance of any machinery duplicating this table would be purely coincidental.

Notes:

1. Actual wheel diameters, and speed ranges over which they are used, will vary from manufacturer to manufacturer. Table 20-1 should be regarded as typical only.
2. A vendor may select a smaller diameter wheel and use more of them rather than use fewer larger wheels, for many reasons. For example, for low-horsepower, high-energy applications, the required steam flow might be too low to utilize high-percentage arc-of-admission nozzle rings. The stage efficiency is a function of the arc of admission. The use of a smaller diameter wheel may increase the arc of admission, resulting in higher stage efficiency.
3. For multi-stage turbines, the biggest effect the selected diameter will have on program results will be in the calculated number of stages. Any effect on efficiency or steam rate will be negligible.

Table 20-2
Turbine Types for Program 20

Type of Turbine	TYPE
1. Single-stage and single-valve multi-stage, back-pressure	1
2. Single-stage and single-valve multi-stage, condensing	2
3. Multi-valve, multi-stage, back-pressure	3
4. Multi-valve, multi-stage, condensing	4

Upon entering all the data, the program estimates the number of stages, efficiency, steam rate, discharge enthalpy, and required steam flow for either a single-stage or multi-stage turbine.

The program is set up for continuous usage, without the need for complete data reentry. Therefore, only the parameters of interest need be changed.

Table 20-3 is the nomenclature printed by the program; Table 20-4 shows the data registers used by the program.

Table 20-3
Program 20: Printer Nomenclature

Program Term	Definition	Units
MVMS	multi-valve, multi-stage	—
SVMS	single-valve, multi-stage	—
SING ST	single-stage, general-purpose	—
D	wheel diameter	inches
EFF	steam-turbine efficiency	dimensionless
G	steam flowrate	lbm/hr
H1	inlet enthalpy	Btu/lbm
H2	actual exhaust enthalpy	Btu/lbm
H2S	isentropic exhaust enthalpy based on P_1	Btu/lbm
H2S'	isentropic exhaust enthalpy based on P_1'	Btu/lbm
N	rotational speed	rpm
NOST	number of stages	dimensionless
PWR	power required from turbine	hp
P1	steam inlet pressure	psig
P1'	steam pressure downstream of governor valve	psia
SR	steam rate	lbm/hp-hr
TYPE	type of turbine from Table 20-2	dimensionless

Table 20-4
Data Registers Used by Program 20

00	not used	09	N	18	h_2
01	not used	10	PWR	19	$h_1 - h_{2s}$
02	not used	11	P_1'	20	η_{st}
03	P_1	12	P_1'/P_1	21	SR
04	h_1	13	u	22	G
05	h_{2s}	14	no. stages	23	0.94 or 0.88
06	h_{2s}'	15	$h_1 - h_{2s}'$	24	0.94 or 0.88
07	TYPE	16	V_{rat}		
08	d_w	17	η_b		

Notes:

1. P_1'/P_1 is the multiplier applied to the steam inlet pressure to obtain the pressure downstream of the governor valve. It equals 0.92 for single-valve turbines, including the single-stage turbine, and 0.95 for multi-valve turbines.

2. η_b is the basic efficiency from Table 20-1, uncorrected for steam-path losses.

3. The values in registers 23 and 24 are the steam-path loss multipliers applied to the efficiency obtained from Figure 20-1. For single-stage turbines, the multiplier is 0.94; for multi-stage turbines, the multiplier is 0.94 for condensing turbines and 0.88 for backpressure (noncondensing) turbines.

Labels Used by Program 20

004	11	A	391	23	LNX	
009	12	B	447	33	X²	
014	13	C	457	35	1/X	
019	14	D	467	42	STO	
024	16	A'	488	43	RCL	
114	34	ΓX	509	44	SUM	
158	17	B'	529	25	CLR	
163	18	C'	536	65	X	
168	19	D'	549	52	EE	
173	15	E	682	55	÷	
273	45	YX	691	61	GTO	
284	10	E'	712	75	-	
358	32	X¦T				

Program 20 Usage

Program 20 is executed by using the user-defined keys. The definition for the user-defined keys can be found in Table 20-5.

After entering the steam pressure through user-defined key A, the type of turbine from Table 20-2 is entered through A'. The program calculates the pressure downstream of the governor valve. The inlet enthalpy (h_1), the isentropic exhaust enthalpy based on $P_1(h_{2s})$, and the isentropic exhaust enthalpy based on $P_1'(h_{2s}')$ are obtained from the steam Mollier chart and entered through B, C, and D, respectively.

The diameter is entered through B'. If manufacturer's data are unavailable, it can be obtained from Table 20-1. To determine the diameter from Table 20-1, use the tabulated speed closest to the actual required speed. It is good practice to run the program twice, using the diameter listed for speeds above and below the required speed. The average of the two runs will normally better approximate turbine performance for the single-stage turbine and the number of stages for the multi-stage turbine.

The speed and power required from the turbine are entered through C' and D' respectively.

Multi-stage turbine estimates, either single valve or multi-valve, are obtained through user-defined key E. Single-stage turbine estimates are obtained through E'.

Subsequent calculations can be made by changing only those terms desired.

Note that the calculator must be repartitioned to 719.29 before loading or keying in the program.

Table 20-5
Program 20: Definitions of User-Defined Keys

A	P1	A'	TYPE
B	H1	B'	D
C	H2S	C'	N
D	H2S'	D'	PWR
E	Calculate, multi-stage turbines	E'	Calculate, single-stage turbines

Sample Problem 20-1

Determine the efficiency, steam rate, discharge enthalpy, and required steam flow for an application requiring a single-stage turbine to deliver 1000 hp at 6000 rpm.

The steam conditions are as follows:

Inlet pressure = 600 psig
Inlet temperature = 700°F
Exhaust pressure = 50 psig

The state points should be plotted on a steam Mollier chart to confirm the enthalpies.

Sample Problem 20-1: User Instructions

Step	Procedure	Enter	Press	Display
1.	Partition calculator.	3	2nd OP 17	719.29
2.	Load program.			
3.	Enter inlet pressure.	600	A	600
4.	Enter TYPE from Table 20-2.	1	2nd A'	0.88 (value in register 24)
5.	Enter inlet enthalpy from steam Mollier chart.	1350	B	1350
6.	Enter isentropic exhaust enthalpy based on P_1 from steam Mollier chart.	1137	C	1137

(continued on next page)

Sample Problem 20-1: User Instructions continued

Step	Procedure	Enter	Press	Display
7.	Enter isentropic exhaust enthalpy based on P'_1 from steam Mollier chart.	1145	D	1145
8.	Enter required speed.	6000	2nd C'	6000
9.	Enter required power.	1000	2nd D'	1000
10.	Enter diameter from Table 20-1.	20	2nd B'	20
11.	Calculate.		2nd E'	

Sample Problem 20-1: Program Printout

```
STM TURB ESTIMATES


    600.      P1
      1.      TYPE
    565.      P1'


    SING ST

   1000.      PWR
   6000.        N
     20.        D
   1350.       H1
   1137.      H2S
   1145.      H2S'

      1.     NOST
   0.48      EFF
   24.9       SR
  24901.       G
   1245.       H2
```

Sample Problem 20-2

For the same steam conditions as Sample Problem 20-1, determine the efficiency, steam rate, discharge enthalpy, and required steam flow for an application requiring a single-valve, multi-stage turbine to deliver 5000 hp at 6000 rpm.

For this sample problem, the program was run twice, with diameters representing speeds tabulated above and below the required speed. Note that the only effect of the change in diameter was the calculated number of stages.

Sample Problem 20-2: User Instructions

Step	Procedure	Enter	Press	Display
1–8	Refer to Sample Problem 20-1, User Instructions.			
9.	Enter required power.	5000	2nd D′	5000
10.	Enter diameter from Table 20-1.	30	2nd B′	30
11.	Calculate.		E	
12.	Since the required speed is between two speeds in Table 20-1, try another diameter in order that results might be averaged.	25	2nd B′	25
13.	Calculate.		E	

Sample Problem 20-2: Program Printout

```
STM TURB ESTIMATES              SVMS

                        5000.      PWR
          600.    P1    6000.        N
            1.    TYPE    25.        D
          565.    P1'   1350.       H1
                        1137.      H2S
                        1145.      H2S'

          SVMS             4.     NOST
                          0.71     EFF
         5000.    PWR     16.9      SR
         6000.      N   84679.       G
           30.      D    1196.      H2
         1350.     H1
         1137.    H2S
         1145.    H2S'

            3.    NOST
          0.71     EFF
          16.9      SR
        84679.       G
         1196.      H2
```

Program 20 Listing

000	03	3		050	01	1		100	69	⏹P
001	69	⏹P		051	07	7		101	06	06
002	17	17		052	03	3		102	03	3
003	76	LBL		053	06	6		103	32	X⁁T
004	11	A		054	03	3		104	43	RCL
005	42	STⅡ		055	07	7		105	07	07
006	03	03		056	02	2		106	77	GE
007	91	R/S		057	04	4		107	33	X²
008	76	LBL		058	69	⏹P		108	93	.
009	12	B		059	03	03		109	09	9
010	42	STⅡ		060	03	3		110	02	2
011	04	04		061	00	0		111	42	STⅡ
012	91	R/S		062	01	1		112	12	12
013	76	LBL		063	03	3		113	76	LBL
014	13	C		064	03	3		114	34	⌐X
015	42	STⅡ		065	07	7		115	65	×
016	05	05		066	01	1		116	53	(
017	91	R/S		067	07	7		117	43	RCL
018	76	LBL		068	03	3		118	03	03
019	14	D		069	06	6		119	85	+
020	42	STⅡ		070	69	⏹P		120	01	1
021	06	06		071	04	04		121	05	5
022	91	R/S		072	69	⏹P		122	54	)
023	76	LBL		073	05	05		123	95	=
024	16	A'		074	69	⏹P		124	42	STⅡ
025	42	STⅡ		075	00	00		125	11	11
026	07	07		076	98	ADV		126	03	3
027	98	ADV		077	98	ADV		127	03	3
028	69	⏹P		078	03	3		128	00	0
029	00	00		079	03	3		129	02	2
030	03	3		080	00	0		130	06	6
031	06	6		081	02	2		131	05	5
032	03	3		082	69	⏹P		132	69	⏹P
033	07	7		083	04	04		133	04	04
034	03	3		084	43	RCL		134	43	RCL
035	00	0		085	03	03		135	11	11
036	69	⏹P		086	69	⏹P		136	59	INT
037	01	01		087	06	06		137	69	⏹P
038	03	3		088	03	3		138	06	06
039	07	7		089	07	7		139	03	3
040	04	4		090	04	4		140	32	X⁁T
041	01	1		091	05	5		141	43	RCL
042	03	3		092	03	3		142	07	07
043	05	5		093	03	3		143	67	EQ
044	01	1		094	01	1		144	75	-
045	04	4		095	07	7		145	01	1
046	69	⏹P		096	69	⏹P		146	32	X⁁T
047	02	02		097	04	04		147	43	RCL
048	00	0		098	43	RCL		148	07	07
049	00	0		099	07	07		149	67	EQ

Program 20 Listing continued

150	75	–	200	55	÷	250	05	5
151	93	.	201	53	(	251	32	X⁞T
152	09	9	202	43	RCL	252	43	RCL
153	04	4	203	04	04	253	16	16
154	42	STO	204	75	–	254	77	GE
155	24	24	205	43	RCL	255	43	RCL
156	92	RTN	206	06	06	256	43	RCL
157	76	LBL	207	54	)	257	16	16
158	17	B'	208	42	STO	258	45	Yˣ
159	42	STO	209	15	15	259	93	.
160	08	08	210	95	=	260	09	9
161	91	R/S	211	35	1/X	261	07	7
162	76	LBL	212	59	INT	262	01	1
163	18	C'	213	42	STO	263	65	×
164	42	STO	214	14	14	264	03	3
165	09	09	215	55	÷	265	93	.
166	91	R/S	216	43	RCL	266	00	0
167	76	LBL	217	15	15	267	01	1
168	19	D'	218	95	=	268	01	1
169	42	STO	219	35	1/X	269	95	=
170	10	10	220	34	ГX	270	42	STO
171	91	R/S	221	65	×	271	17	17
172	76	LBL	222	02	2	272	76	LBL
173	15	E	223	02	2	273	45	Yˣ
174	43	RCL	224	04	4	274	71	SBR
175	24	24	225	55	÷	275	23	LNX
176	42	STO	226	43	RCL	276	71	SBR
177	23	23	227	13	13	277	44	SUM
178	89	⫪	228	95	=	278	71	SBR
179	65	×	229	35	1/X	279	52	EE
180	43	RCL	230	42	STO	280	69	OP
181	08	08	231	16	16	281	00	00
182	65	×	232	93	.	282	92	RTN
183	43	RCL	233	04	4	283	76	LBL
184	09	09	234	32	X⁞T	284	10	E'
185	55	÷	235	43	RCL	285	93	.
186	07	7	236	16	16	286	09	9
187	02	2	237	77	GE	287	04	4
188	00	0	238	35	1/X	288	42	STO
189	95	=	239	93	.	289	23	23
190	42	STO	240	02	2	290	89	⫪
191	13	13	241	05	5	291	65	×
192	55	÷	242	32	X⁞T	292	43	RCL
193	01	1	243	43	RCL	293	08	08
194	00	0	244	16	16	294	65	×
195	00	0	245	77	GE	295	43	RCL
196	93	.	246	42	STO	296	09	09
197	08	8	247	93	.	297	55	÷
198	95	=	248	01	1	298	07	7
199	33	Xᶻ	249	02	2	299	02	2

(continued on next page)

Program 20 Listing continued

300	00	0	350	03	3	400	43	RCL
301	95	=	351	93	.	401	04	04
302	42	STO	352	06	6	402	95	=
303	13	13	353	08	8	403	42	STO
304	01	1	354	95	=	404	18	18
305	42	STO	355	42	STO	405	94	+/-
306	14	14	356	17	17	406	85	+
307	43	RCL	357	76	LBL	407	43	RCL
308	04	04	358	32	X:T	408	04	04
309	75	-	359	71	SBR	409	95	=
310	43	RCL	360	23	LNX	410	55	÷
311	06	06	361	69	OP	411	53	(
312	95	=	362	00	00	412	43	RCL
313	42	STO	363	98	ADV	413	04	04
314	15	15	364	98	ADV	414	75	-
315	34	ГX	365	03	3	415	43	RCL
316	65	x	366	06	6	416	05	05
317	02	2	367	02	2	417	54	)
318	02	2	368	04	4	418	42	STO
319	04	4	369	69	OP	419	19	19
320	55	÷	370	02	02	420	65	x
321	43	RCL	371	03	3	421	93	.
322	13	13	372	01	1	422	09	9
323	95	=	373	02	2	423	08	8
324	35	1/X	374	02	2	424	95	=
325	42	STO	375	00	0	425	42	STO
326	16	16	376	00	0	426	20	20
327	93	.	377	03	3	427	65	x
328	02	2	378	06	6	428	43	RCL
329	32	X:T	379	03	3	429	19	19
330	43	RCL	380	07	7	430	55	÷
331	16	16	381	69	OP	431	02	2
332	77	GE	382	03	03	432	05	5
333	55	÷	383	69	OP	433	04	4
334	93	.	384	05	05	434	05	5
335	00	0	385	71	SBR	435	95	=
336	09	9	386	52	EE	436	35	1/X
337	32	X:T	387	69	OP	437	42	STO
338	43	RCL	388	00	00	438	21	21
339	16	16	389	92	RTN	439	65	x
340	77	GE	390	76	LBL	440	43	RCL
341	61	GTO	391	23	LNX	441	10	10
342	43	RCL	392	65	x	442	95	=
343	16	16	393	43	RCL	443	42	STO
344	45	YX	394	23	23	444	22	22
345	93	.	395	65	x	445	92	RTN
346	09	9	396	43	RCL	446	76	LBL
347	02	2	397	15	15	447	33	X²
348	02	2	398	94	+/-	448	93	.
349	65	x	399	85	+	449	09	9

Program 20 Listing continued

450	05	5	500	05	5	550	98	ADV
451	42	STO	501	05	5	551	03	3
452	12	12	502	95	=	552	03	3
453	71	SBR	503	42	STO	553	04	4
454	34	ГX	504	17	17	554	03	3
455	92	RTN	505	71	SBR	555	03	3
456	76	LBL	506	45	YX	556	05	5
457	35	1/X	507	92	RTN	557	69	OP
458	93	.	508	76	LBL	558	04	04
459	08	8	509	44	SUM	559	43	RCL
460	05	5	510	69	OP	560	10	10
461	42	STO	511	00	00	561	69	OP
462	17	17	512	98	ADV	562	06	06
463	71	SBR	513	98	ADV	563	03	3
464	45	YX	514	03	3	564	01	1
465	92	RTN	515	32	X!T	565	69	OP
466	76	LBL	516	43	RCL	566	04	04
467	42	STO	517	07	07	567	43	RCL
468	43	RCL	518	77	GE	568	09	09
469	16	16	519	65	X	569	69	OP
470	45	YX	520	03	3	570	06	06
471	93	.	521	06	6	571	01	1
472	04	4	522	04	4	572	06	6
473	04	4	523	02	2	573	69	OP
474	04	4	524	03	3	574	04	04
475	65	X	525	00	0	575	43	RCL
476	01	1	526	03	3	576	08	08
477	93	.	527	06	6	577	69	OP
478	02	2	528	76	LBL	578	06	06
479	07	7	529	25	CLR	579	02	2
480	07	7	530	69	OP	580	03	3
481	95	=	531	03	03	581	00	0
482	42	STO	532	69	OP	582	02	2
483	17	17	533	05	05	583	69	OP
484	71	SBR	534	92	RTN	584	04	04
485	45	YX	535	76	LBL	585	43	RCL
486	92	RTN	536	65	X	586	04	04
487	76	LBL	537	03	3	587	69	OP
488	43	RCL	538	00	0	588	06	06
489	43	RCL	539	04	4	589	02	2
490	16	16	540	02	2	590	03	3
491	45	YX	541	03	3	591	00	0
492	93	.	542	00	0	592	03	3
493	07	7	543	03	3	593	03	3
494	08	8	544	06	6	594	06	6
495	07	7	545	71	SBR	595	69	OP
496	65	X	546	25	CLR	596	04	04
497	02	2	547	92	RTN	597	43	RCL
498	93	.	548	76	LBL	598	05	05
499	00	0	549	52	EE	599	69	OP

(continued on next page)

Program 20 Listing continued

600	06	06	640	58	FIX	680	92	RTN
601	02	2	641	02	02	681	76	LBL
602	03	3	642	69	DP	682	55	÷
603	00	0	643	06	06	683	93	.
604	03	3	644	22	INV	684	06	6
605	03	3	645	58	FIX	685	42	STD
606	06	6	646	03	3	686	17	17
607	06	6	647	06	6	687	71	SBR
608	05	5	648	03	3	688	32	X:T
609	69	DP	649	05	5	689	92	RTN
610	04	04	650	69	DP	690	76	LBL
611	43	RCL	651	04	04	691	61	GTD
612	06	06	652	43	RCL	692	43	RCL
613	69	DP	653	21	21	693	16	16
614	06	06	654	58	FIX	694	45	Yˣ
615	98	ADV	655	01	01	695	93	.
616	03	3	656	69	DP	696	05	5
617	01	1	657	06	06	697	00	0
618	03	3	658	22	INV	698	08	8
619	02	2	659	58	FIX	699	65	×
620	03	3	660	02	2	700	01	1
621	06	6	661	02	2	701	93	.
622	03	3	662	69	DP	702	03	3
623	07	7	663	04	04	703	05	5
624	69	DP	664	43	RCL	704	09	9
625	04	04	665	22	22	705	95	=
626	43	RCL	666	59	INT	706	42	STD
627	14	14	667	69	DP	707	17	17
628	69	DP	668	06	06	708	71	SBR
629	06	06	669	02	2	709	32	X:T
630	01	1	670	03	3	710	92	RTN
631	07	7	671	00	0	711	76	LBL
632	02	2	672	03	3	712	75	-
633	01	1	673	69	DP	713	93	.
634	02	2	674	04	04	714	08	8
635	01	1	675	43	RCL	715	08	8
636	69	DP	676	18	18	716	42	STD
637	04	04	677	59	INT	717	24	24
638	43	RCL	678	69	DP	718	91	R/S
639	20	20	679	06	06	719	92	RTN

Program 21

Motor Acceleration Time

Background

The time it takes a motor to accelerate a compressor from zero to full speed is proportional to the inertia of the entire rotating string and the area between the compressor and motor speed-torque curves, typically shown in Figure 21-1.

The rigorous equation for the acceleration time is Equation 21-1:

$$t = \frac{2\pi \, WK^2}{60 g_c} \int_0^N \frac{dN}{\tau_a} \tag{21-1}$$

where:

t = acceleration time, sec
π = mathematical pi, 3.14159
WK^2 = inertia of entire rotating string, lbm-ft^2
N = full-load rotational speed, rpm
τ_a = torque available for acceleration, equal to the difference between the torque delivered by the motor and the torque required by the compressor, ft-lbf
g_c = universal gravitational constant, 32.2 ft-lbm/lbf-sec^2

An approximate solution to Equation 21-1 results from dividing the area between the curves into a series of rectangles and calculating the approximate time increment for each speed increment. A convenient speed increment is 10% of the full-load speed. The acceleration time is then the sum of the incremental time elements:

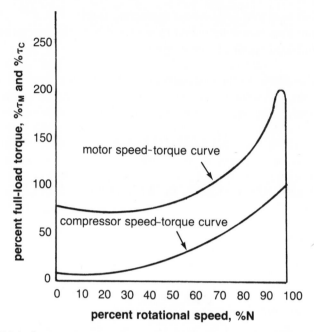

Figure 21-1. Compressor and motor speed-torque curve for Sample Problem 21-1.

$$t \approx \frac{2\pi \, WK^2}{60g_c} \sum_{\Delta N=0.1N}^{N} \frac{\Delta N}{(\tau_a)_{\Delta N}} \qquad (21\text{-}2)$$

where:

   ΔN = speed increment, $0.1N$

   $(\tau_a)_{\Delta N}$ = torque available for acceleration for speed increment ΔN

The compressor torque and motor torque are given by:

$$\tau_C = \frac{5250 \, PWR_C}{N_C} \qquad (21\text{-}3)$$

$$\tau_M = \frac{5250 \, PWR_M}{N_M} \qquad (21\text{-}4)$$

where:

   τ_C = full-load torque required by compressor, ft-lbf

   PWR_C = full-load power required by compressor, hp

   N_C = full-load speed of compressor, rpm

τ_M = full-load torque delivered by motor, ft-lbf
PWR_M = full-load power delivered by motor, i.e. nameplate power, hp
N_M = full-load speed of motor, rpm

The torque available for acceleration for each speed increment is the difference between the motor torque and the compressor torque at that speed increment. Note, however, that the torque available for acceleration varies with speed and can be calculated with reference to either the compressor shaft speed or the motor shaft speed. Therefore, in order to calculate the torque available for acceleration, it is necessary to get all values of incremental torque on the same speed basis. For simplicity, the compressor speed will be considered the basis for calculating $(\tau_a)_{\Delta N}$. Thus, $(\tau_a)_{\Delta N}$ is given by Equation 21-5:

$$(\tau_a)_{\Delta N} = \frac{(\% \tau_M)(\tau_M)}{r_g} - (\% \tau_C)(\tau_C) \tag{21-5}$$

where:
$\% \tau_M$ = percent full-load motor torque at speed increment ΔN, expressed as a fraction.
$\% \tau_C$ = percent full-load compressor torque at speed increment ΔN, expressed as a fraction
r_g = gear ratio = N_c/N_M

The value of the rotor inertia is also dependent on the speed reference. It is therefore necessary to convert all system component inertias to the same speed reference. Since the compressor speed was used as the speed basis previously, it will be used as the speed basis for calculating the inertia, also. Any component inertia given in terms of the motor shaft speed can be converted to compressor shaft-speed reference by Equation 21-6:

$$(WK^2)_C = \frac{(WK^2)_M}{r_g^2} \tag{21-6}$$

where:
$(WK^2)_C$ = component inertia based on compressor speed, lbm-ft^2
$(WK^2)_M$ = component inertia based on motor speed, lbm-ft^2

Program 21 Description

Program 21, Motor Acceleration Time, calculates and prints the results of Equations 21-2, 21-3, and 21-4.

In order to execute the program, the following must be known:

1. Inertia of the entire rotating system, referenced to the compressor shaft, $(WK^2)_C$
2. Power required by the compresor at full load, PWR_C
3. Power delivered by the motor at full load, (i.e. motor nameplate power), PWR_M
4. Full-load speed of compressor, N_C
5. Full-load speed of motor, N_M

In addition, compressor and motor speed-torque curves are required. Regardless of how they are presented, they must be converted to percent speed versus percent torque and superimposed on a single graph in order to use the program.

There are two ways to superimpose the compressor and motor speed-torque curves. The rigorous method is to base both curves on the same power reference, preferably the motor nameplate power, since it is the higher value. With this method, 100% torque is a single value applicable to both the compressor and the motor. Therefore:

$$100\%\tau_C = 100\%\tau_M = \frac{5250\ PWR_M}{N_M} \tag{21-7}$$

The compressor and motor torques for each speed increment are calculated and compared to the results of Equation 21-7 to establish $\%\tau_C$ and $\%\tau_M$ in order to construct the speed-torque curve. The resulting curve is a true graphical representation of the torque available for acceleration and of the acceleration time (area between the curves).

A less rigorous but generally more easily applied method is to utilize a compressor speed-torque curve with compressor full-load power as reference, and a motor speed-torque curve with motor nameplate power as reference. Superimposing these two curves on the same axes is not absolutely correct, but will work just as well as the former method as long as the compressor torques at each speed increment are calculated based on the compressor full-load torque, and as long as the motor torques at each speed increment are calculated based on the motor full-load torque.

This program is based on the latter method of speed-torque curve construction. Machinery manufacturers do not normally furnish superimposed curves. Rather, the compressor manufacturer will normally furnish a percent speed versus percent torque curve with compressor full-load power as reference, and the motor manufacturer will furnish a similar curve with motor nameplate power as reference. By basing the program on the latter method, the two curves can be directly superimposed without correction. (Note that with a curve drawn based on the former method, this program will provide a conservative estimate of acceleration time, i.e. a higher value than the actual acceleration time.)

After entering the compressor and motor speed-torque curves, the program approximates the area between them by the summation of rectangular areas.

The inertia of each rotating element must be considered, i.e. of the compressor, motor, gear, couplings, etc. Each must be referenced to the compressor shaft. Those that are not can be converted by using Equation 21-6. The sum of the inertias of each component is the total inertia required for the program.

The program must be reinitialized before each run, and the compressor and motor speed-torque curves must be reentered before program reexecution.

Table 21-1 is the nomenclature printed by the program; Table 21-2 shows the data registers used by the program.

Table 21-1
Program 21: Printer Nomenclature

Program Term	Definition	Units
CT	full-load compressor torque	ft-lbf
%CT	fraction of full-load compressor torque at speed increment considered	dimensionless
DELT	acceleration time	seconds
GR	gear ratio	dimensionless
MT	full-load motor torque	ft-lbf
%MT	fraction of full-load motor torque at speed increment considered	dimensionless
NC	full-load compressor speed	rpm
NM	full-load motor speed	rpm
PWRC	power required by compressor at full load	hp
PWRM	power delivered by motor at full load, i.e. nameplate	hp
WK2C	inertia of entire rotating string, referenced to compressor shaft	lbm-ft^2

Labels Used by Program 21

```
001   10 E'        098   11  A
073   13  C        119   12  B
078   16 A'        138   15  E
083   17 B'        326   33  X²
088   18 C'        350   34  ΓX
093   19 D'        377   45  Y×
```

Table 21-2
Data Registers Used by Program 21

00	not used	13 ⎫		26 ⎫	
01	not used	14 ⎪		27 ⎪	
02	not used	15 ⎪		28 ⎬ $\%\tau_M$ and $\dfrac{(\%\tau_M)(\tau_M)}{r_g}$	
				29 ⎪	
03	counter	16 ⎬ $\%\tau_C$ and $(\%\tau_C)(\tau_C)$		30 ⎪	
04	counter	17 ⎪		31 ⎭	
05	pointer, $\%\tau_C$ and $(\%\tau_C)(\tau_C)$	18 ⎪		32 t	
06	pointer, $\%\tau_M$ and $\dfrac{(\%\tau_M)(\tau_M)}{r_g}$	19 ⎪			
07	$(WK^2)_C$	20 ⎪		33 r_g	
08	PWR_C	21 ⎭		34 τ_C	
09	N_C	22 ⎫		35 τ_M	
10	PWR_M	23 ⎬ $\%\tau_M$ and $\dfrac{(\%\tau_M)(\tau_M)}{r_g}$		36 $0.1N_C$	
11	N_M	24 ⎪			
12	$\%\tau_C$ and $(\%\tau_C)(\tau_C)$	25 ⎭			

Table 21-3
Program 21: Definitions of User-Defined Keys

A	%CT		A′	PWRC
B	%MT		B′	NC
C	WK2C		C′	PWRM
			D′	NM
E	Calculate		E′	Initialize

Program 21 Usage

Program 21 is executed by using the user-defined keys. The definitions for the user-defined keys can be found in Table 21-3.

After initializing, the compressor and motor speed-torque curves are entered through user-defined keys A and B, respectively. The program requires 10 entries of percent torque, entered as a fraction, for both the compressor and the motor. The first entry is the average percent torque occurring over the speed range from 0% N–10% N; the second entry is the average percent torque over the speed range 10% N–20% N; the third, 20% N–30% N; and so on.

The compressor full-load power and full-load speed and the motor full-load power (i.e. nameplate) and full-load speed are entered through user-defined keys A′, B′, C′, and D′, respectively. Note that the motor speed entered should be the full-load speed, not the nominal speed. Therefore, the full-load speed for an 1800-rpm induction motor is on the order of 1750 rpm, and the full-load speed of a 3600-rpm induction motor is on the order of 3550 rpm.

The operator calculates, if necessary, the total inertia of the rotating masses in units of lbm-ft^2 and enters the value through C. It is important that all rotating masses be considered, i.e. all compressors, the motor, the gear, and all couplings. Also note that all inertias must be referenced to the compressor shaft speed in order to be added and useful in the program.

The program is not set up for continuous usage. Therefore, data reentry will be required prior to program reexecution.

Sample Problem 21-1

Given an application for a compressor requiring 5000 hp at 7500 rpm, driven by a 6000-hp, 1800-rpm induction motor, calculate the acceleration time of the motor, assuming that the speed-torque curve is Figure 21-1. (Note that Figure 21-1 was constructed by using the compressor full-load power requirement as the basis for the compressor speed-torque curve, and by using the motor nameplate power as the basis for the motor speed-torque curve.)

The total inertia of the rotating string is 1000 lbm-ft^2, referenced to the compressor shaft. The full-load speed of the motor will be approximately 1750 rpm.

Sample Problem 21-1: User Instructions

Step	Procedure	Enter	Press	Display
1.	Load program.			
2.	Initialize.		2nd E′	0
3.	Enter percent compressor torque for speed increment 0% N–10% N from speed-torque curve, Figure 21-1, as a fraction.	0.06	A	0.06
4.	Enter percent motor torque for speed increment 0% N–10% N from speed-torque curve, Figure 21-1, as a fraction.	0.8	B	0.8

(continued on next page)

Sample Problem 21-1: User Instructions continued

Step	Procedure	Enter	Press	Display
5.	Repeat steps 3 and 4 for each of the 10 speed increments.			
6.	Enter compressor full-load power requirement.	5000	2nd A'	5000
7.	Enter compressor full-load speed.	7500	2nd B'	7500
8.	Enter motor nameplate power.	6000	2nd C'	6000
9.	Enter motor full-load speed.	1750	2nd D'	1750
10.	Enter total inertia.	1000	C	1000
11.	Calculate.		E	

Sample Problem 21-1: Program Printout

```
MOTOR ACCELERATION


        0.06    %CT              5000.    PWRC
         0.8    %MT              7500.      NC
        0.07    %CT              6000.    PWRM
        0.75    %MT              1750.      NM
         0.1    %CT              1000.    WK2C
        0.75    %MT
        0.13    %CT
         0.8    %MT             4.286       GR
         0.2    %CT             3500.       CT
        0.85    %MT            18000.       MT
         0.3    %CT
         0.9    %MT             8.26       DELT
         0.4    %CT
          1.    %MT
        0.65    %CT
        1.13    %MT
        0.75    %CT
         1.4    %MT
         0.9    %CT
        1.75    %MT
```

Program 21 Listing

000	76	LBL	050	04	04	100	05	05	
001	10	E'	051	69	OP	101	06	6	
002	98	ADV	052	05	05	102	01	1	
003	69	OP	053	98	ADV	103	01	1	
004	00	00	054	98	ADV	104	05	5	
005	03	3	055	69	OP	105	03	3	
006	00	0	056	00	00	106	07	7	
007	03	3	057	00	0	107	69	OP	
008	02	2	058	42	STO	108	04	04	
009	03	3	059	03	03	109	73	RC*	
010	07	7	060	01	1	110	05	05	
011	03	3	061	02	2	111	69	OP	
012	02	2	062	42	STO	112	06	06	
013	69	OP	063	05	05	113	69	OP	
014	01	01	064	02	2	114	25	25	
015	03	3	065	02	2	115	69	OP	
016	05	5	066	42	STO	116	23	23	
017	00	0	067	06	06	117	91	R/S	
018	00	0	068	00	0	118	76	LBL	
019	01	1	069	42	STO	119	12	B	
020	03	3	070	32	32	120	72	ST*	
021	01	1	071	91	R/S	121	06	06	
022	05	5	072	76	LBL	122	06	6	
023	01	1	073	13	C	123	01	1	
024	05	5	074	42	STO	124	03	3	
025	69	OP	075	07	07	125	00	0	
026	02	02	076	91	R/S	126	03	3	
027	01	1	077	76	LBL	127	07	7	
028	07	7	078	16	A'	128	69	OP	
029	02	2	079	42	STO	129	04	04	
030	07	7	080	08	08	130	73	RC*	
031	01	1	081	91	R/S	131	06	06	
032	07	7	082	76	LBL	132	69	OP	
033	03	3	083	17	B'	133	06	06	
034	05	5	084	42	STO	134	69	OP	
035	01	1	085	09	09	135	26	26	
036	03	3	086	91	R/S	136	91	R/S	
037	69	OP	087	76	LBL	137	76	LBL	
038	03	03	088	18	C'	138	15	E	
039	03	3	089	42	STO	139	43	RCL	
040	07	7	090	10	10	140	03	03	
041	02	2	091	91	R/S	141	42	STO	
042	04	4	092	76	LBL	142	04	04	
043	03	3	093	19	D'	143	43	RCL	
044	02	2	094	42	STO	144	09	09	
045	03	3	095	11	11	145	55	÷	
046	01	1	096	91	R/S	146	43	RCL	
047	00	0	097	76	LBL	147	11	11	
048	00	0	098	11	A	148	95	=	
049	69	OP	099	72	ST*	149	42	STO	

(continued on next page)

Program 21 Listing continued

150	33	33	200	98	ADV	250	04	4
151	01	1	201	98	ADV	251	03	3
152	02	2	202	03	3	252	02	2
153	42	STO	203	03	3	253	06	6
154	05	05	204	04	4	254	00	0
155	02	2	205	03	3	255	03	3
156	02	2	206	03	3	256	01	1
157	42	STO	207	05	5	257	05	5
158	06	06	208	01	1	258	69	OP
159	05	5	209	05	5	259	04	04
160	02	2	210	69	OP	260	43	RCL
161	05	5	211	04	04	261	07	07
162	00	0	212	43	RCL	262	69	OP
163	65	×	213	08	08	263	06	06
164	43	RCL	214	69	OP	264	98	ADV
165	08	08	215	06	06	265	02	2
166	55	÷	216	03	3	266	02	2
167	43	RCL	217	01	1	267	03	3
168	09	09	218	01	1	268	05	5
169	95	=	219	05	5	269	69	OP
170	42	STO	220	69	OP	270	04	04
171	34	34	221	04	04	271	43	RCL
172	05	5	222	43	RCL	272	33	33
173	02	2	223	09	09	273	58	FIX
174	05	5	224	69	OP	274	03	03
175	00	0	225	06	06	275	69	OP
176	65	×	226	03	3	276	06	06
177	43	RCL	227	03	3	277	22	INV
178	10	10	228	04	4	278	58	FIX
179	55	÷	229	03	3	279	01	1
180	43	RCL	230	03	3	280	05	5
181	11	11	231	05	5	281	03	3
182	95	=	232	03	3	282	07	7
183	42	STO	233	00	0	283	69	OP
184	35	35	234	69	OP	284	04	04
185	71	SBR	235	04	04	285	43	RCL
186	33	X²	236	43	RCL	286	34	34
187	71	SBR	237	10	10	287	58	FIX
188	34	ΓX	238	69	OP	288	00	00
189	43	RCL	239	06	06	289	69	OP
190	09	09	240	03	3	290	06	06
191	65	×	241	01	1	291	03	3
192	00	0	242	03	3	292	00	0
193	93	.	243	00	0	293	03	3
194	01	1	244	69	OP	294	07	7
195	95	=	245	04	04	295	69	OP
196	42	STO	246	43	RCL	296	04	04
197	36	36	247	11	11	297	43	RCL
198	71	SBR	248	69	OP	298	35	35
199	45	YX	249	06	06	299	58	FIX

Program 21 Listing continued

300	00	00	341	04	04	382	73	RC*
301	69	OP	342	42	STO	383	06	06
302	06	06	343	03	03	384	75	-
303	98	ADV	344	01	1	385	73	RC*
304	01	1	345	02	2	386	05	05
305	06	6	346	42	STO	387	54	)
306	01	1	347	05	05	388	95	=
307	07	7	348	92	RTN	389	44	SUM
308	02	2	349	76	LBL	390	32	32
309	07	7	350	34	⌐X	391	69	OP
310	03	3	351	73	RC*	392	26	26
311	07	7	352	06	06	393	69	OP
312	69	OP	353	65	×	394	25	25
313	04	04	354	43	RCL	395	97	DSZ
314	43	RCL	355	35	35	396	03	03
315	32	32	356	55	÷	397	45	Y×
316	58	FIX	357	43	RCL	398	43	RCL
317	02	02	358	33	33	399	32	32
318	69	OP	359	95	=	400	65	×
319	06	06	360	72	ST*	401	02	2
320	22	INV	361	06	06	402	65	×
321	58	FIX	362	69	OP	403	89	π
322	69	OP	363	26	26	404	65	×
323	00	00	364	97	DSZ	405	43	RCL
324	91	R/S	365	03	03	406	07	07
325	76	LBL	366	34	⌐X	407	55	÷
326	33	X²	367	43	RCL	408	01	1
327	73	RC*	368	04	04	409	09	9
328	05	05	369	42	STO	410	03	3
329	65	×	370	03	03	411	02	2
330	43	RCL	371	02	2	412	95	=
331	34	34	372	02	2	413	42	STO
332	95	=	373	42	STO	414	32	32
333	72	ST*	374	06	06	415	92	RTN
334	05	05	375	92	RTN	416	00	0
335	69	OP	376	76	LBL	417	00	0
336	25	25	377	45	Y×	418	00	0
337	97	DSZ	378	43	RCL	419	00	0
338	03	03	379	36	36	420	00	0
339	33	X²	380	55	÷	421	00	0
340	43	RCL	381	53	(	422	00	0

Program 22

Gear Mechanical Check

Background

The American Petroleum Institute sets the mechanical rating standards for special-purpose gearing in API Standard 613, Second Edition, 1977. The API standards are in addition to the American Gear Manufacturer's standards.

Five major mechanical points are considered in API 613:

1. The gear rated horsepower.
2. The gear service factor.
3. The tooth pitting index, or K factor.
4. The bending stress number for both the pinion and the gear.
5. The maximum ratio of the total width of the gear to the pinion diameter, or L/d_p.

API Standard 613 sets the minimum limits on the gear rated horsepower. The minimum service factors are tabulated for several applications. The reader is referred to API 613, Second Edition, for these values.

The tooth pitting index, or K factor, is given by Equation 22-1:

$$K = \frac{W_t}{Fd_p} \left[\frac{(r_g + 1)}{r_g} \right] \tag{22-1}$$

where:
K = tooth pitting index, psi

F = net face width (total helix width), inches
d_p = pinion diameter, inches
r_g = gear ratio

and:

$$W_t = \frac{126000}{N_p d_p} \qquad (22\text{-}2)$$

where:
W_t = transmitted load at the operating pitch diameter, lbf
N_p = pinion speed, rpm

The calculated K factor must be compared to an allowable K factor, which is a function of the material index number:

$$\text{allowable } K = \frac{\text{material index number}}{SF} \qquad (22\text{-}3)$$

where:
SF = gear service factor

The material index number, in turn, is a function of material hardness. API 613 graphically displays the material index number as a function of gear hardness for thru-hardened teeth, quenched and tempered steels bath or gas nitrided, nitriding steels gas nitrided, and carburized teeth. The K factor is based on the gear hardness, not the pinion hardness, since the pinion is always harder than the gear.

The bending stress number is given by Equation 22-4:

$$S_t = \frac{(W_t)(P_{nd})(SF)}{F} \left[\frac{1.8 \cos \Psi}{J} \right] \qquad (22\text{-}4)$$

where:
S_t = bending stress number, psi
P_{nd} = normal diametral pitch, number of teeth/inch
Ψ = helix angle, degrees
J = geometry factor (from AGMA 226)

The bending stress number must be calculated for both the pinion and the gear. The values in Equation 22-4 will only differ in the value of the geometry factor. Once the actual bending stress numbers are known, they must be compared to the allowable values. API 613 graphically displays the allowable bending stress numbers as a function of material hardness for thru-hardened teeth, the core of nitrided teeth, and carburized teeth. (Note that API 613 states that when idler gears are used, the calculated bending stress numbers cannot exceed 70% of the allowable bending stress numbers.)

The L/d_p ratio is given by Equation 22-5:

$$L/d_p = \frac{F + GAP}{d_p} \tag{22-5}$$

where:

L/d_p = ratio of the total width of the gear to the pinion diameter
GAP = the gap between the two helix faces of the gear, inches

API 613 tabulates maximum values of L/d_p for both single and double helical gears as a function of the material index number.

There are four material combinations considered in API 613, Second Edition, that generally occur in the industry:

1. Thru-hardened gear and thru-hardened pinion.
2. Thru-hardened gear and nitrided pinion.
3. Nitrided gear and nitrided pinion.
4. Carburized gear and carburized pinion.

Combinations 1 and 4 are the most common.

Program 22 Description

Program 22, Gear Mechanical Check, calculates and prints the results of Equations 22-1, 22-3, 22-4, and 22-5. Curve fits for the material index number and the allowable bending stress number for the more common material combinations are in the program. Therefore, the program calculates the allowable K factors and allowable bending stress numbers as indicated in Table 22-1.

In order to execute the program, the following must be known:

1. Gear rated horsepower, PWR_{gr}
2. Gear service factor, SF
3. Pinion diameter, d_p
4. Normal diametral pitch, P_{nd}
5. Pinion hardness (Brinell for thru-hardened and Rockwell C for carburized)

Table 22-1
Types of Material Combinations for Program 22

Material Combination			Allowables Calculated by Program		
Gear	Pinion	Type	K	Gear S_t	Pinion S_t
Thru-hardened	Thru-hardened	1	yes	yes	yes
Thru-hardened	Nitrided	2	yes	yes	no
Nitrided	Nitrided	3	no	no	no
Carburized	Carburized	4	yes	yes	yes

6. Gear hardness (Brinell for thru-hardened and Rockwell C for carburized)
7. Geometry factor for pinion, J_p
8. Geometry factor for gear, J_g
9. Net face width, F
10. Helix angle, Ψ
11. Type of gear, TYPE

In addition, the gap between the two helix faces of the gear should be known in order to obtain an accurate value of L/d_p.

All of the preceding information, except the type of gear, is requested on the API 613, Second Edition, data sheet, and should, therefore, be furnished by the vendor with his proposal. The type of gear refers to the material combination and comes from Table 22-1.

The program calculates the allowable tooth pitting index (K factor) from a material index number which is based on gear hardness.

After calculating and printing the material index number, actual and allowable K factors, and actual and allowable bending stress numbers for the pinion and gear, the program stops to allow the operator to enter the gap between the helix faces. If the gear is double helical and the gap is known, the operator enters the value and the program calculates an L/d_p, which can be compared to the maximum allowables in API 613. If the gear is single helical or the gap is not known, the operator can enter zero. The program then calculates an L/d_p value which is actually the ratio of the net face width to the pinion diameter, and less than the L/d_p for a double helical gear. Note that for the single helical gear, the L/d_p and F/d_p are the same, since there is no gap.

The program is not set up for continuous usage. Therefore, complete data reentry will be required prior to program reexecution.

Table 22-2 is the nomenclature printed by the program; Table 22-3 shows the data registers used by the program.

Table 22-2
Program 22: Printer Nomenclature

Program Term	Definition	Units
DP	pinion diameter	inches
F	net face width	inches
GAP	gap between helix faces	inches
GRHP	gear-rated horsepower	hp
HA	helix angle	degrees
HARG	gear hardness (Brinell or Rockwell C; refer to API 613)	dimensionless
HARP	pinion hardness (Brinell or Rockwell C; refer to API 613)	dimensionless
JG	geometry factor for gear	dimensionless
JP	geometry factor for pinion	dimensionless
KF	actual tooth-pitting index	psi
KFA	allowable tooth-pitting index	psi
L/D	ratio of total width of gear to pinion diameter	dimensionless
MIDX	material index number	psi
NG	rotational speed of gear	rpm
NP	rotational speed of pinion	rpm
PND	normal diametral pitch	number of teeth/inch
SF	gear service factor	dimensionless
SG	actual gear bending-stress number	psi
SGA	allowable gear bending-stress number	psi
SP	actual pinion bending-stress number	psi
SPA	allowable pinion bending-stress number	psi
TYPE	type of gear from Table 22-1	dimensionless

Labels Used by Program 22

```
004   10 E'        106   18 C'
061   11 A         111   19 D'
068   12 B         196   35 1/X
075   13 C         347   44 SUM
082   14 D         482   34 ΓX
089   15 E         507   42 STO
096   16 A'        657   43 RCL
101   17 B'        702   45 YX
```

Program 22 Usage

Program 22 is executed by using the user-defined keys and the R/S key. The definitions of the user-defined and R/S keys can be found in Table 22-4.

After initializing, all the data required by user-defined keys A through E and A' through C' are entered. Where two entries are required by a user-defined key, they must be entered in the order listed in Table 22-4. For example, both pinion and gear speeds are entered through user-defined key B; however, the pinion speed must be entered first.

User-defined key D' is used to execute the program. The program will calculate the *K* factor and all bending stress numbers. It will then request the gap between the helix faces and stop. After entering the gap, the R/S key is used to continue program execution.

Note that the calculator must be repartitioned to 719.29 before loading or keying in the program.

Sample Problem 22-1

Check the mechanical rating of a gear with thru-hardened teeth and the following parameters:

$$PWR_{gr} = 5000 \text{ hp}$$
$$SF = 1.3$$
$$N_p = 6000 \text{ rpm}$$
$$N_g = 1750 \text{ rpm}$$
$$d = 10 \text{ inches}$$
$$P_{nd} = 5 \text{ teeth/inch}$$
$$J_p = 0.51$$
$$J_g = 0.54$$
$$F = 9 \text{ inches}$$
$$\Psi = 30°$$
$$\text{pinion hardness} = 341 \text{ Brinell}$$
$$\text{gear hardness} = 302 \text{ Brinell}$$
$$GAP = 1.5 \text{ inches}$$

Sample Problem 22-1: User Instructions

Step	Procedure	Enter	Press	Display
1.	Partition program.	3	2nd OP 17	719.29
2.	Load program.			
3.	Initialize.		2nd E'	18
4.	Enter gear rated horse-power.	5000	A	5000
5.	Enter gear service factor.	1.3	A	1.3

(continued on next page)

Table 22-3

Data Registers Used by Program 22

00	not used	10	PWR_{gr}
01	not used	11	SF
02	not used	12	N_p
03	pointer, PWR_{gr} and SF	13	N_g
04	pointer, N_p and N_g	14	d_p
05	pointer, d_p and P_{nd}	15	P_{nd}
06	pointer, hardness, pinion and gear	16	pinion hardness
07	pointer, J_p and J_g	17	gear hardness
08	TYPE	18	J_p
09	W_t	19	J_g

20	F		
21	ψ		
22	material index number and $(S_t)(J)$		
23	pinion S_t		
24	gear S_t		
25	allowable pinion S_t		
26	allowable gear S_t		
27	K and GAP		
28	allowable K and L/d_p		
29	r_g		

Table 22-4

Program 22: Definitions of User-Defined and *R/S* Keys

A	GRHP, SF	A'	F
B	NP, NG	B'	HA
C	DP, PND	C'	TYPE
D	HARP, HARG	D'	Calculate
E	JP, JG	E'	Initialize
		R/S	GAP, continue execution

Sample Problem 22-1: User Instructions continued

Step	Procedure	Enter	Press	Display
6.	Enter pinion speed.	6000	B	6000
7.	Enter gear speed.	1750	B	1750
8.	Enter pinion diameter.	10	C	10
9.	Enter normal diameter pitch.	5	C	5
10.	Enter pinion hardness.	341	D	341
11.	Enter gear hardness.	302	D	302
12.	Enter pinion geometry factor.	0.51	E	0.51
13.	Enter gear geometry factor.	0.54	E	0.54
14.	Enter net face width.	9	2nd A′	9
15.	Enter helix angle.	30	2nd B′	30
16.	Enter TYPE from Table 22-1 based on pinion and gear material. Since both are thru-hardened, enter 1.	1	2nd C′	1
17.	Calculate		2nd D′	
18.	Enter GAP.	1.5	R/S	

Sample Problem 22-1: Program Printout

```
GEAR CHECK                          23178.      SP
                                    28661.      SPA
                                    21891.      SG
                                    25887.      SGA
     5000.    GRHP
        1.3     SF
     6000.     NP
     1750.     NG             ENTER GAP,   R/S
       10.     DP
        5.    PND
      341.    HARP                    1.5     GAP
      302.    HARG                  1.050     L/D
      0.51     JP
      0.54     JG
        9.      F
       30.     HA
        1.    TYPE


      200.    MIDX
      150.     KF
      154.    KFA
```

Sample Problem 22-2

Check the mechanical rating of a gear with the same parameters as Sample Problem 22-1, except:

pinion hardness = 55 Rockwell C (carburized)
gear hardness = 55 Rockwell C (carburized)

Sample Problem 22-2: User Instructions

Step	Procedure	Enter	Press	Display
1–15	Refer to Sample Problem 22-1, User Instructions.			
16.	Enter TYPE from Table 22-1. Since both gear and pinion are carburized, enter 4.	4	2nd C′	4
17–18	Refer to Sample Problem 22-1, User Instructions.			

Sample Problem 22-2: Program Printout

```
GEAR CHECK
                              409.    MIDX
                              150.    KF
                              315.    KFA
     5000.     GRHP
        1.3    SF
     6000.     NP            23178.    SP
     1750.     NG            36283.    SPA
       10.     DP            21891.    SG
        5.     PND           36283.    SGA
       55.     HARP
       55.     HARG
       0.51    JP
       0.54    JG       ENTER GAP,   R/S
        9.     F
       30.     HA             1.5     GAP
        4.     TYPE           1.050   L/D
```

Program 22 Listing

000	03	3	050	05	05	100	76	LBL
001	69	OP	051	01	1	101	17	B'
002	17	17	052	06	6	102	42	STO
003	76	LBL	053	42	STO	103	21	21
004	10	E'	054	06	06	104	91	R/S
005	47	CMS	055	01	1	105	76	LBL
006	98	ADV	056	08	8	106	18	C'
007	69	OP	057	42	STO	107	42	STO
008	00	00	058	07	07	108	08	08
009	02	2	059	91	R/S	109	91	R/S
010	02	2	060	76	LBL	110	76	LBL
011	01	1	061	11	A	111	19	D'
012	07	7	062	72	ST*	112	71	SBR
013	01	1	063	03	03	113	42	STO
014	03	3	064	69	OP	114	43	RCL
015	03	3	065	23	23	115	12	12
016	05	5	066	91	R/S	116	55	÷
017	00	0	067	76	LBL	117	43	RCL
018	00	0	068	12	B	118	13	13
019	69	OP	069	72	ST*	119	95	=
020	02	02	070	04	04	120	42	STO
021	01	1	071	69	OP	121	29	29
022	05	5	072	24	24	122	01	1
023	02	2	073	91	R/S	123	02	2
024	03	3	074	76	LBL	124	06	6
025	01	1	075	13	C	125	00	0
026	07	7	076	72	ST*	126	00	0
027	01	1	077	05	05	127	00	0
028	05	5	078	69	OP	128	65	×
029	02	2	079	25	25	129	43	RCL
030	06	6	080	91	R/S	130	10	10
031	69	OP	081	76	LBL	131	55	÷
032	03	03	082	14	D	132	43	RCL
033	69	OP	083	72	ST*	133	12	12
034	05	05	084	06	06	134	55	÷
035	69	OP	085	69	OP	135	43	RCL
036	00	00	086	26	26	136	14	14
037	98	ADV	087	91	R/S	137	95	=
038	98	ADV	088	76	LBL	138	42	STO
039	01	1	089	15	E	139	09	09
040	00	0	090	72	ST*	140	65	×
041	42	STO	091	07	07	141	53	(
042	03	03	092	69	OP	142	43	RCL
043	01	1	093	27	27	143	29	29
044	02	2	094	91	R/S	144	85	+
045	42	STO	095	76	LBL	145	01	1
046	04	04	096	16	A'	146	54	)
047	01	1	097	42	STO	147	55	÷
048	04	4	098	20	20	148	43	RCL
049	42	STO	099	91	R/S	149	29	29

(continued on next page)

Program 22 Listing continued

150	55	÷	200	43	RCL	250	55	÷
151	43	RCL	201	11	11	251	43	RCL
152	20	20	202	95	=	252	20	20
153	55	÷	203	42	STO	253	65	×
154	43	RCL	204	28	28	254	43	RCL
155	14	14	205	03	3	255	11	11
156	95	=	206	00	0	256	65	×
157	42	STO	207	02	2	257	01	1
158	27	27	208	04	4	258	93	.
159	04	4	209	01	1	259	08	8
160	32	X:T	210	06	6	260	65	×
161	43	RCL	211	04	4	261	43	RCL
162	08	08	212	04	4	262	21	21
163	77	GE	213	69	OP	263	39	COS
164	34	ГX	214	04	04	264	95	=
165	03	3	215	43	RCL	265	42	STO
166	32	X:T	216	22	22	266	22	22
167	43	RCL	217	59	INT	267	55	÷
168	08	08	218	69	OP	268	43	RCL
169	77	GE	219	06	06	269	18	18
170	35	1/X	220	02	2	270	95	=
171	04	4	221	06	6	271	42	STO
172	00	0	222	02	2	272	23	23
173	93	.	223	01	1	273	43	RCL
174	06	6	224	69	OP	274	22	22
175	06	6	225	04	04	275	55	÷
176	65	×	226	43	RCL	276	43	RCL
177	53	(	227	27	27	277	19	19
178	43	RCL	228	59	INT	278	95	=
179	17	17	229	69	OP	279	42	STO
180	65	×	230	06	06	280	24	24
181	93	.	231	02	2	281	04	4
182	00	0	232	06	6	282	32	X:T
183	00	0	233	02	2	283	43	RCL
184	05	5	234	01	1	284	08	08
185	02	2	235	01	1	285	77	GE
186	09	9	236	03	3	286	43	RCL
187	54	)	237	69	OP	287	03	3
188	22	INV	238	04	04	288	32	X:T
189	23	LNX	239	43	RCL	289	43	RCL
190	95	=	240	28	28	290	08	08
191	42	STO	241	59	INT	291	77	GE
192	22	22	242	69	OP	292	44	SUM
193	71	SBR	243	06	06	293	01	1
194	35	1/X	244	98	ADV	294	01	1
195	76	LBL	245	43	RCL	295	07	7
196	35	1/X	246	09	09	296	07	7
197	43	RCL	247	65	×	297	00	0
198	22	22	248	43	RCL	298	65	×
199	55	÷	249	15	15	299	53	(

Program 22 Listing continued

300	43	RCL	350	03	3	400	01	1
301	16	16	351	03	3	401	07	7
302	65	×	352	69	OP	402	03	3
303	93	.	353	04	04	403	01	1
304	00	0	354	43	RCL	404	03	3
305	00	0	355	23	23	405	07	7
306	02	2	356	59	INT	406	01	1
307	06	6	357	69	OP	407	07	7
308	01	1	358	06	06	408	03	3
309	54	)	359	03	3	409	05	5
310	22	INV	360	06	6	410	69	OP
311	23	LNX	361	03	3	411	01	01
312	95	=	362	03	3	412	02	2
313	42	STO	363	01	1	413	02	2
314	25	25	364	03	3	414	01	1
315	01	1	365	69	OP	415	03	3
316	01	1	366	04	04	416	03	3
317	07	7	367	43	RCL	417	03	3
318	07	7	368	25	25	418	05	5
319	00	0	369	59	INT	419	07	7
320	65	×	370	69	OP	420	69	OP
321	53	(	371	06	06	421	02	02
322	43	RCL	372	03	3	422	03	3
323	17	17	373	06	6	423	05	5
324	65	×	374	02	2	424	06	6
325	93	.	375	02	2	425	03	3
326	00	0	376	69	OP	426	03	3
327	00	0	377	04	04	427	06	6
328	02	2	378	43	RCL	428	69	OP
329	06	6	379	24	24	429	03	03
330	01	1	380	59	INT	430	69	OP
331	54	)	381	69	OP	431	05	05
332	22	INV	382	06	06	432	69	OP
333	23	LNX	383	03	3	433	00	00
334	95	=	384	06	6	434	98	ADV
335	42	STO	385	02	2	435	00	0
336	26	26	386	02	2	436	91	R/S
337	02	2	387	01	1	437	42	STO
338	32	X:T	388	03	3	438	27	27
339	43	RCL	389	69	OP	439	85	+
340	08	08	390	04	04	440	43	RCL
341	77	GE	391	43	RCL	441	20	20
342	45	YX	392	26	26	442	95	=
343	71	SBR	393	59	INT	443	55	÷
344	44	SUM	394	69	OP	444	43	RCL
345	92	RTN	395	06	06	445	14	14
346	76	LBL	396	98	ADV	446	95	=
347	44	SUM	397	98	ADV	447	42	STO
348	03	3	398	69	OP	448	28	28
349	06	6	399	00	00	449	02	2

(continued on next page)

Program 22 Listing continued

450	02	2		500	95	=		550	69	OP
451	01	1		501	42	STO		551	06	06
452	03	3		502	22	22		552	01	1
453	03	3		503	71	SBR		553	06	6
454	03	3		504	35	1/X		554	03	3
455	69	OP		505	92	RTN		555	03	3
456	04	04		506	76	LBL		556	69	OP
457	43	RCL		507	42	STO		557	04	04
458	27	27		508	02	2		558	43	RCL
459	69	OP		509	02	2		559	14	14
460	06	06		510	03	3		560	69	OP
461	02	2		511	05	5		561	06	06
462	07	7		512	02	2		562	03	3
463	06	6		513	03	3		563	03	3
464	03	3		514	03	3		564	03	3
465	01	1		515	03	3		565	01	1
466	06	6		516	69	OP		566	01	1
467	69	OP		517	04	04		567	06	6
468	04	04		518	43	RCL		568	69	OP
469	43	RCL		519	10	10		569	04	04
470	28	28		520	69	OP		570	43	RCL
471	58	FIX		521	06	06		571	15	15
472	03	03		522	03	3		572	69	OP
473	69	OP		523	06	6		573	06	06
474	06	06		524	02	2		574	02	2
475	22	INV		525	01	1		575	03	3
476	58	FIX		526	69	OP		576	01	1
477	69	OP		527	04	04		577	03	3
478	00	00		528	43	RCL		578	03	3
479	91	R/S		529	11	11		579	05	5
480	92	RTN		530	69	OP		580	03	3
481	76	LBL		531	06	06		581	03	3
482	34	ГX		532	03	3		582	69	OP
483	01	1		533	01	1		583	04	04
484	01	1		534	03	3		584	43	RCL
485	05	5		535	03	3		585	16	16
486	93	.		536	69	OP		586	69	OP
487	07	7		537	04	04		587	06	06
488	65	×		538	43	RCL		588	02	2
489	53	(		539	12	12		589	03	3
490	43	RCL		540	69	OP		590	01	1
491	17	17		541	06	06		591	03	3
492	65	×		542	03	3		592	03	3
493	93	.		543	01	1		593	05	5
494	00	0		544	02	2		594	02	2
495	02	2		545	02	2		595	02	2
496	03	3		546	69	OP		596	69	OP
497	54	)		547	04	04		597	04	04
498	22	INV		548	43	RCL		598	43	RCL
499	23	LNX		549	13	13		599	17	17

Program 22 Listing continued

600	69	OP	639	06	06	678	01	1	
601	06	06	640	03	3	679	03	3	
602	02	2	641	07	7	680	04	4	
603	05	5	642	04	4	681	08	8	
604	03	3	643	05	5	682	02	2	
605	03	3	644	03	3	683	65	×	
606	69	OP	645	03	3	684	53	(	
607	04	04	646	01	1	685	43	RCL	
608	43	RCL	647	07	7	686	17	17	
609	18	18	648	69	OP	687	65	×	
610	69	OP	649	04	04	688	93	.	
611	06	06	650	43	RCL	689	00	0	
612	02	2	651	08	08	690	01	1	
613	05	5	652	69	OP	691	08	8	
614	02	2	653	06	06	692	54	)	
615	02	2	654	98	ADV	693	22	INV	
616	69	OP	655	92	RTN	694	23	LNX	
617	04	04	656	76	LBL	695	95	=	
618	43	RCL	657	43	RCL	696	42	STO	
619	19	19	658	01	1	697	26	26	
620	69	OP	659	03	3	698	71	SBR	
621	06	06	660	04	4	699	44	SUM	
622	02	2	661	08	8	700	92	RTN	
623	01	1	662	02	2	701	76	LBL	
624	69	OP	663	65	×	702	45	YX	
625	04	04	664	53	(	703	00	0	
626	43	RCL	665	43	RCL	704	42	STO	
627	20	20	666	16	16	705	25	25	
628	69	OP	667	65	×	706	71	SBR	
629	06	06	668	93	.	707	44	SUM	
630	02	2	669	00	0	708	92	RTN	
631	03	3	670	01	1	709	00	0	
632	01	1	671	08	8	710	00	0	
633	03	3	672	54	)	711	00	0	
634	69	OP	673	22	INV	712	00	0	
635	04	04	674	23	LNX	713	00	0	
636	43	RCL	675	95	=	714	00	0	
637	21	21	676	42	STO	715	00	0	
638	69	OP	677	25	25	716	00	0	

Program 23

Gas Turbine Site Rating

Background

Gas-turbine manufacturers publish the power ratings of their gas turbines as ISO ratings. The ISO power is the zero-loss output at an ambient temperature of 59°F at sea level. Several factors affect the power output that can be realized at the operating site. The heat input necessary to obtain the power is also affected by some of these factors, which are:

1. Ambient temperature.
2. Altitude.
3. Inlet and exhaust ducting losses.
4. Gear efficiency, when applicable.

The power output and the heat input are both inversely proportional to the ambient temperature. A survey of current equipment and data shows that the ambient-temperature effects on power output are approximately linear above and below 59°F, and that the following points establish good approximations of temperature effects:

at $T_a = 30°F$ $PWR_d = 112\% \ PWR_i$
at $T_a = 59°F$ $PWR_d = 100\% \ PWR_i$
at $T_a = 120°F$ $PWR_d = 73\% \ PWR_i$

where:
    PWR_d = site rated horsepower, hp
     PWR_i = ISO rated horsepower, hp
       T_a = ambient temperature, °F

The survey also shows that the specified heat input is well approximated by a single straight line through the following points:

$$T_a = 59°F \qquad SHI = 100\% \; SHI_i$$
$$T_a = 120°F \qquad SHI = 107.5\% \; SHI_i$$

where:
    SHI = site rated specific heat input, Btu/hp-hr
    SHI_i = ISO rated specific heat input, Btu/hp-hr

The effect of altitude is to reduce the power output and the heat input by approximately 3.5% per 1000 feet above sea level. The heat input is measured in Btu/hr. Note that the specific heat input (Btu/hp-hr) is not affected by altitude.

The inlet and exhaust ducting losses are variables based on the gas-turbine installation. A good approximation for the total of these losses is a three-percent reduction in gas-turbine power output. These losses do not reduce the required heat input.

The gear efficiency directly reduces the power output from the gas turbine—gear combination. It does not reduce the required heat input.

Considering the foregoing, the power output from the gas turbine is given by Equation 23-1:

$$PWR_d = PWR_i \; (C_{tp})(C_{ap})(C_{dp})(\eta_g) \tag{23-1}$$

where:
    C_{tp} = temperature correction on power
    C_{ap} = altitude correction on power
    C_{dp} = ducting loss correction on power
    η_g = gear efficiency

The specific heat input is given by Equation 23-2:

$$SHI = SHI_i(C_{th}) \tag{23-2}$$

where:
    C_{th} = temperature correction on specific heat input

The heat input is given by Equation 23-3:

$$HI = SHI(PWR_i)(C_{tp})(C_{ap}) \tag{23-3}$$

where:
    HI = heat input, Btu/hr

The specific fuel consumption is given by Equation 23-4:

$$SFC = \frac{HI}{(PWR_d)(LHV)} \tag{23-4}$$

where:

    SFC = specific fuel consumption, with units of SCF/hp-hr for gas fuels and lbm/hp-hr for liquid fuels

    LHV = lower heating value of the fuel, with units of Btu/SCF for gas fuels and Btu/lbm for liquid fuels.

The SCF is standard cubic feet normally measured at 60°F, 14.7 psia.

Program 23 Description

Program 23, Gas-Turbine Site Rating, calculates and prints the results of Equations 23-1, 23-2, 23-3, and 23-4, with expected accuracy of ±5%. In order to execute the program, the following must be known:

1. ISO rated horsepower, PWR_i
2. ISO rated specific heat input, SHI_i
3. Ambient temperature, T_a
4. Altitude, A_{sl}
5. Lower heating value of the fuel, LHV
6. Gear efficiency (when applicable), η_g

The ISO rated horsepower is the zero-loss horsepower at an ambient temperature of 59°F. Normally this value is taken at 100% nominal gas-turbine speed. However, if a different speed is required, the zero-loss power for an ambient temperature of 59°F corresponding to the required speed can be entered as the ISO rated horsepower.

The ISO rated specific heat input must correspond to the selected ISO rated horsepower.

The program has the option to accept the lower heating value for either gas or liquid fuels. The program output will correspond to the type of fuel entered.

The program automatically sets the gear efficiency at 1.0 (100%) unless a gear efficiency is entered.

Should the operator only desire the site rated horsepower exclusive of the required heat input or specific fuel consumption, the ISO rated specific heat input and the lower heating value can be ignored.

The program is set up for continuous usage without the need for complete data reentry. Therefore, only the parameters of interest need to be changed for program reexecution.

Table 23-1 is the nomenclature printed by the program; Table 23-2 shows the data registers used by the program.

Table 23-1
Nomenclature Printed by Program 23

Program Term	Definition	Units
ALT	altitude	feet
EFFG	gear efficiency	dimensionless
HI	heat input	Btu/hr
LHVG	lower heating value—gas fuels	Btu/SCF
LHVL	lower heating value—liquid fuels	Btu/lbm
PWRD	site rated shaft horsepower	hp
PWRI	ISO rated shaft horsepower	hp
SFCG	specific fuel consumption—gas fuels	SCF/hp-hr
SFCL	specific fuel consumption—liquid fuels	lbm/hp-hr
SHI	site rated specific heat input	Btu/hp-hr
SHII	ISO rated specific heat input	Btu/hp-hr
TA	ambient temperature	°F

Table 23-2
Data Registers Used by Program 23

00	not used	06	A_{sl}	12	PWR_d
01	not used	07	η_g	13	SHI
02	not used	08	LHV_g	14	HI
03	PWR_i	09	LHV_l	15	SFC_g
04	SHI_i	10	C_{ap}	16	SFC_l
05	T_a	11	C_{tp}		

Labels Used by Program 23

```
001   10   E·
059   11   A              147   34   ΓX
064   12   B              220   45   YX
069   13   C              307   43   RCL
074   14   D              381   44   SUM
079   17   B·             405   33   X²
087   18   C·             428   35   1/X
095   19   D·             448   42   STO
100   15   E              467   32   X:T
```

Table 23-3
Program 23: Definitions of User-Defined Keys

A	PWRI			
B	SHII	B'	LHVG	
C	TA	C'	LHVL	
D	ALT	D'	EFFG	
E	Calculate	E'	Initialize	

Program 23 Usage

Program 23 is executed by using the user-defined keys, the definitions for which can be found in Table 23-3.

Initializing the program prints the title and sets the gear efficiency at 1.0 (100%). Therefore, if there is no gear, there is no need to enter the gear efficiency through user-defined key D'.

If the fuel is a gas, its lower heating value is entered through B'. If the fuel is a liquid, its lower heating value is entered through C'. Only the lower heating value for one type of fuel can be entered.

If the site rated horsepower is all that is desired, entries through user-defined keys B, B', and C' do not have to be made. Therefore, only the ISO rated horsepower, ambient temperature, and altitude are necessary to calculate the site rated horsepower.

After all required data are entered, program execution is initiated through user-defined key E. Subsequent calculations can be made by changing only the parameters of interest.

Sample Problem 23-1

Given a gas turbine with an ISO rated power of 10,000 hp and an ISO rated specific heat input of 14,000 Btu/hp-hr, what is the site rated horsepower and specific fuel consumption for gas and liquid fuels for an ambient temperature of 100°F and an altitude of 1500 feet? The gas turbine is to drive through a gear, with an efficiency of 98%. The lower heating value of the gas fuel is 1000 Btu/SCF; the lower heating value of the liquid fuel is 18,300 Btu/lbm.

Sample Problem 23-1: User Instructions

Step	Procedure	Enter	Press	Display
1.	Load program.			
2.	Initialize.		2nd E'	1

Sample Problem 23-1: User Instructions continued

Step	Procedure	Enter	Press	Display
3.	Enter ISO rated horse-power.	10000	A	10000
4.	Enter ISO rated specific heat input.	14000	B	14000
5.	Enter ambient temperature.	100	C	100
6.	Enter altitude.	1500	D	1500
7.	Enter lower heating value of gas fuel.	1000	2nd B′	0
8.	Enter gear efficiency.	0.98	2nd D′	0.98
9.	Calculate.		E	
10.	Enter lower heating value of liquid fuel.	18300	2nd C′	0
11.	Calculate.		E	

Sample Problem 23-1: Program Printout

```
GAS TURBINE POWER                        7358.      PWRD
                                        14700.       SHI
                                       113.79 06    HI
                                         0.845      SFCL
      10000.      PWRI
      14000.      SHII
        100.       TA
       1500.      ALT
        0.98      EFFG
       1000.      LHVG


       7358.      PWRD
      14700.       SHI
      113.79 06    HI
        15.5      SFCG



      10000.      PWRI
      14000.      SHII
        100.       TA
       1500.      ALT
        0.98      EFFG
      18300.      LHVL
```

Program 23 Listing

000	76	LBL	054	01	1	108	00	0
001	10	E'	055	42	STO	109	00	0
002	98	ADV	056	07	07	110	00	0
003	69	OP	057	91	R/S	111	65	×
004	00	00	058	76	LBL	112	93	.
005	47	CMS	059	11	A	113	00	0
006	02	2	060	42	STO	114	03	3
007	02	2	061	03	03	115	05	5
008	01	1	062	91	R/S	116	54	)
009	03	3	063	76	LBL	117	95	=
010	03	3	064	12	B	118	42	STO
011	06	6	065	42	STO	119	10	10
012	69	OP	066	04	04	120	05	5
013	01	01	067	91	R/S	121	09	9
014	03	3	068	76	LBL	122	32	X:T
015	07	7	069	13	C	123	43	RCL
016	04	4	070	42	STO	124	05	05
017	01	1	071	05	05	125	77	GE
018	03	3	072	91	R/S	126	33	X²
019	05	5	073	76	LBL	127	43	RCL
020	01	1	074	14	D	128	05	05
021	04	4	075	42	STO	129	65	×
022	69	OP	076	06	06	130	93	.
023	02	02	077	91	R/S	131	00	0
024	02	2	078	76	LBL	132	00	0
025	04	4	079	17	B'	133	03	3
026	03	3	080	42	STO	134	04	4
027	01	1	081	08	08	135	05	5
028	01	1	082	00	0	136	94	+/-
029	07	7	083	42	STO	137	85	+
030	00	0	084	09	09	138	01	1
031	00	0	085	91	R/S	139	93	.
032	03	3	086	76	LBL	140	02	2
033	03	3	087	18	C'	141	95	=
034	69	OP	088	42	STO	142	42	STO
035	03	03	089	09	09	143	11	11
036	03	3	090	00	0	144	71	SBR
037	02	2	091	42	STO	145	34	ГХ
038	04	4	092	08	08	146	76	LBL
039	03	3	093	91	R/S	147	34	ГХ
040	01	1	094	76	LBL	148	43	RCL
041	07	7	095	19	D'	149	03	03
042	03	3	096	42	STO	150	65	×
043	05	5	097	07	07	151	43	RCL
044	00	0	098	91	R/S	152	11	11
045	00	0	099	76	LBL	153	65	×
046	69	OP	100	15	E	154	43	RCL
047	04	04	101	01	1	155	10	10
048	69	OP	102	75	-	156	65	×
049	05	05	103	53	(	157	43	RCL
050	69	OP	104	43	RCL	158	07	07
051	00	00	105	06	06	159	65	×
052	98	ADV	106	55	÷	160	93	.
053	98	ADV	107	01	1	161	09	9

Program 23 Listing continued

162	07	7	216	71	SBR	270	06	06
163	95	=	217	45	YX	271	01	1
164	42	STD	218	92	RTN	272	07	7
165	12	12	219	76	LBL	273	02	2
166	43	RCL	220	45	YX	274	01	1
167	05	05	221	03	3	275	02	2
168	65	×	222	03	3	276	01	1
169	93	.	223	04	4	277	02	2
170	00	0	224	03	3	278	02	2
171	00	0	225	03	3	279	69	DP
172	01	1	226	05	5	280	04	04
173	02	2	227	02	2	281	43	RCL
174	03	3	228	04	4	282	07	07
175	85	+	229	69	DP	283	69	DP
176	93	.	230	04	04	284	06	06
177	09	9	231	43	RCL	285	43	RCL
178	02	2	232	03	03	286	08	08
179	07	7	233	69	DP	287	67	EQ
180	95	=	234	06	06	288	42	STD
181	65	×	235	03	3	289	02	2
182	43	RCL	236	06	6	290	07	7
183	04	04	237	02	2	291	02	2
184	95	=	238	03	3	292	03	3
185	42	STD	239	02	2	293	04	4
186	13	13	240	04	4	294	02	2
187	65	×	241	02	2	295	02	2
188	43	RCL	242	04	4	296	02	2
189	03	03	243	69	DP	297	69	DP
190	65	×	244	04	04	298	04	04
191	43	RCL	245	43	RCL	299	43	RCL
192	11	11	246	04	04	300	08	08
193	65	×	247	69	DP	301	69	DP
194	43	RCL	248	06	06	302	06	06
195	10	10	249	03	3	303	71	SBR
196	95	=	250	07	7	304	43	RCL
197	42	STD	251	01	1	305	92	RTN
198	14	14	252	03	3	306	76	LBL
199	00	0	253	69	DP	307	43	RCL
200	32	X¦T	254	04	04	308	98	ADV
201	43	RCL	255	43	RCL	309	03	3
202	08	08	256	05	05	310	03	3
203	67	EQ	257	69	DP	311	04	4
204	35	1/X	258	06	06	312	03	3
205	43	RCL	259	01	1	313	03	3
206	14	14	260	03	3	314	05	5
207	55	÷	261	02	2	315	01	1
208	43	RCL	262	07	7	316	06	6
209	12	12	263	03	3	317	69	DP
210	55	÷	264	07	7	318	04	04
211	43	RCL	265	69	DP	319	43	RCL
212	08	08	266	04	04	320	12	12
213	95	=	267	43	RCL	321	59	INT
214	42	STD	268	06	06	322	69	DP
215	15	15	269	69	DP	323	06	06

(continued on next page)

Program 23 Listing continued

324	03	3	375	58	FIX	426	92	RTN
325	06	6	376	69	OP	427	76	LBL
326	02	2	377	00	00	428	35	1/X
327	03	3	378	91	R/S	429	43	RCL
328	02	2	379	92	RTN	430	09	09
329	04	4	380	76	LBL	431	67	EQ
330	69	OP	381	44	SUM	432	32	X:T
331	04	04	382	03	3	433	43	RCL
332	43	RCL	383	06	6	434	14	14
333	13	13	384	02	2	435	55	÷
334	59	INT	385	01	1	436	43	RCL
335	69	OP	386	01	1	437	12	12
336	06	06	387	05	5	438	55	÷
337	02	2	388	02	2	439	43	RCL
338	03	3	389	07	7	440	09	09
339	02	2	390	69	OP	441	95	=
340	04	4	391	04	04	442	42	STO
341	69	OP	392	43	RCL	443	16	16
342	04	04	393	16	16	444	71	SBR
343	43	RCL	394	58	FIX	445	45	Y×
344	14	14	395	03	03	446	92	RTN
345	57	ENG	396	69	OP	447	76	LBL
346	58	FIX	397	06	06	448	42	STO
347	02	02	398	22	INV	449	02	2
348	69	OP	399	58	FIX	450	07	7
349	06	06	400	69	OP	451	02	2
350	22	INV	401	00	00	452	03	3
351	58	FIX	402	91	R/S	453	04	4
352	22	INV	403	92	RTN	454	02	2
353	57	ENG	404	76	LBL	455	02	2
354	43	RCL	405	33	X²	456	07	7
355	08	08	406	43	RCL	457	69	OP
356	67	EQ	407	05	05	458	04	04
357	44	SUM	408	65	×	459	43	RCL
358	03	3	409	93	.	460	09	09
359	06	6	410	00	0	461	69	OP
360	02	2	411	00	0	462	06	06
361	01	1	412	04	4	463	71	SBR
362	01	1	413	04	4	464	43	RCL
363	05	5	414	03	3	465	92	RTN
364	02	2	415	94	+/-	466	76	LBL
365	02	2	416	85	+	467	32	X:T
366	69	OP	417	01	1	468	00	0
367	04	04	418	93	.	469	42	STO
368	43	RCL	419	02	2	470	15	15
369	15	15	420	06	6	471	42	STO
370	58	FIX	421	95	=	472	16	16
371	01	01	422	42	STO	473	71	SBR
372	69	OP	423	11	11	474	45	Y×
373	06	06	424	71	SBR	475	92	RTN
374	22	INV	425	34	ГX	476	00	0

Part VI

Miscellaneous Aids for Centrifugal Compressor Calculations and Analysis

Program 24

Inlet Flow Conversions

Background

A book of compressor estimating programs would not be complete without discussing the conversion of flow values from one set of units to another. Compressor flow may be specified in ICFM (inlet cubic feet per minute), SCFM (standard cubic feet per minute), or MMSCFD (millions of standard cubic feet per day). It is necessary to convert these units to lbm/min in order to use the compressor estimating programs, Programs 1, 2, and 3. Furthermore, if the inlet flow is specified in metric units, it will be necessary to convert these units to lbm/min. There are also several other reasons to convert from one set of units to another.

The inlet volume flow is related to the inlet mass flow by Equation 24-1:

$$Q_1 = 10.729 \frac{m_1 Z_1 T_1}{(MW)(P_1)} \tag{24-1}$$

The standard inlet volume flow is related to the inlet mass flow by Equation 24-2:

$$SVF = 10.729 \frac{m_1 Z_{std} T_{std}}{(MW)(P_{std})} \tag{24-2}$$

where:
  SVF = standard volume flow in SCFM

265

and where the subscript std refers to standard conditions.

The standard inlet volume flow in SCFM is related to the standard inlet volume flow in MMSCFD by Equation 24-3:

$$SVF = \frac{SVF_{MMSCFD}}{0.00144} \tag{24-3}$$

where:

SVF_{MMSCFD} = standard volume flow in MMSCFD

The inlet mass flow in lbm/min is related to the inlet mass flow in kg/h by Equation 24-4:

$$m_{lbm/min} = 0.03674 \, m_{kg/h} \tag{24-4}$$

where:

$m_{lbm/min}$ = mass flow in lbm/min
$m_{kg/h}$ = mass flow in kg/h

The actual inlet volume flow in ICFM is related to the actual inlet volume flow in m³/h by Equation 24-5:

$$Q_{ICFM} = \frac{Q_{m^3/h}}{1.699} \tag{24-5}$$

where:

Q_{ICFM} = inlet volume flow in ICFM
$Q_{m^3/h}$ = inlet volume flow in m³/h

The standard inlet volume flow in standard cubic meters per hour is related to the inlet mass flow in kg/h by Equation 24-6:

$$SVFM = 8.314 \frac{m_1 Z_{std} T_{std}}{(MW)(P_{std})} \tag{24-6}$$

where:

$SVFM$ = metric standard volume flow in standard m³/h
T_{std} = standard temperature in K
P_{std} = standard pressure in kPa

The preceding equations considered all flows as inlet in order to form a common reference point. Inlet was used because it is by far of most concern for compressor estimates. Provided the corresponding pressures, temperatures, and compressibilities are used, the preceding equations are good for discharge flows also. Note, however, that the standard volume flows do not change, since they are based on standard temperature, standard pressure, and standard compressibility, regardless of process values.

Program 24 Description

Inlet Flow Conversions, Program 24, considers Equations 24-1, 24-2, 24-3, 24-4, 24-5, and 24-6 in order to convert the inlet flow from the units given to the units desired.

In order to execute the program, the following must be known:

1. Standard temperature, T_{std}
2. Standard pressure, P_{std}
3. Standard Z-value, Z_{std}
4. Inlet temperature, T_1
5. Inlet pressure, P_1
6. Inlet Z-value, Z_1
7. Molecular weight, MW

Note that these standard values are only necessary when the flow is specified in, or being converted to, standard units.

When using the metric-English conversions available in this program, the standard temperature and pressure must be entered in metric units, °C and kPa respectively. The inlet temperature and pressure, however, must be entered in English units, °F and psia respectively.

The program is set up for continuous usage, without the need for complete data reentry. Therefore, as many conversions as needed can be made by changing only the pertinent data.

Table 24-1 is the nomenclature printed by the program; Table 24-2 shows the data registers used by the program.

Labels Used by Program 24

004	10	E'	384	14	D
173	11	A	455	33	X²
186	16	A'	500	34	ΓX
199	12	B	559	43	RCL
217	17	B'	600	42	STO
266	13	C	677	35	1/X
297	18	C'	725	44	SUM
341	15	E	758	45	YX

Table 24-1
Program 24: Printer Nomenclature

Program Term	Definition	Units
ICFM	actual inlet volume flow	ICFM
KG/H	mass flow—metric	kg/h
LB/M	mass flow	lbm/min
M3/H	actual inlet volume flow—metric	m^3/h
M3HS	standard volume flow—metric	m^3/h
MMSD	standard volume flow	MMSCFD
MW	molecular weight	lbm/lbm-mol
P1	actual inlet pressure	psia
PS	standard pressure	psia or kPa
SCFM	standard volume flow	SCFM
T1	actual inlet temperature	°F
TS	standard temperature	°F or °C
Z1	actual inlet compressibility	dimensionless
ZS	standard compressibility	dimensionless

Table 24-2
Data Registers Used by Program 24

00	not used	06	T_1	12	SVF_{SCFM}
01	not used	07	P_1	13	SVF_{MMSCFD}
02	not used	08	Z_1	14	$SVFM$
03	T_{std}	09	MW	15	$Q_{m3/h}$
04	P_{std}	10	$m_{lbm/min}$	16	$m_{kg/h}$
05	Z_{std}	11	Q_{ICFM}		

Program 24 Usage

Program 24 is executed by using the user-defined keys and by following the instructions prompted by the program. The definitions for the user-defined keys can be found in Table 24-3.

Once initialized, the program prints instructions to store the standard temperature, standard pressure, standard compressibility, inlet temperature, inlet pressure, inlet compressibility, and molecular weight. A typical instruction is "TS-3," which means to store the standard temperature in data-register 03.

Each conversion is made through a user-defined key, as specified in Table 24-3. Subsequent conversions can be made by changing only the pertinent data.

Note that the calculator must be repartitioned to 799.19 before loading or keying in the program.

Table 24-3
Program 24: Definitions of User-Defined Keys

A	LB/M to ICFM	A'	ICFM to LB/M
B	SCFM to ICFM, LB/M, MMSD	B'	ICFM to SCFM, LB/M, MMSD
C	MMSD to ICFM, SCFM, LB/M	C'	KG/H to ICFM, LB/M
D	M3HS to ICFM, LB/M		
E	M3/H to ICFM, LB/M	E'	Initialize

Sample Problem 24-1

Consider the following:

$T_1 = 100°F$
$P_1 = 15$ psia
$Z_1 = 0.99$
$MW = 30$

and the following English and metric standard conditions:

English	**metric**
$T_{std} = 60°F$	$T_{std} = 0°C$
$P_{std} = 14.7$ psia	$P_{std} = 101.3$ kPa
$Z_{std} = 1.0$	$Z_{std} = 1.0$

Convert the following:

2500 lbm/min to ICFM
50,000 ICFM to lbm/min
35,000 SCFM to ICFM
40,000 ICFM to SCFM
25.0 MMSCFD to ICFM
60,000 kg/h to ICFM
75,000 standard m^3/h to ICFM
65,000 m^3/h to ICFM

Sample Problem 24-1: User Instructions

Step	Procedure	Enter	Press	Display
1.	Partition calculator.	2	2nd OP 17	799.19
2.	Load program.			
3.	Initialize.		2nd E'	3043201200

(continued on next page)

Sample Problem 24-1: User Instructions continued

Step	Procedure	Enter	Press	Display
4.	Enter standard temperature	60	STO 03	60
5.	Enter standard pressure.	14.7	STO 04	14.7
6.	Enter standard compressibility.	1	STO 05	1
7.	Enter inlet temperature.	100	STO 06	100
8.	Enter inlet pressure.	15	STO 07	15
9.	Enter inlet compressibility.	0.99	STO 08	0.99
10.	Enter molecular weight.	30	STO 09	30
11.	Convert 2500 lbm/min to ICFM.	2500	A	
12.	Convert 50,000 ICFM to lbm/min.	50000	2nd A′	
13.	Convert 35,000 SCFM to ICFM.	35000	B	
14.	Convert 40,000 ICFM to SCFM.	40000	2nd B′	
15.	Convert 25.0 MMSCFD to ICFM.	25	C	
16.	Enter metric standard temperature.	0	STO 03	0
17.	Enter metric standard pressure.	101.3	STO 04	101.3
18.	Convert 60,000 kg/h to ICFM.	60000	2nd C′	
19.	Convert 75,000 standard m^3/h to ICFM.	75000	D	
20.	Convert 65,000 m^3/h to ICFM.	65000	E	

Sample Problem 24-1: Program Printout

```
    FLOW CONVERSIONS                    100.        T1
                                       15.00        P1
                                       0.990        Z1
                                       30.00        MW
  TS-3, PS-4, ZS-5
  T1-6, P1-7, Z1-8
  MW-9                                33045.        ICFM
                                       2500.        LB/M
```

Sample Problem 24-1: Program Printout continued

100.	T1
15.00	P1
0.990	Z1
30.00	MW

50000.	ICFM
3783.	LB/M

60.	TS
14.70	PS
1.000	ZS

100.	T1
15.00	P1
0.990	Z1
30.00	MW

35000.	SCFM
36569.	ICFM
2767.	LB/M
50.40	MMSD

60.	TS
14.70	PS
1.000	ZS

100.	T1
15.00	P1
0.990	Z1
30.00	MW

38284.	SCFM
40000.	ICFM
3026.	LB/M
55.13	MMSD

60.	TS
14.70	PS
1.000	ZS

100.	T1
15.00	P1
0.990	Z1
30.00	MW

17361.	SCFM
18139.	ICFM
1372.	LB/M
25.00	MMSD

60000.	KG/H

100.	T1
15.00	P1
0.990	Z1
30.00	MW

29138.	ICFM
2204.	LB/M

75000.	M3HS

0.	TS
101.30	PS
1.000	ZS

100.	T1
15.00	P1
0.990	Z1
30.00	MW

48767.	ICFM
3689.	LB/M

65000.	M3/H

100.	T1
15.00	P1
0.990	Z1
30.00	MW

38258.	ICFM
2894.	LB/M

Program 24 Listing

000	02	2	054	98	ADV	108	02	2
001	69	OP	055	98	ADV	109	00	0
002	17	17	056	03	3	110	00	0
003	76	LBL	057	07	7	111	07	7
004	10	E'	058	03	3	112	05	5
005	69	OP	059	06	6	113	07	7
006	00	00	060	02	2	114	69	OP
007	98	ADV	061	00	0	115	01	01
008	02	2	062	00	0	116	03	3
009	01	1	063	04	4	117	03	3
010	02	2	064	05	5	118	00	0
011	07	7	065	07	7	119	02	2
012	03	3	066	69	OP	120	02	2
013	02	2	067	01	01	121	00	0
014	69	OP	068	03	3	122	01	1
015	01	01	069	03	3	123	00	0
016	04	4	070	03	3	124	69	OP
017	03	3	071	06	6	125	02	02
018	00	0	072	02	2	126	05	5
019	00	0	073	00	0	127	07	7
020	01	1	074	00	0	128	00	0
021	05	5	075	05	5	129	00	0
022	03	3	076	69	OP	130	04	4
023	02	2	077	02	02	131	06	6
024	03	3	078	05	5	132	00	0
025	01	1	079	07	7	133	02	2
026	69	OP	080	00	0	134	02	2
027	02	02	081	00	0	135	00	0
028	04	4	082	04	4	136	69	OP
029	02	2	083	06	6	137	03	03
030	01	1	084	03	3	138	01	1
031	07	7	085	06	6	139	01	1
032	03	3	086	02	2	140	00	0
033	05	5	087	00	0	141	00	0
034	03	3	088	69	OP	142	00	0
035	06	6	089	03	03	143	00	0
036	02	2	090	00	0	144	00	0
037	04	4	091	06	6	145	00	0
038	69	OP	092	00	0	146	00	0
039	03	03	093	00	0	147	00	0
040	03	3	094	00	0	148	69	OP
041	02	2	095	00	0	149	04	04
042	03	3	096	00	0	150	69	OP
043	01	1	097	00	0	151	05	05
044	03	3	098	00	0	152	69	OP
045	06	6	099	00	0	153	00	00
046	00	0	100	69	OP	154	03	3
047	00	0	101	04	04	155	00	0
048	00	0	102	69	OP	156	04	4
049	00	0	103	05	05	157	03	3
050	69	OP	104	03	3	158	02	2
051	04	04	105	07	7	159	00	0
052	69	OP	106	00	0	160	01	1
053	05	05	107	02	2	161	02	2

Program 24 Listing continued

162	00	0	216	76	LBL	270	55	÷	
163	00	0	217	17	B'	271	01	1	
164	69	OP	218	98	ADV	272	93	.	
165	01	01	219	42	STO	273	04	4	
166	69	OP	220	11	11	274	04	4	
167	05	05	221	55	÷	275	52	EE	
168	69	OP	222	43	RCL	276	03	3	
169	00	00	223	04	04	277	94	+/-	
170	98	ADV	224	65	×	278	95	=	
171	91	R/S	225	43	RCL	279	22	INV	
172	76	LBL	226	07	07	280	52	EE	
173	11	A	227	55	÷	281	42	STO	
174	98	ADV	228	53	(	282	12	12	
175	42	STO	229	43	RCL	283	71	SBR	
176	10	10	230	06	06	284	35	1/X	
177	71	SBR	231	85	+	285	71	SBR	
178	44	SUM	232	04	4	286	44	SUM	
179	71	SBR	233	06	6	287	71	SBR	
180	34	ΓX	234	00	0	288	33	X²	
181	98	ADV	235	54	)	289	98	ADV	
182	71	SBR	236	65	×	290	71	SBR	
183	43	RCL	237	53	(	291	34	ΓX	
184	91	R/S	238	43	RCL	292	98	ADV	
185	76	LBL	239	03	03	293	71	SBR	
186	16	A'	240	85	+	294	42	STO	
187	98	ADV	241	04	4	295	91	R/S	
188	42	STO	242	06	6	296	76	LBL	
189	11	11	243	00	0	297	18	C'	
190	71	SBR	244	54	)	298	98	ADV	
191	45	YX	245	55	÷	299	42	STO	
192	71	SBR	246	43	RCL	300	16	16	
193	34	ΓX	247	08	08	301	02	2	
194	98	ADV	248	65	×	302	06	6	
195	71	SBR	249	43	RCL	303	02	2	
196	43	RCL	250	05	05	304	02	2	
197	91	R/S	251	95	=	305	06	6	
198	76	LBL	252	42	STO	306	03	3	
199	12	B	253	12	12	307	02	2	
200	98	ADV	254	71	SBR	308	03	3	
201	42	STO	255	35	1/X	309	69	OP	
202	12	12	256	71	SBR	310	04	04	
203	71	SBR	257	33	X²	311	43	RCL	
204	35	1/X	258	98	ADV	312	16	16	
205	71	SBR	259	71	SBR	313	58	FIX	
206	44	SUM	260	34	ΓX	314	00	00	
207	71	SBR	261	98	ADV	315	69	OP	
208	33	X²	262	71	SBR	316	06	06	
209	98	ADV	263	42	STO	317	22	INV	
210	71	SBR	264	91	R/S	318	58	FIX	
211	34	ΓX	265	76	LBL	319	43	RCL	
212	98	ADV	266	13	C	320	16	16	
213	71	SBR	267	42	STO	321	65	×	
214	42	STO	268	13	13	322	93	.	
215	91	R/S	269	98	ADV	323	00	0	

(continued on next page)

Program 24 Listing continued

324	03	3	377	71	SBR	430	43	RCL	
325	06	6	378	34	ГX	431	04	04	
326	07	7	379	98	ADV	432	65	×	
327	04	4	380	71	SBR	433	93	.	
328	95	=	381	43	RCL	434	00	0	
329	42	STD	382	91	R/S	435	03	3	
330	10	10	383	76	LBL	436	06	6	
331	71	SBR	384	14	D	437	07	7	
332	44	SUM	385	98	ADV	438	04	4	
333	98	ADV	386	42	STD	439	95	=	
334	71	SBR	387	14	14	440	42	STD	
335	34	ГX	388	03	3	441	10	10	
336	98	ADV	389	00	0	442	71	SBR	
337	71	SBR	390	00	0	443	44	SUM	
338	43	RCL	391	04	4	444	98	ADV	
339	91	R/S	392	02	2	445	71	SBR	
340	76	LBL	393	03	3	446	33	X²	
341	15	E	394	03	3	447	98	ADV	
342	98	ADV	395	06	6	448	71	SBR	
343	42	STD	396	69	DP	449	34	ГX	
344	15	15	397	04	04	450	98	ADV	
345	03	3	398	43	RCL	451	71	SBR	
346	00	0	399	14	14	452	43	RCL	
347	00	0	400	58	FIX	453	91	R/S	
348	04	4	401	00	00	454	76	LBL	
349	06	6	402	69	DP	455	33	X²	
350	03	3	403	06	06	456	03	3	
351	02	2	404	22	INV	457	07	7	
352	03	3	405	58	FIX	458	03	3	
353	69	DP	406	43	RCL	459	06	6	
354	04	04	407	14	14	460	69	DP	
355	43	RCL	408	55	÷	461	04	04	
356	15	15	409	08	8	462	43	RCL	
357	58	FIX	410	93	.	463	03	03	
358	00	00	411	03	3	464	58	FIX	
359	69	DP	412	01	1	465	00	00	
360	06	06	413	04	4	466	69	DP	
361	22	INV	414	55	÷	467	06	06	
362	58	FIX	415	43	RCL	468	22	INV	
363	43	RCL	416	05	05	469	58	FIX	
364	15	15	417	55	÷	470	03	3	
365	55	÷	418	53	(	471	03	3	
366	01	1	419	43	RCL	472	03	3	
367	93	.	420	03	03	473	06	6	
368	06	6	421	85	+	474	69	DP	
369	09	9	422	02	2	475	04	04	
370	09	9	423	07	7	476	43	RCL	
371	95	=	424	03	3	477	04	04	
372	42	STD	425	54	)	478	58	FIX	
373	11	11	426	65	×	479	02	02	
374	71	SBR	427	43	RCL	480	69	DP	
375	45	YX	428	09	09	481	06	06	
376	98	ADV	429	65	×	482	22	INV	

Program 24 Listing continued

483	58	FIX	536	08	08	589	10	10
484	04	4	537	58	FIX	590	58	FIX
485	06	6	538	03	03	591	00	00
486	03	3	539	69	OP	592	69	OP
487	06	6	540	06	06	593	06	06
488	69	OP	541	22	INV	594	22	INV
489	04	04	542	58	FIX	595	58	FIX
490	43	RCL	543	03	3	596	69	OP
491	05	05	544	00	0	597	00	00
492	58	FIX	545	04	4	598	92	RTN
493	03	03	546	03	3	599	76	LBL
494	69	OP	547	69	OP	600	42	STO
495	06	06	548	04	04	601	03	3
496	22	INV	549	43	RCL	602	06	6
497	58	FIX	550	09	09	603	01	1
498	92	RTN	551	58	FIX	604	05	5
499	76	LBL	552	02	02	605	02	2
500	34	ΓX	553	69	OP	606	01	1
501	03	3	554	06	06	607	03	3
502	07	7	555	22	INV	608	00	0
503	00	0	556	58	FIX	609	69	OP
504	02	2	557	92	RTN	610	04	04
505	69	OP	558	76	LBL	611	43	RCL
506	04	04	559	43	RCL	612	12	12
507	43	RCL	560	02	2	613	58	FIX
508	06	06	561	04	4	614	00	00
509	58	FIX	562	01	1	615	69	OP
510	00	00	563	05	5	616	06	06
511	69	OP	564	02	2	617	22	INV
512	06	06	565	01	1	618	58	FIX
513	22	INV	566	03	3	619	02	2
514	58	FIX	567	00	0	620	04	4
515	03	3	568	69	OP	621	01	1
516	03	3	569	04	04	622	05	5
517	00	0	570	43	RCL	623	02	2
518	02	2	571	11	11	624	01	1
519	69	OP	572	58	FIX	625	03	3
520	04	04	573	00	00	626	00	0
521	43	RCL	574	69	OP	627	69	OP
522	07	07	575	06	06	628	04	04
523	58	FIX	576	22	INV	629	43	RCL
524	02	02	577	58	FIX	630	11	11
525	69	OP	578	02	2	631	58	FIX
526	06	06	579	07	7	632	00	00
527	22	INV	580	01	1	633	69	OP
528	58	FIX	581	04	4	634	06	06
529	04	4	582	06	6	635	22	INV
530	06	6	583	03	3	636	58	FIX
531	00	0	584	03	3	637	02	2
532	02	2	585	00	0	638	07	7
533	69	OP	586	69	OP	639	01	1
534	04	04	587	04	04	640	04	4
535	43	RCL	588	43	RCL	641	06	6

(continued on next page)

Program 24 Listing continued

642	03	3	694	12	12	746	54	)
643	03	3	695	55	÷	747	55	÷
644	00	0	696	01	1	748	43	RCL
645	69	OP	697	00	0	749	07	07
646	04	04	698	93	.	750	55	÷
647	43	RCL	699	07	7	751	43	RCL
648	10	10	700	02	2	752	09	09
649	58	FIX	701	09	9	753	95	=
650	00	00	702	55	÷	754	42	STO
651	69	OP	703	43	RCL	755	11	11
652	06	06	704	05	05	756	92	RTN
653	22	INV	705	55	÷	757	76	LBL
654	58	FIX	706	53	(	758	45	Y×
655	03	3	707	43	RCL	759	43	RCL
656	00	0	708	03	03	760	11	11
657	03	3	709	85	+	761	55	÷
658	00	0	710	04	4	762	01	1
659	03	3	711	06	6	763	00	0
660	06	6	712	00	0	764	93	.
661	01	1	713	54	)	765	07	7
662	06	6	714	65	×	766	02	2
663	69	OP	715	43	RCL	767	09	9
664	04	04	716	04	04	768	55	÷
665	43	RCL	717	65	×	769	43	RCL
666	13	13	718	43	RCL	770	08	08
667	58	FIX	719	09	09	771	55	÷
668	02	02	720	95	=	772	53	(
669	69	OP	721	42	STO	773	43	RCL
670	06	06	722	10	10	774	06	06
671	22	INV	723	92	RTN	775	85	+
672	58	FIX	724	76	LBL	776	04	4
673	69	OP	725	44	SUM	777	06	6
674	00	00	726	43	RCL	778	00	0
675	92	RTN	727	10	10	779	54	)
676	76	LBL	728	65	×	780	65	×
677	35	1/X	729	01	1	781	43	RCL
678	43	RCL	730	00	0	782	07	07
679	12	12	731	93	.	783	65	×
680	65	×	732	07	7	784	43	RCL
681	01	1	733	02	2	785	09	09
682	93	.	734	09	9	786	95	=
683	04	4	735	65	×	787	42	STO
684	04	4	736	43	RCL	788	10	10
685	52	EE	737	08	08	789	92	RTN
686	03	3	738	65	×	790	00	0
687	94	+/-	739	53	(	791	00	0
688	95	=	740	43	RCL	792	00	0
689	22	INV	741	06	06	793	00	0
690	52	EE	742	85	+	794	00	0
691	42	STO	743	04	4	795	00	0
692	13	13	744	06	6	796	00	0
693	43	RCL	745	00	0	797	00	0

Program 25

Efficiency Conversions

Background

It is often interesting, and sometimes necessary, to change the basis for an efficiency, either to gain more appreciation for its magnitude or to compare two vendors quoting on different bases.

Process compressors are normally quoted based on polytropic efficiency; air compressors, especially the low-head variety, on adiabatic efficiency; and fans on isometric efficiency. Consider a medium-head-requirement, high-volume-flow air compressor. One vendor may quote a process centrifugal compressor for which available data are in terms of polytropic efficiency. Another vendor may quote an axial compressor for which available data are in terms of adiabatic efficiency. The actual efficiency of the two vendors cannot be compared and checked unless the engineer has the ability to convert from one efficiency base to another.

The polytropic, adiabatic, and isometric efficiencies are related as follows:

$$\eta_{ad} = \frac{r_p^{(k-1)/k} - 1}{r_p^{(n-1)/n} - 1} \tag{25-1}$$

$$\eta_p = \frac{(k-1)[\log_e (r_p)]}{k \log_e \left[\dfrac{r_p^{(k-1)/k} - 1}{\eta_{ad}} + 1 \right]} \tag{25-2}$$

$$\eta_{ad} = \frac{\eta_{im}\, k(r_p^{(k-1)/k} - 1)}{(k-1)(r_p - 1)} \tag{25-3}$$

$$\eta_{im} = \frac{\eta_{ad}\,(k-1)(r_p - 1)}{k\,(r_p^{(k-1)/k} - 1)} \tag{25-4}$$

where:
η_{im} = isometric efficiency

The isometric efficiency assumes that the inlet volume flow equals the discharge volume flow, making the process incompressible. Thus, the isometric efficiency is only applicable to low-pressure-ratio fans.

Program 25 Description

Efficiency Conversions, Program 25, calculates and prints the results of Equations 25-1, 25-2, 25-3, and 25-4.
In order to execute the program, the following must be known:

1. Inlet pressure, P_1
2. Discharge pressure, P_2
3. Average k-value, k_a
4. Inlet temperature, T_1
5. Specified efficiency, η_p, η_{ad}, or η_{im}

The program provides an option to enter the pressure ratio, r_p, instead of the inlet and discharge pressures.
If the specified efficiency is adiabatic, the program can convert the efficiency to either polytropic or polytropic and isometric. The latter option would be used for low-pressure-ratio fans, the former for all other applications.
The program is set up for continuous usage, without the need for complete data reentry, except when the inlet and discharge pressures entry option is used. The discharge pressure can be varied without reentering the inlet pressure. However, if the inlet pressure is changed, the discharge pressure must be reentered. Otherwise, only the parameters of interest need be changed.
Table 25-1 is the nomenclature printed by the program; Table 25-2 shows the data registers used by the program.

Table 25-1
Program 25: Printer Nomenclature

Program Term	Definition	Units
EFFA	adiabatic efficiency	dimensionless
EFFM	isometric efficiency	dimensionless
EFFP	polytropic efficiency	dimensionless
KA	average ratio of specific heats	dimensionless
RP	pressure ratio	dimensionless
T1	inlet temperature	°F
T2	discharge temperature	°F

Table 25-2
Data Registers Used by Program 25

00	not used	05	r_p	10	η_{im}
01	not used	06	k_a	11	$r_p^{(k-1)/k} - 1$
02	not used	07	T_1	12	$(k-1)/k$
03	P_1	08	η_p	13	$(n-1)/n$
04	P_2	09	η_{ad}	14	T_2

Labels Used by Program 25

001	11	A
006	12	B
017	13	C
022	14	D
036	15	E
046	16	A'
099	17	B'
151	19	D'
179	18	C'
210	33	X²
344	34	⌈X

Program 25 Usage

Program 25 is executed by using the user-defined keys. The definitions for the user-defined keys can be found in Table 25-3.

Either the inlet and discharge pressures must be entered through user-defined keys A and B, respectively, or the pressure ratio must be entered through C. If the inlet and discharge pressures are entered, the inlet pressure must be entered first.

Table 25-3
Program 25: Definitions of User-Defined Keys

A	P1	A'	η_p to η_{ad}
B	P2	B'	η_{ad} to η_p
C	RP	C'	η_{im} to η_{ad} and η_p
D	KA	D'	η_{ad} to η_{im} and η_p
E	T1		

After entering the inlet and discharge pressures (or the pressure ratio), the average k-value, and the inlet temperature, the efficiency is entered through the user-defined key specified in Table 25-3. Note that the adiabatic efficiency can be entered through two user-defined keys. B' is used when only the polytropic efficiency is desired; D' is used when both the polytropic and isometric efficiencies are desired.

Subsequent conversions can be made by changing only the pertinent data. Note, however, that when the inlet pressure is changed, the discharge pressure must be reentered.

Sample Problem 25-1

Given the following:

$P_1 = 15$ psia
$P_2 = 45$ psia
$k_a = 1.3$
$T_1 = 100°F$

convert a polytropic efficiency of 78% to adiabatic efficiency.

Sample Problem 25-1: User Instructions

Step	Procedure	Enter	Press	Display
1.	Load program.			
2.	Enter inlet pressure.	15	A	15
3.	Enter discharge pressure.	45	B	3 (r_p)
4.	Enter average k-value.	1.3	D	$.2307\dots\left(\dfrac{k-1}{k}\right)$
5.	Enter inlet temperature.	100(°F)	E	560(°R)
6.	Enter polytropic efficiency as a fraction and calculate.	0.78	2nd A'	

Sample Problem 25-1: Program Printout

```
EFFICIENCY          315.      T2

3.000      RP      0.751    EFFA
 100.      T1      0.780    EFFP
  1.3      KA
```

Sample Problem 25-2

Given the following:

$$r_p = 1.15$$
$$k_a = 1.4$$
$$T_1 = 90°F$$

convert an isometric efficiency of 85% to adiabatic efficiency and polytropic efficiency.

Sample Problem 25-2: User Instructions

Step	Procedure	Enter	Press	Display
1.	Load program.			
2.	Enter pressure ratio.	1.15	C	1.15
3.	Enter average k-value.	1.4	D	$.2857\ldots\left(\dfrac{k-1}{k}\right)$
4.	Enter inlet temperature.	90(°F)	E	550(°R)
5.	Enter isometric efficiency as a fraction and calculate.	0.85	2nd C'	

Sample Problem 25-2: Program Printout

```
EFFICIENCY

1.150      RP      118.      T2
  90.      T1
  1.4      KA
                   0.808    EFFA
                   0.812    EFFP
                   0.850    EFFM
```

Program 25 Listing

000	76	LBL	050	43	RCL	100	42	STO
001	11	A	051	12	12	101	09	09
002	42	STO	052	35	1/X	102	43	RCL
003	03	03	053	95	=	103	05	05
004	91	R/S	054	35	1/X	104	45	Y×
005	76	LBL	055	42	STO	105	43	RCL
006	12	B	056	13	13	106	12	12
007	42	STO	057	43	RCL	107	75	-
008	04	04	058	05	05	108	01	1
009	55	÷	059	45	Y×	109	95	=
010	43	RCL	060	43	RCL	110	42	STO
011	03	03	061	12	12	111	11	11
012	95	=	062	75	-	112	55	÷
013	42	STO	063	01	1	113	43	RCL
014	05	05	064	95	=	114	09	09
015	91	R/S	065	42	STO	115	95	=
016	76	LBL	066	11	11	116	85	+
017	13	C	067	55	÷	117	01	1
018	42	STO	068	53	(	118	95	=
019	05	05	069	43	RCL	119	23	LNX
020	91	R/S	070	05	05	120	55	÷
021	76	LBL	071	45	Y×	121	43	RCL
022	14	D	072	43	RCL	122	05	05
023	42	STO	073	13	13	123	23	LNX
024	06	06	074	75	-	124	95	=
025	75	-	075	01	1	125	35	1/X
026	01	1	076	54	)	126	65	×
027	95	=	077	95	=	127	43	RCL
028	55	÷	078	42	STO	128	12	12
029	43	RCL	079	09	09	129	95	=
030	06	06	080	43	RCL	130	42	STO
031	95	=	081	11	11	131	08	08
032	42	STO	082	65	×	132	43	RCL
033	12	12	083	43	RCL	133	11	11
034	91	R/S	084	07	07	134	65	×
035	76	LBL	085	55	÷	135	43	RCL
036	15	E	086	43	RCL	136	07	07
037	85	+	087	09	09	137	55	÷
038	04	4	088	95	=	138	43	RCL
039	06	6	089	85	+	139	09	09
040	00	0	090	43	RCL	140	95	=
041	95	=	091	07	07	141	85	+
042	42	STO	092	95	=	142	43	RCL
043	07	07	093	42	STO	143	07	07
044	91	R/S	094	14	14	144	95	=
045	76	LBL	095	71	SBR	145	42	STO
046	16	A'	096	33	X²	146	14	14
047	42	STO	097	91	R/S	147	71	SBR
048	08	08	098	76	LBL	148	33	X²
049	65	×	099	17	B'	149	92	RTN

Program 25 Listing continued

150	76	LBL	200	05	05	250	43	RCL
151	19	D'	201	75	-	251	05	05
152	17	B'	202	01	1	252	58	FIX
153	43	RCL	203	54	)	253	03	03
154	11	11	204	95	=	254	69	OP
155	65	×	205	17	B'	255	06	06
156	43	RCL	206	71	SBR	256	22	INV
157	12	12	207	34	ΓX	257	58	FIX
158	35	1/X	208	91	R/S	258	03	3
159	95	=	209	76	LBL	259	07	7
160	35	1/X	210	33	X²	260	00	0
161	65	×	211	98	ADV	261	02	2
162	53	(	212	69	OP	262	69	OP
163	43	RCL	213	00	00	263	04	04
164	05	05	214	01	1	264	43	RCL
165	75	-	215	07	7	265	07	07
166	01	1	216	02	2	266	75	-
167	54	)	217	01	1	267	04	4
168	95	=	218	02	2	268	06	6
169	65	×	219	01	1	269	00	0
170	43	RCL	220	02	2	270	95	=
171	09	09	221	04	4	271	69	OP
172	95	=	222	01	1	272	06	06
173	42	STO	223	05	5	273	02	2
174	10	10	224	69	OP	274	06	6
175	71	SBR	225	02	02	275	01	1
176	34	ΓX	226	02	2	276	03	3
177	91	R/S	227	04	4	277	69	OP
178	76	LBL	228	01	1	278	04	04
179	18	C'	229	07	7	279	43	RCL
180	42	STO	230	03	3	280	06	06
181	10	10	231	01	1	281	69	OP
182	43	RCL	232	01	1	282	06	06
183	05	05	233	05	5	283	98	ADV
184	45	Y×	234	04	4	284	03	3
185	43	RCL	235	05	5	285	07	7
186	12	12	236	69	OP	286	00	0
187	75	-	237	03	03	287	03	3
188	01	1	238	69	OP	288	69	OP
189	95	=	239	05	05	289	04	04
190	65	×	240	69	OP	290	43	RCL
191	43	RCL	241	00	00	291	14	14
192	12	12	242	98	ADV	292	75	-
193	35	1/X	243	98	ADV	293	04	4
194	65	×	244	03	3	294	06	6
195	43	RCL	245	05	5	295	00	0
196	10	10	246	03	3	296	95	=
197	55	÷	247	03	3	297	58	FIX
198	53	(	248	69	OP	298	00	00
199	43	RCL	249	04	04	299	69	OP

(continued on next page)

Program 25 Listing continued

300	06	06	323	07	7	346	07	7
301	22	INV	324	02	2	347	02	2
302	58	FIX	325	01	1	348	01	1
303	98	ADV	326	02	2	349	02	2
304	01	1	327	01	1	350	01	1
305	07	7	328	03	3	351	03	3
306	02	2	329	03	3	352	00	0
307	01	1	330	69	OP	353	69	OP
308	02	2	331	04	04	354	04	04
309	01	1	332	43	RCL	355	43	RCL
310	01	1	333	08	08	356	10	10
311	03	3	334	58	FIX	357	58	FIX
312	69	OP	335	03	03	358	03	03
313	04	04	336	69	OP	359	69	OP
314	43	RCL	337	06	06	360	06	06
315	09	09	338	22	INV	361	22	INV
316	58	FIX	339	58	FIX	362	58	FIX
317	03	03	340	69	OP	363	69	OP
318	69	OP	341	00	00	364	00	00
319	06	06	342	92	RTN	365	92	RTN
320	22	INV	343	76	LBL	366	00	0
321	58	FIX	344	34	ΓX	367	00	0
322	01	1	345	01	1	368	00	0

Program 26

Compressor Efficiency from Specific Speed

Background

Baljé* presented the efficiency map shown in Figure 26-1 as a means of relating compressor efficiency to the similarity parameters specific speed and specific diameter.

The specific speed and specific diameter are defined by Equations 26-1 and 26-2, respectively:

$$N_{ss} = \frac{N \sqrt{Q_1/60}}{H_{ad}^{0.75}} \tag{26-1}$$

$$D_{sd} = \frac{d_w H_{ad}^{0.25}}{12 \sqrt{Q_1/60}} \tag{26-2}$$

where:
N_{ss} = specific speed
D_{sd} = specific diameter
N = rotational speed, rpm
Q_1 = inlet volume flow, ICFM
H_{ad} = adiabatic head, ft-lbf/lbm
d_w = impeller diameter, inches

---

*Baljé, O. E., "A Study on Design Criteria and Matching of Turbomachines: Part B—Compressor and Pump Performance and Matching of Turbocomponents," *Journal of Engineering for Power*, Transactions of the ASME, Series A, Vol. 84, 1962, pp. 103–114.

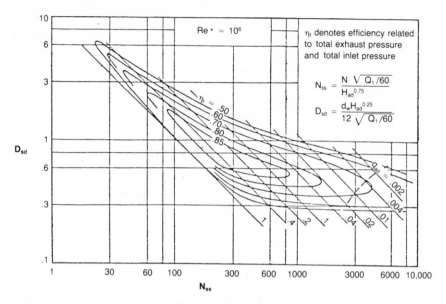

Figure 26-1. Baljé specific speed-specific diameter diagram for centrifugal compressor efficiency. (Reprinted by permission of ASME, *Journal of Engineering for Power,* Transactions of ASME, Series A, Vol. 84, 1962, p. 107.)

The Baljé diagram can be used to estimate the expected efficiency from a centrifugal compressor or to compare specific speeds and specific diameters between manufacturers for optimum selection with regards to efficiency.

Even though the Baljé chart is based on adiabatic head, the pressure ratio from a single stage of a centrifugal compressor is low enough that the difference between the polytropic and adiabatic heads and efficiencies are usually within the tolerance of this diagram. Therefore, it is suggested that either the polytropic or the adiabatic head be used to calculate the specific speed and specific diameter, and that the efficiency, η_t, be read directly as polytropic or adiabatic efficiency, respectively.

For multi-stage centrifugal compressors, the specific speed and specific diameter is based on the polytropic head produced by each impeller. Furthermore, a rigorous analysis requires that the efficiency for each stage be determined from the inlet volume flow to that stage. However, a reasonable compromise at average efficiency can be obtained by estimating the polytropic head per stage from Program 4 and calculating an average inlet volume flow from Equation 26-3:

$$Q_{1a} = \frac{Q_1 + Q_2}{2}$$

(26-3)

where:

Q_{1a} = average inlet volume flow

The polytropic head per stage and the average inlet volume flow are then used to calculate the specific speed and specific diameter needed to estimate the efficiency from Figure 26-1.

The efficiency read from Figure 26-1 should probably be reduced two to four points to account for internal losses due to recirculation, and for the fact that the impeller will not be specifically "designed" for the application.

Program 26 Description

Program 26, Compressor Efficiency from Specific Speed, calculates and prints the results of Equations 26-1 and 26-2.

In order to execute the program, the following must be known:

1. Average inlet volume flow, Q_{1a}
2. Polytropic head per stage, H_p/stage, or adiabatic head, H_{ad}
3. Impeller (wheel) diameter, d_w
4. Rotational speed, N

The average inlet volume flow can be calculated from Equation 26-3. Note that for single-stage compressors the average inlet volume flow is identical to the compressor inlet volume flow.

The polytropic head per stage can be estimated from Program 4. In order to do this, Program 2 or 3 would have had to be run with an estimated efficiency. For single-stage compressors the adiabatic head is used instead of the polytropic head per stage.

The program is set up for continuous usage, without the need for complete data reentry. Therefore, only the parameters of interest need be changed.

Table 26-1 is the nomenclature printed by the program; Table 26-2 shows the data registers used by the program.

Labels Used by Program 26

```
001   11   A
006   12   B
011   13   C
016   14   D
021   15   E
```

Table 26-1
Program 26: Printer Nomenclature

Program Term	Definition	Units
D	impeller diameter	inches
DSD	specific diameter	similarity parameter
H/ST	polytropic head per stage	ft-lbf/lbm
N	rotational speed	rpm
NSS	specific speed	similarity parameter
Q1A	average inlet volume flow	ICFM

Table 26-2
Data Registers Used by Program 26

00	not used	04	H_p/stage	08	N_{ss}
01	not used	05	d_w	09	D_{sd}
02	not used	06	N		
03	Q_{1a}	07	$\sqrt{Q_1/60}$		

Table 26-3
Program 26: Definitions of User-Defined Keys

A	Q1A	D	N
B	H/ST	E	Calculate
C	D		

Program 26 Usage

Program 26 is executed by using the user-defined keys, the definitions of which can be found in Table 26-3.

After all the data are entered, program execution is initiated through user-defined key E. Subsequent calculations can be made by changing only the parameters of interest.

Sample Problem 26-1

Given the following:

$$Q_{1a} = 20,000 \text{ ICFM}$$
$$H_p/\text{stage} = 10,000 \text{ ft-lbf/lbm}$$
$$d_w = 30 \text{ inches}$$
$$N = 5900 \text{ rpm}$$

calculate the specific speed and specific diameter.

Sample Problem 26-1: User Instructions

Step	Procedure	Enter	Press	Display
1.	Load program.			
2.	Enter average inlet volume flow.	20000	A	20000
3.	Enter polytropic head per stage.	10000	B	10000
4.	Enter impeller diameter.	30	C	30
5.	Enter rotational speed.	5900	D	5900
6.	Calculate.		E	

Sample Problem 26-1: Program Printout

```
EFF - SPECIFIC SPEED


      20000.      Q1A          108.      NSS
      10000.      H/ST         1.37      DSD
         30.      D
       5900.      N
```

Program 26 Listing

000	76	LBL	017	42	STD	034	43	RCL
001	11	A	018	06	06	035	07	07
002	42	STD	019	91	R/S	036	55	÷
003	03	03	020	76	LBL	037	43	RCL
004	91	R/S	021	15	E	038	04	04
005	76	LBL	022	43	RCL	039	45	Y*
006	12	B	023	03	03	040	93	.
007	42	STD	024	55	÷	041	07	7
008	04	04	025	06	6	042	05	5
009	91	R/S	026	00	0	043	95	=
010	76	LBL	027	95	=	044	42	STD
011	13	C	028	34	ΓX	045	08	08
012	42	STD	029	42	STD	046	43	RCL
013	05	05	030	07	07	047	05	05
014	91	R/S	031	43	RCL	048	65	×
015	76	LBL	032	06	06	049	43	RCL
016	14	D	033	65	×	050	04	04

(continued on next page)

Program 26 Listing continued

051	45	YˣX	102	06	6	153	03	3
052	93	.	103	03	3	154	01	1
053	02	2	104	03	3	155	69	OP
054	05	5	105	01	1	156	04	04
055	55	÷	106	07	7	157	43	RCL
056	43	RCL	107	01	1	158	06	06
057	07	07	108	07	7	159	69	OP
058	55	÷	109	01	1	160	06	06
059	01	1	110	06	6	161	98	ADV
060	02	2	111	69	OP	162	03	3
061	95	=	112	04	04	163	01	1
062	42	STO	113	69	OP	164	03	3
063	09	09	114	05	05	165	06	6
064	98	ADV	115	69	OP	166	03	3
065	69	OP	116	00	00	167	06	6
066	00	00	117	98	ADV	168	69	OP
067	01	1	118	98	ADV	169	04	04
068	07	7	119	03	3	170	43	RCL
069	02	2	120	04	4	171	08	08
070	01	1	121	00	0	172	58	FIX
071	02	2	122	02	2	173	00	00
072	01	1	123	01	1	174	69	OP
073	00	0	124	03	3	175	06	06
074	00	0	125	69	OP	176	22	INV
075	02	2	126	04	04	177	58	FIX
076	00	0	127	43	RCL	178	01	1
077	69	OP	128	03	03	179	06	6
078	01	01	129	69	OP	180	03	3
079	03	3	130	06	06	181	06	6
080	06	6	131	02	2	182	01	1
081	03	3	132	03	3	183	06	6
082	03	3	133	06	6	184	69	OP
083	01	1	134	03	3	185	04	04
084	07	7	135	03	3	186	43	RCL
085	01	1	136	06	6	187	09	09
086	05	5	137	03	3	188	58	FIX
087	69	OP	138	07	7	189	02	02
088	02	02	139	69	OP	190	69	OP
089	02	2	140	04	04	191	06	06
090	04	4	141	43	RCL	192	22	INV
091	02	2	142	04	04	193	58	FIX
092	01	1	143	69	OP	194	69	OP
093	02	2	144	06	06	195	00	00
094	04	4	145	01	1	196	91	R/S
095	01	1	146	06	6	197	00	0
096	05	5	147	69	OP	198	00	0
097	00	0	148	04	04	199	00	0
098	00	0	149	43	RCL	200	00	0
099	69	OP	150	05	05	201	00	0
100	03	03	151	69	OP	202	00	0
101	03	3	152	06	06	203	00	0

Program 27

Compressor Inlet Nozzle Velocity

Background

An inlet nozzle must be sized to obtain a low enough inlet velocity in order to maintain a reasonable inlet pressure drop and a good flow distribution into the eye of the first impeller. It is good practice to check inlet velocities of compressors quoted by vendors.

The inlet velocity is given by Equation 27-1:

$$V_a = \frac{Q_1}{60\,A} \tag{27-1}$$

where:
  V_a = actual inlet velocity, ft/sec
  A = area of the inlet nozzle, ft^2

The area of the inlet nozzle is in turn given by Equation 27-2:

$$A = \frac{\pi}{4}\left[\frac{d_n}{12}\right]^2 \tag{27-2}$$

where:
  π = mathematical pi, 3.14159
  d_n = inlet nozzle diameter, inches

A good rule of thumb is to set the maximum inlet velocity at 140 ft/sec for air and lighter gases.

Since high inlet Mach numbers lead to poor flow distribution, the maximum inlet velocity for heavier gases and for processes with low inlet temperatures must be reduced. The Mach-number effect is best handled by comparing the sonic velocity of the subject gas to the sonic velocity of air at 80°F. Consider Equation 2-14, which was used to determine the maximum polytropic head per stage:

$$\theta = \sqrt{\frac{26.1\,MW}{k_1 Z_1 T_1}} \tag{2-14}$$

The inverse of Equation 2-14, coupled with the maximum inlet velocity of 140 ft/sec for air and lighter gases, establishes the maximum inlet velocity for any case:

$$V_{max} = 140\sqrt{\frac{k_1 Z_1 T_1}{26.1\,MW}} \leq 140 \text{ ft/sec} \tag{27-3}$$

where:
V_{max} = maximum acceptable inlet velocity, ft/sec

Note that Equation 27-3 is not an absolute equation. Inlet velocities above V_{max} may be satisfactory with good, sound, inlet piping, but they should be avoided if possible. If the inlet velocity approaches or exceeds V_{max}, the vendor should be asked to review the inlet piping for his recommendation.

Program 27 Description

Compressor Inlet Nozzle Velocity, Program 27, calculates and prints the results of Equations 27-1 and 27-3.

In order to execute the program, the following must be known:

1. Inlet volume flow, Q_1
2. Inlet nozzle diameter, d_n
3. Inlet temperature, T_1
4. Molecular weight, MW
5. Inlet k-value, k_1
6. Inlet Z-value, Z_1

The program calculates the actual inlet velocity and the maximum inlet velocity for the gas conditions and compares the two. If the actual inlet velocity exceeds the maximum allowable, the program prints the warning

VELOCITY TOO HIGH and proceeds to calculate a minimum satisfactory inlet nozzle diameter, d_{min}.

Program 27 is set up for continuous usage, without, the need for complete data reentry. Therefore, only the parameters of interest need to be reentered.

Table 27-1 is the nomenclature printed by the program; Table 27-2 shows the data registers used by the program.

Table 27-1
Program 27: Printer Nomenclature

Program Term	Definition	Units
DMIN	minimum acceptable inlet nozzle diameter	inches
DN	actual inlet nozzle diameter	inches
K1	inlet ratio of specific heats	dimensionless
MW	molecular weight	lbm/lbm-mol
Q1	inlet volume flow	ICFM
T1	inlet temperature	°F
VEL	actual inlet velocity	ft/sec
VMAX	maximum acceptable inlet velocity	ft/sec
Z1	inlet compressibility	dimensionless

Table 27-2
Data Registers Used by Program 27

00	not used	05	T_1	10	V_{max}
01	not used	06	MW	11	$\sqrt{(k_1 Z_1 T_1)/(26.1\,MW)}$
02	not used	07	k_1	12	d_{min}
03	Q_1	08	Z_1		
04	d_n	09	V_a		

Labels Used by Program 27

001	11	A	031	18	C'
006	12	B	036	15	E
011	13	C	099	34	ΓX
021	16	A'	350	33	X^2
026	17	B'	360	35	$1/X$

Program 27 Usage

Program 27 is executed by using the user-defined keys. The definitions for these can be found in Table 27-3.

Table 27-3
Program 27: Definitions of User-Defined Keys

A	Q1		A′	MW
B	DN		B′	K1
C	T1		C′	Z1
E	Calculate			

After all the data are entered, program execution is initiated through user-defined key E. Subsequent calculations can be made by changing only the parameters of interest.

Sample Problem 27-1

Consider the following:

$$Q_1 = 25,000 \text{ ICFM}$$
$$T_1 = -50°F$$
$$MW = 44.0$$
$$k_1 = 1.15$$
$$Z_1 = 0.98$$

Check the adequacy of inlet nozzles with diameters of 24 inches and 30 inches.

Sample Problem 27-1: User Instructions

Step	Procedure	Enter	Press	Display
1.	Load program.			
2.	Enter inlet volume flow.	25000	A	25000
3.	Enter inlet nozzle diameter.	24	B	24
4.	Enter inlet temperature.	−50(°F)	C	410(°R)
5.	Enter molecular weight.	44	2nd A′	44
6.	Enter inlet k-value.	1.15	2nd B′	1.15
7.	Enter inlet Z-value.	0.98	2nd C′	0.98
8.	Calculate.		E	
9.	Enter new inlet nozzle diameter.	30	B	30
10.	Calculate.		E	

Sample Problem 27-1: Program Printout

```
NOZZLE VELOCITY              NOZZLE VELOCITY


    25000.      Q1              25000.      Q1
       24.      DN                 30.      DN
      -50.      T1                -50.      T1
       44.      MW                 44.      MW
      1.15      K1                1.15      K1
      0.98      Z1                0.98      Z1


     132.6     VEL                84.9     VEL
      88.8     VMAX               88.8     VMAX


**VELOCITY TOO HIGH*

      29.3     DMIN
```

Program 27 Listing

000	76	LBL	023	06	06	046	89	π
001	11	A	024	91	R/S	047	65	×
002	42	STO	025	76	LBL	048	04	4
003	03	03	026	17	B'	049	55	÷
004	91	R/S	027	42	STO	050	53	(
005	76	LBL	028	07	07	051	43	RCL
006	12	B	029	91	R/S	052	04	04
007	42	STO	030	76	LBL	053	55	÷
008	04	04	031	18	C'	054	01	1
009	91	R/S	032	42	STO	055	02	2
010	76	LBL	033	08	08	056	54	)
011	13	C	034	91	R/S	057	33	X^2
012	85	+	035	76	LBL	058	95	=
013	04	4	036	15	E	059	42	STO
014	06	6	037	69	OP	060	09	09
015	00	0	038	00	00	061	43	RCL
016	95	=	039	98	ADV	062	07	07
017	42	STO	040	43	RCL	063	65	×
018	05	05	041	55	÷	064	43	RCL
019	91	R/S	042	55	÷	065	08	08
020	76	LBL	043	06	6	066	65	×
021	16	A'	044	00	0	067	43	RCL
022	42	STO	045	55	÷	068	05	05

(continued on next page)

Program 27 Listing continued

069	55	÷	119	02	2	169	07	7
070	02	2	120	01	1	170	00	0
071	06	6	121	07	7	171	02	2
072	93	.	122	02	2	172	69	OP
073	01	1	123	07	7	173	04	04
074	55	÷	124	03	3	174	43	RCL
075	43	RCL	125	02	2	175	05	05
076	06	06	126	01	1	176	75	-
077	95	=	127	05	5	177	04	4
078	34	ΓX	128	69	OP	178	06	6
079	42	STO	129	03	03	179	00	0
080	11	11	130	02	2	180	95	=
081	01	1	131	04	4	181	69	OP
082	32	X:T	132	03	3	182	06	06
083	43	RCL	133	07	7	183	03	3
084	11	11	134	04	4	184	00	0
085	77	GE	135	05	5	185	04	4
086	33	X^2	136	00	0	186	03	3
087	43	RCL	137	00	0	187	69	OP
088	11	11	138	00	0	188	04	04
089	65	×	139	00	0	189	43	RCL
090	01	1	140	69	OP	190	06	06
091	04	4	141	04	04	191	69	OP
092	00	0	142	69	OP	192	06	06
093	95	=	143	05	05	193	02	2
094	42	STO	144	69	OP	194	06	6
095	10	10	145	00	00	195	00	0
096	71	SBR	146	98	ADV	196	02	2
097	34	ΓX	147	98	ADV	197	69	OP
098	76	LBL	148	03	3	198	04	04
099	34	ΓX	149	04	4	199	43	RCL
100	03	3	150	00	0	200	07	07
101	01	1	151	02	2	201	69	OP
102	03	3	152	69	OP	202	06	06
103	02	2	153	04	04	203	04	4
104	69	OP	154	43	RCL	204	06	6
105	01	01	155	03	03	205	00	0
106	04	4	156	69	OP	206	02	2
107	06	6	157	06	06	207	69	OP
108	04	4	158	01	1	208	04	04
109	06	6	159	06	6	209	43	RCL
110	02	2	160	03	3	210	08	08
111	07	7	161	01	1	211	69	OP
112	01	1	162	69	OP	212	06	06
113	07	7	163	04	04	213	98	ADV
114	00	0	164	43	RCL	214	04	4
115	00	0	165	04	04	215	02	2
116	69	OP	166	69	OP	216	01	1
117	02	02	167	06	06	217	07	7
118	04	4	168	03	3	218	02	2

Program 27 Listing continued

219	07	7	269	34	ГX	319	05	5
220	69	OP	270	65	×	320	01	1
221	04	04	271	01	1	321	69	OP
222	43	RCL	272	02	2	322	04	04
223	09	09	273	95	=	323	69	OP
224	58	FIX	274	42	STO	324	05	05
225	01	01	275	12	12	325	69	OP
226	69	OP	276	98	ADV	326	00	00
227	06	06	277	05	5	327	98	ADV
228	22	INV	278	01	1	328	01	1
229	58	FIX	279	05	5	329	06	6
230	04	4	280	01	1	330	03	3
231	02	2	281	04	4	331	00	0
232	03	3	282	02	2	332	02	2
233	00	0	283	01	1	333	04	4
234	01	1	284	07	7	334	03	3
235	03	3	285	02	2	335	01	1
236	04	4	286	07	7	336	69	OP
237	04	4	287	69	OP	337	04	04
238	69	OP	288	01	01	338	43	RCL
239	04	04	289	03	3	339	12	12
240	43	RCL	290	02	2	340	58	FIX
241	10	10	291	01	1	341	01	01
242	58	FIX	292	05	5	342	69	OP
243	01	01	293	02	2	343	06	06
244	69	OP	294	04	4	344	22	INV
245	06	06	295	03	3	345	58	FIX
246	22	INV	296	07	7	346	69	OP
247	58	FIX	297	04	4	347	00	00
248	43	RCL	298	05	5	348	91	R/S
249	10	10	299	69	OP	349	76	LBL
250	32	X:T	300	02	02	350	33	X²
251	43	RCL	301	03	3	351	01	1
252	09	09	302	07	7	352	04	4
253	22	INV	303	03	3	353	00	0
254	77	GE	304	02	2	354	42	STO
255	35	1/X	305	03	3	355	10	10
256	43	RCL	306	02	2	356	71	SBR
257	03	03	307	00	0	357	34	ГX
258	55	÷	308	00	0	358	92	RTN
259	06	6	309	69	OP	359	76	LBL
260	00	0	310	03	03	360	35	1/X
261	55	÷	311	02	2	361	91	R/S
262	43	RCL	312	03	3	362	92	RTN
263	10	10	313	02	2	363	00	0
264	65	×	314	04	4	364	00	0
265	04	4	315	02	2	365	00	0
266	55	÷	316	02	2	366	00	0
267	89	π	317	02	2	367	00	0
268	95	=	318	03	3	368	00	0

Program 28

Thrust-Error Analysis

Background

Impeller thrust results from the differential pressure distribution between the back and front faces of the impeller. Since the pressure is higher on the back face of the impeller, the impeller thrust always acts toward the inlet of the impeller. The rotor thrust is the algebraic sum of the individual impeller thrusts.

The thrust of each impeller is a function of its area, the pressure rise across the impeller, and an empirically determined thrust factor, which is a function of impeller geometry. Since only the manufacturer knows the thrust factors, and since they will vary greatly from one impeller to another, even within a manufacturer's line, there is no real way for the purchaser's engineer to estimate rotor thrust with any degree of accuracy.

Manufacturers usually install a balance piston to compensate for a large amount of the rotor thrust, normally on the order of 75%. The compensating thrust resulting from the balance piston is a function of its area and, in most cases, the pressure rise across the entire compressor, and it acts toward compressor discharge.

While there is no real way for the purchaser's engineer to estimate net rotor thrust, it is necessary that he be able to analyze the thrust bearing selected by the manufacturer. This is easily accomplished with data that the manufacturer should provide on the API 617 Fourth Edition, data sheets.

The accuracy of the manufacturer's calculated rotor thrust is highly dependent on the accuracy of the empirically determined thrust factors. As a result, it is not beyond reason for the calculated rotor thrust to be in error by as much as ±10%. Once the balance piston is sized, it will compensate for a fixed amount of thrust, depending only on its area and the pressure differential across the compressor. Any additional thrust, including any error in calculated rotor thrust, must be accommodated by the thrust bearing. It is the effect of this potential error on thrust bearing loading that the engineer can and should analyze.

The force on the thrust bearing is given by Equation 28-1:

$$F_{tb} = P_{tb}A_{tb} \tag{28-1}$$

where:

F_{tb} = thrust bearing load, lbf
P_{tb} = thrust bearing pressure, tabulated on the API 617 data sheets, psi
A_{tb} = active area of the thrust bearing, tabulated on the API 617 data sheets, in.^{2}

The total rotor thrust calculated by the manufacturer is given by Equation 28-2:

$$F_r = F_{tb} + F_{bp} \tag{28-2}$$

where:

F_r = total rotor thrust calculated by the manufacturer, lbf
F_{bp} = balance piston compensating load, tabulated on the API 617 data sheets, lbf

A positive 10% error would raise the thrust bearing pressure according to Equation 28-3:

$$(P_{tb})_{+10\%F_r} = \frac{1.1\,F_r - F_{bp}}{A_{tb}} \tag{28-3}$$

A negative 10% error would lower the thrust bearing pressure according to Equation 28-4:

$$(P_{tb})_{-10\%F_r} = \frac{\left(\dfrac{F_r}{1.1}\right) - F_{bp}}{A_{tb}} \tag{28-4}$$

Equations 28-3 and 28-4 will normally bracket the range of the actual thrust bearing pressure. The maximum value from Equation 28-3 can then be compared to the thrust bearing manufacturer's rating.

Program 28 Description

Thrust-Error Analysis, Program 28, calculates and prints the results of Equations 28-1, 28-2, 28-3, and 28-4.

In order to execute the program, the following must be known:

1. Thrust bearing pressure, P_{tb}
2. Active thrust bearing area, A_{tb}
3. Balance piston compensating load, F_{bp}

All of these can be obtained from the compressor manufacturer and should be tabulated on the data sheet.

The program calculates the thrust bearing pressure resulting from both a $+10\%$ error in calculated rotor thrust and a -10% error.

Program 28 is set up for continuous usage, without the need for complete data reentry. Therefore, only the parameters of interest need to be reentered.

Table 28-1 is the nomenclature printed by the program; Table 28-2 shows the data registers used by the program.

Table 28-1
Program 28: Printer Nomenclature

Program Term	Definition	Units
ATB	active area of thrust bearing	in.^{2}
FBP	balance piston compensating load	lbf
FR	total rotor thrust	lbf
FTP	thrust bearing load	lbf
PTB	thrust bearing pressure	psi

Table 28-2
Data Registers Used by Program 28

00	not used	04	A_{tb}	08	P_{tb} with $\pm 10\%$ error
01	not used	05	F_{bp}	09	PTB (title)
02	not used	06	F_{tb}	10	10% (title)
03	P_{tb}	07	F_r		

Table 28-3
Program 28: Definitions of User-Defined Keys

A	PTB		C	FBP
B	ATB		E	Calculate

Lables Used by Program 28

```
001   11   A
006   12   B
011   13   C
016   15   E
210   33   X²
```

Program 28 Usage

Program 28 is executed by using the user-defined keys, the definitions for which can be found in Table 28-3.

After entering all the data, program execution is initiated through user-defined key E. Subsequent calculations can be made by changing only the parameters of interest.

Sample Problem 28-1

Given the following information on the API 617 data sheets:

$$P_{tb} = 150 \text{ psi}$$
$$A_{tb} = 50 \text{ in}^2$$
$$F_{bp} = 22{,}500 \text{ lbf}$$

calculate the thrust bearing pressure resulting from both a $+10\%$ error and a -10% error in the calculated rotor thrust.

Sample Problem 28-1: User Instructions

Step	Procedure	Enter	Press	Display
1.	Load program.			
2.	Enter thrust bearing pressure.	150	A	150
3.	Enter thrust bearing area.	50	B	50
4.	Enter balance piston compensating load.	22500	C	22500
5.	Calculate.		E	

Sample Problem 28-1: Program Printout

```
THRUST ERROR


      150.       PTB
       50.       ATB     FR + 10%
   22500.        FBP              210.0        PTB
    7500.        FTB

                         FR - 10%
   30000.        FR               95.5         PTB
```

Program 28 Listing

000	76	LBL	032	69	OP	064	69	OP
001	11	A	033	00	00	065	05	05
002	42	STO	034	03	3	066	69	OP
003	03	03	035	07	7	067	00	00
004	91	R/S	036	02	2	068	98	ADV
005	76	LBL	037	03	3	069	98	ADV
006	12	B	038	69	OP	070	03	3
007	42	STO	039	01	01	071	03	3
008	04	04	040	03	3	072	03	3
009	91	R/S	041	05	5	073	07	7
010	76	LBL	042	04	4	074	01	1
011	13	C	043	01	1	075	04	4
012	42	STO	044	03	3	076	42	STO
013	05	05	045	06	6	077	09	09
014	91	R/S	046	03	3	078	69	OP
015	76	LBL	047	07	7	079	04	04
016	15	E	048	00	0	080	43	RCL
017	43	RCL	049	00	0	081	03	03
018	03	03	050	69	OP	082	69	OP
019	65	×	051	02	02	083	06	06
020	43	RCL	052	01	1	084	01	1
021	04	04	053	07	7	085	03	3
022	95	=	054	03	3	086	03	3
023	42	STO	055	05	5	087	07	7
024	06	06	056	03	3	088	01	1
025	85	+	057	05	5	089	04	4
026	43	RCL	058	03	3	090	69	OP
027	05	05	059	02	2	091	04	04
028	95	=	060	03	3	092	43	RCL
029	42	STO	061	05	5	093	04	04
030	07	07	062	69	OP	094	69	OP
031	98	ADV	063	03	03	095	06	06

Program 28 Listing continued

096	02	2	145	03	3	194	10	10
097	01	1	146	05	5	195	69	OP
098	01	1	147	00	0	196	02	02
099	04	4	148	00	0	197	69	OP
100	03	3	149	04	4	198	05	05
101	03	3	150	07	7	199	43	RCL
102	69	OP	151	00	0	200	07	07
103	04	04	152	00	0	201	55	÷
104	43	RCL	153	69	OP	202	01	1
105	05	05	154	01	01	203	93	.
106	69	OP	155	00	0	204	01	1
107	06	06	156	02	2	205	75	-
108	02	2	157	00	0	206	71	SBR
109	01	1	158	01	1	207	33	X²
110	03	3	159	06	6	208	91	R/S
111	07	7	160	01	1	209	76	LBL
112	01	1	161	00	0	210	33	X²
113	04	4	162	00	0	211	43	RCL
114	69	OP	163	00	0	212	05	05
115	04	04	164	00	0	213	95	=
116	43	RCL	165	42	STO	214	55	÷
117	06	06	166	10	10	215	43	RCL
118	58	FIX	167	69	OP	216	04	04
119	00	00	168	02	02	217	95	=
120	69	OP	169	69	OP	218	42	STO
121	06	06	170	05	05	219	08	08
122	22	INV	171	43	RCL	220	43	RCL
123	58	FIX	172	07	07	221	09	09
124	98	ADV	173	65	×	222	69	OP
125	02	2	174	01	1	223	04	04
126	01	1	175	93	.	224	43	RCL
127	03	3	176	01	1	225	08	08
128	05	5	177	75	-	226	58	FIX
129	69	OP	178	71	SBR	227	01	01
130	04	04	179	33	X²	228	69	OP
131	43	RCL	180	98	ADV	229	06	06
132	07	07	181	02	2	230	22	INV
133	58	FIX	182	01	1	231	58	FIX
134	00	00	183	03	3	232	69	OP
135	69	OP	184	05	5	233	00	00
136	06	06	185	00	0	234	92	RTN
137	22	INV	186	00	0	235	00	0
138	58	FIX	187	02	2	236	00	0
139	69	OP	188	00	0	237	00	0
140	00	00	189	00	0	238	00	0
141	98	ADV	190	00	0	239	00	0
142	98	ADV	191	69	OP	240	00	0
143	02	2	192	01	01	241	00	0
144	01	1	193	43	RCL	242	00	0

Program 29

Labyrinth Leakage

Background

For some applications it is necessary to calculate the leakage through a labyrinth seal. Of most concern on a centrifugal compressor are the external seals and the balance piston seal.

The external seals of a centrifugal compressor are often buffered, i.e. some gas, either process gas or gas from an external source, is injected in the seal to prevent either the inward leakage of air or oil carryover along the shaft or the outward leakage of process gas. Consider the process air compressor. Discharge temperatures may reach 450°F. It is necessary to block the high-temperature discharge from the bearing housing to eliminate the possibility of auto ignition and a resulting catastrophy. In this case, buffer gas is used to prevent outward leakage of process gas.

If the process gas was toxic or combustible, buffer gas could also be used to prevent its outward leakage.

Consider a process having a sub-atmospheric inlet pressure where air would be considered a contaminant. In this case, buffer gas could be used to prevent the inward leakage of air.

Note that for whatever reason the buffer gas is used, it must be injected at a higher pressure than that which occurs at either side of the seal. (The common rule of thumb is to supply buffer gas at three to five psig above the highest sealed pressure). As a result, buffer gas will flow in both directions, toward the process and toward the bearing housing. The buffer gas must therefore be compatible with the process gas and cannot be toxic, combustible, or harmful in any way to the environment or to personnel. Note also that any buffer gas flowing toward the process on the inlet end of the compressor will affect performance and must be considered in the power requirement.

The other seal of concern is the balance piston labyrinth. Centrifugal compressors nearly always have a balance piston to compensate for a good portion of the rotor thrust. One side of the balance piston is essentially at discharge pressure. In order to obtain a pressure differential, and therefore a force opposing the rotor thrust, the other side is usually connected to the inlet of the compressor. Some leakage will occur across the balance piston seal and is normally referred to as balance piston flow or balance piston leakage. The magnitude of this leakage is the manufacturer's responsibility, and he must consider it in compressor selection and when calculating performance and power requirement. The purchaser's engineer may wish to check the leakage to see what power penalty is being paid for it.

Mark's Standard Handbook for Mechanical Engineers, Eighth Edition presents the following equation for the calculation of the leakage through a labyrinth seal on page 9-46 (note that some of the nomenclature has been changed):

$$m_l = 25C_L A_L \sqrt{\frac{(P_1/v_1)\,[1 - (P_2/P_1)^2]}{NTP - \log_e(P_2/P_1)}} \tag{29-1}$$

where:
m_l = leakage, lbm/hr
C_L = experimentally determined coefficient
A_L = flow area through the clearance space, in^2
P_1 = inlet pressure to the labyrinth, psia
P_2 = pressure downstream of the labyrinth, psia
v_1 = inlet specific volume to the labyrinth, ft^3/lbm
NTP = number of throttling points, i.e. the number of labyrinth teeth between the point of gas entry and the point gas exhaust

Mark's Handbook suggests that the value of C_L is on the order of 50 for interlocking labryrinths, regardless of clearance. For non-interlocking labyrinths, *Mark's Handbook* suggests that the value of C_L is on the order of 120 when the tooth spacing is 5 times the radial clearance, and that it is reduced to 50 when the tooth spacing is 50 times the radial clearance.

If one assumes that C_L varies linearly between the end points given for non-interlocking seals, the following equations can be derived for labyrinth leakage:

For non-interlocking seals:

$$m_l = 0.4\left[127.8 - 1.556\left(\frac{TSPA}{\delta}\right)\right]\delta D_s P_1\sqrt{\frac{\dfrac{MW}{Z_1 T_1}[1-(P_2/P_1)^2]}{NTP - \log_e(P_2/P_1)}} \quad (29\text{-}2)$$

For interlocking seals:

$$m_l = 0.4(50)\,\delta\,D_s P_1\sqrt{\frac{\dfrac{MW}{Z_1 T_1}[1-(P_2/P_1)^2]}{NTP - \log_e(P_2/P_1)}} \quad (29\text{-}3)$$

where:
D_s = shaft diameter, inches
$TSPA$ = tooth spacing, inches
δ = radial clearance, inches

Refer to Figure 29-1 for the nomenclature of Equations 29-2 and 29-3. An interlocking seal would be similar to Figure 29-1, except that there would be teeth emanating from and attached to the shaft between the stationary teeth. The number of teeth will increase by a factor of $2w - 1$, where w is the number of teeth for a non-interlocking seal.

Equation 29-2 predicted leakages within 10%–35% of one compressor manufacturer's procedure. This is well within the acceptable tolerance for this calculation. Consider the two main purposes for the leakage calculation.

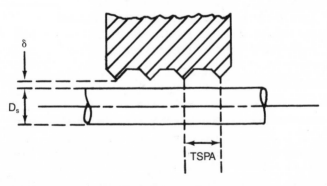

NTP = 4

Figure 29-1. Schematic of noninterlocking labyrinth seal, with nomenclature.

The first is to determine the amount of buffer flow required for the external seals. In this case, the main concern would be with lost product and the power penalty if the buffer gas was process gas, and with the buffer-gas inventory and power penalty if the buffer was from an external source. Except in rare cases, the required buffer flow will not be any greater than 3%–5% of the process gas flow, and usually much less. For a calculated buffer-gas flow equal to 3% of process flow, an error of 35% will convert to .5% error on total product loss and a .25% error on total power penalty. (Note that since the buffer gas flows inward and outward on both ends, only about half of the flow goes to lost product, and only about one quarter of the flow enters the compressor on the inlet end and affects power requirement. Refer to Figure 29-2.) Furthermore, when calculating external-source buffer-gas inventory, the engineer is more interested in magnitude than absolute numbers, as he will probably at least double the requirement to determine the inventory.

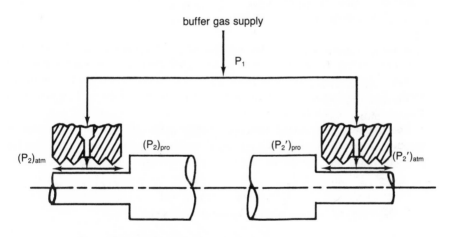

P_1 = inlet pressure to seal

$(P_2)_{atm}$ = pressure downstream of seal, inlet end, bearing-housing side

$(P_2)_{pro}$ = pressure downstream of seal, inlet end, process side

$(P_2')_{atm}$ = pressure downstream of seal, discharge end, bearing-housing side

$(P_2')_{pro}$ = pressure downstream of seal, discharge end, process side

Figure 29-2. Leakage schematic for buffered external seals.

The second purpose of this procedure is to determine the balance piston leakage to assess its effects on compressor performance and the power penalty. The balance piston leakage is normally on the order of 1%–5% of process flow. A 35% error in this case would affect performance and power a maximum of 2%, but usually much less. In the rare cases where the balance piston leakage exceeds 5%, the manufacturer should be consulted.

The external-seal labyrinth leakage must be determined both toward the process side and toward the bearing housing on both ends of the compressor. The total leakage is then the sum of the calculated leakages. Refer to Figure 29-2 for the illustration.

Program 29 Description

Labyrinth Leakage, Program 29, calculates and prints the results of Equations 29-2 and 29-3. In addition, since there has been much interest in the past few years in obtaining leakage values at twice new clearances, the program also calculates the labyrinth leakage for twice the radial clearace entered.

In order to execute the program, the following must be known:

1. Inlet pressure to seal, P_1
2. Pressure downstream of seal, P_2
3. Inlet temperature to seal, T_1
4. Molecular weight of gas flowing to seal, MW
5. Z-value of gas flowing to seal, Z_1
6. Shaft diameter, D_s
7. Radial clearance of seal, δ
8. Number of seal throttling points (teeth), NTP
9. Tooth spacing (centerline to centerline), $TSPA$

The program is set up to calculate the leakage for the radial clearance and for twice the radial clearance for a non-interlocking seal, since this is the seal type used for most applications. If he desires, the operator can actuate continued program execution to obtain leakages at radial clearance and at twice radial clearance for an interlocking seal.

If the seal is interlocking, the user must enter the number of teeth on the side, stationary or rotating, that contains the maximum number. Therefore, for an interlocking seal composed of four stationary teeth and three rotating teeth, enter 4 for NTP. The program will automatically change the number of teeth to $2w - 1$.

The program is set up for continuous usage, without the need for complete data reentry, unless the interlocking labyrinth option is exercised. Under this circumstance, the number of throttling points must be reentered prior to program reexecution. Otherwise, only the parameters of interest need to be changed.

Table 29-1 is the nomenclature printed by the program; Table 29-2 shows the data registers used by the program.

Table 29-1
Program 29: Printer Nomenclature

Program Term	Definition	Units
DS	shaft diameter	inches
MW	molecular weight to seal	lbm/lbm-mol
M1IN	leakage based on radial clearance for interlocking seal	lbm/min
M2IN	leakage based on 2 × radial clearance for interlocking seal	lbm/min
M1RC	leakage based on radial clearance for non-interlocking seal	lbm/min
M2RC	leakage based on 2 × radial clearance for non-interlocking seal	lbm/min
NTP	number of throttling points (teeth)	dimensionless
P1	inlet pressure to seal	psia
P2	pressure downstream of seal	psia
TSPA	tooth spacing (centerline to centerline)	inches
T1	inlet temperature to seal	°F
Z1	inlet compressibility to seal	dimensionless
1RC	radial clearance of seal	inches
2RC	2 × radial clearance of seal	inches

Table 29-2
Data Registers Used by Program 29

00	not used	07	MW	14	m_{2rc}
01	not used	08	Z_1	15	δ and 2δ
02	not used	09	NTP	16	C_{1rc} and C_{2rc}
03	P_1	10	$TSPA$	17	C_{1rc}
04	P_2	11	δ	18	C_{2rc}
05	T_1	12	m_{1rc}	19	m_{1in}
06	D_s	13	2δ	20	m_{2in}

Labels Used by Program 29

```
001   11   A        026   16   A'        046   10   E'
006   12   B        031   17   B'        056   15   E
011   13   C        036   18   C'        373   34   ΓX
021   14   D        041   19   D'        394   33   X²
```

Program 29 Usage

Program 29 is executed by using the user-defined and R/S keys, the definitions of which can be found in Table 29-3.

After the data are entered and program execution is initiated through user-defined key E, the program calculates the leakage for a non-interlocking seal and stops. The leakage is calculated for both the radial clearance entered and two times the radial clearance.

If the leakages for interlocking seals are desired, the user can obtain them by depressing the R/S key. The program automatically increases the number of teeth to $2w - 1$ and calculates the leakage for interlocking seals for both the radial clearance entered and two times the radial clearance.

Subsequent calculations can be made by changing only the parameters of interest. Note, however, that if the interlocking seal leakage option is exercised, the number of throttling points must be reentered prior to program reexecution.

Sample Problem 29-1

Buffer flow is to be injected into the inlet end seal of a centrifugal compressor that operates with an inlet pressure of 15 psia. The buffer flow will be nitrogen ($MW = 28.01$) at 100°F and 20 psia. $Z = 1.0$. The geometry is as follows:

$$D_s = 5.5 \text{ inches}$$
$$\delta = 0.008 \text{ inches}$$
$$NTP = 4$$
$$TSPA = 0.1875 \text{ inches}$$

Calculate the leakage into the compressor for the radial clearance given and two times the radial clearance for both a non-interlocking seal and an interlocking seal.

Note that in order to determine the total buffer flow required for the inlet end seal, the program would have to be run for the bearing housing side also. The sum of the leakages would then be the total required buffer flow for the inlet end seal.

Table 29-3
Program 29: Definitions of User-Defined and R/S Keys

A	P1	A'	MW
B	P2	B'	Z1
C	T1	C'	NTP
D	DS	D'	TSPA
E	Calculate	E'	1RC
		R/S	Continue execution for interlocking seals

Sample Problem 29-1: User Instructions

Step	Procedure	Enter	Press	Display
1.	Load program.			
2.	Enter inlet pressure to seal.	20	A	20
3.	Enter pressure downstream of seal	15	B	15
4.	Enter inlet temperature to seal.	100(°F)	C	560(°R)
5.	Enter molecular weight of gas flowing to seal.	28.01	2nd A'	28.01
6.	Enter compressibility of gas flowing to seal.	1.0	2nd B'	1
7.	Enter shaft diameter.	5.5	D	5.5
8.	Enter number of throttling points	4	2nd C'	4
9.	Enter tooth spacing.	0.1875	2nd D'	0.1875
10.	Enter radial clearance.	0.008	2nd E'	0.016 (2δ)
11.	Calculate for non-interlocking seal.		E	
12.	Calculate for interlocking seal.		R/S	

Sample Problem 29-1: Program Printout

```
LABYRINTH LEAKAGE               0.1875    TSPA
                                0.008     1RC
                                0.016     2RC

          20.      P1
          15.      P2          2.3      M1RC
         100.      T1          5.5      M2RC
           5.5     DS
          28.01    MW
           1.      Z1          1.0      M1IN
           4.      NTP         1.9      M2IN
```

Program 29 Listing

000	76	LBL	050	02	2	100	00	0
001	11	A	051	95	=	101	00	0
002	42	STO	052	42	STO	102	69	OP
003	03	03	053	13	13	103	04	04
004	91	R/S	054	91	R/S	104	69	OP
005	76	LBL	055	76	LBL	105	05	05
006	12	B	056	15	E	106	98	ADV
007	42	STO	057	69	OP	107	98	ADV
008	04	04	058	00	00	108	03	3
009	91	R/S	059	98	ADV	109	03	3
010	76	LBL	060	02	2	110	00	0
011	13	C	061	07	7	111	02	2
012	85	+	062	01	1	112	69	OP
013	04	4	063	03	3	113	04	04
014	06	6	064	01	1	114	43	RCL
015	00	0	065	04	4	115	03	03
016	95	=	066	69	OP	116	69	OP
017	42	STO	067	01	01	117	06	06
018	05	05	068	04	4	118	03	3
019	91	R/S	069	05	5	119	03	3
020	76	LBL	070	03	3	120	00	0
021	14	D	071	05	5	121	03	3
022	42	STO	072	02	2	122	69	OP
023	06	06	073	04	4	123	04	04
024	91	R/S	074	03	3	124	43	RCL
025	76	LBL	075	01	1	125	04	04
026	16	A'	076	03	3	126	69	OP
027	42	STO	077	07	7	127	06	06
028	07	07	078	69	OP	128	03	3
029	91	R/S	079	02	02	129	07	7
030	76	LBL	080	02	2	130	00	0
031	17	B'	081	03	3	131	02	2
032	42	STO	082	00	0	132	69	OP
033	08	08	083	00	0	133	04	04
034	91	R/S	084	02	2	134	43	RCL
035	76	LBL	085	07	7	135	05	05
036	18	C'	086	01	1	136	75	-
037	42	STO	087	07	7	137	04	4
038	09	09	088	01	1	138	06	6
039	91	R/S	089	03	3	139	00	0
040	76	LBL	090	69	OP	140	95	=
041	19	D'	091	03	03	141	69	OP
042	42	STO	092	02	2	142	06	06
043	10	10	093	06	6	143	01	1
044	91	R/S	094	01	1	144	06	6
045	76	LBL	095	03	3	145	03	3
046	10	E'	096	02	2	146	06	6
047	42	STO	097	02	2	147	69	OP
048	11	11	098	01	1	148	04	04
049	65	×	099	07	7	149	43	RCL

Program 29 Listing continued

150	06	06		200	02	2		250	42	STO
151	69	OP		201	03	3		251	12	12
152	06	06		202	05	5		252	43	RCL
153	03	3		203	01	1		253	13	13
154	00	0		204	05	5		254	42	STO
155	04	4		205	69	OP		255	15	15
156	03	3		206	04	04		256	43	RCL
157	69	OP		207	43	RCL		257	18	18
158	04	04		208	11	11		258	42	STO
159	43	RCL		209	69	OP		259	16	16
160	07	07		210	06	06		260	71	SBR
161	69	OP		211	00	0		261	33	X^2
162	06	06		212	03	3		262	42	STO
163	04	4		213	03	3		263	14	14
164	06	6		214	05	5		264	03	3
165	00	0		215	01	1		265	00	0
166	02	2		216	05	5		266	00	0
167	69	OP		217	69	OP		267	02	2
168	04	04		218	04	04		268	03	3
169	43	RCL		219	43	RCL		269	05	5
170	08	08		220	13	13		270	01	1
171	69	OP		221	69	OP		271	05	5
172	06	06		222	06	06		272	69	OP
173	03	3		223	43	RCL		273	04	04
174	01	1		224	11	11		274	43	RCL
175	03	3		225	42	STO		275	12	12
176	07	7		226	15	15		276	58	FIX
177	03	3		227	71	SBR		277	01	01
178	03	3		228	34	ΓX		278	69	OP
179	69	OP		229	42	STO		279	06	06
180	04	04		230	17	17		280	22	INV
181	43	RCL		231	43	RCL		281	58	FIX
182	09	09		232	13	13		282	03	3
183	69	OP		233	42	STO		283	00	0
184	06	06		234	15	15		284	00	0
185	03	3		235	71	SBR		285	03	3
186	07	7		236	34	ΓX		286	03	3
187	03	3		237	42	STO		287	05	5
188	06	6		238	18	18		288	01	1
189	03	3		239	98	ADV		289	05	5
190	03	3		240	43	RCL		290	69	OP
191	01	1		241	11	11		291	04	04
192	03	3		242	42	STO		292	43	RCL
193	69	OP		243	15	15		293	14	14
194	04	04		244	43	RCL		294	58	FIX
195	43	RCL		245	17	17		295	01	01
196	10	10		246	42	STO		296	69	OP
197	69	OP		247	16	16		297	06	06
198	06	06		248	71	SBR		298	22	INV
199	00	0		249	33	X^2		299	58	FIX

(continued on next page)

Program 29 Listing continued

300	69	OP	350	58	FIX	400	95	=
301	00	00	351	03	3	401	33	X²
302	91	R/S	352	00	0	402	94	+/-
303	05	5	353	00	0	403	85	+
304	00	0	354	03	3	404	01	1
305	42	STO	355	02	2	405	95	=
306	16	16	356	04	4	406	65	×
307	43	RCL	357	03	3	407	43	RCL
308	11	11	358	01	1	408	07	07
309	42	STO	359	69	OP	409	55	÷
310	15	15	360	04	04	410	43	RCL
311	43	RCL	361	43	RCL	411	08	08
312	09	09	362	20	20	412	55	÷
313	65	×	363	58	FIX	413	43	RCL
314	02	2	364	01	01	414	05	05
315	75	-	365	69	OP	415	55	÷
316	01	1	366	06	06	416	53	(
317	95	=	367	22	INV	417	43	RCL
318	42	STO	368	58	FIX	418	09	09
319	09	09	369	69	OP	419	75	-
320	71	SBR	370	00	00	420	53	(
321	33	X²	371	91	R/S	421	53	(
322	42	STO	372	76	LBL	422	43	RCL
323	19	19	373	34	√X	423	04	04
324	43	RCL	374	01	1	424	55	÷
325	13	13	375	02	2	425	43	RCL
326	42	STO	376	07	7	426	03	03
327	15	15	377	93	.	427	54	)
328	71	SBR	378	08	8	428	23	LNX
329	33	X²	379	75	-	429	54	)
330	42	STO	380	01	1	430	54	)
331	20	20	381	93	.	431	95	=
332	98	ADV	382	05	5	432	34	√X
333	03	3	383	05	5	433	65	×
334	00	0	384	06	6	434	93	.
335	00	0	385	65	×	435	04	4
336	02	2	386	43	RCL	436	65	×
337	02	2	387	10	10	437	43	RCL
338	04	4	388	55	÷	438	16	16
339	03	3	389	43	RCL	439	65	×
340	01	1	390	15	15	440	43	RCL
341	69	OP	391	95	=	441	15	15
342	04	04	392	92	RTN	442	65	×
343	43	RCL	393	76	LBL	443	43	RCL
344	19	19	394	33	X²	444	06	06
345	58	FIX	395	43	RCL	445	65	×
346	01	01	396	04	04	446	43	RCL
347	69	OP	397	55	÷	447	03	03
348	06	06	398	43	RCL	448	95	=
349	22	INV	399	03	03	449	92	RTN

Program 30

English-Metric Conversions

Program 30 Description

Program 30, English-Metric Conversions can be used for the following conversions:

Pressure:	psia to kPa
	kPa to psia
Mass flow:	lbm/min to kg/h
	kg/h to lbm/min
Volume flow:	ICFM to m^3/h
	m^3/h to ICFM
Head:	ft-lbf/lbm to N·m/kg
	N·m/kg to ft-lbf/lbm
Power:	hp to kw
	kw to hp
Temperature:	°F to °C
	°C to °F

Table 30-1 is the nomenclature printed by the program; Table 30-2 shows the data registers used by the program.

Labels Used by Program 30

004	11	A	216	13	C	428	15	E
056	16	A'	269	18	C'	473	10	E'
108	12	B	322	14	D	518	33	X²
162	17	B'	375	19	D'	573	34	ГX

Table 30-1
Program 30: Printer Nomenclature

Program Term	Definition	Units
DEGC	temperature	°C
DEGF	temperature	°F
FEET	head	ft-lbf/lbm
HP	power	hp
ICFM	inlet volume flow	ICFM
KG/H	mass flow	kg/h
KPA	pressure	kPa
KW	power	kW
LB/M	mass flow	lbm/min
M3/H	inlet volume flow	m³/h
NMKG	head	N·m/kg
PSIA	pressure	psia

Note:

The volume flows are listed as inlet in order to form a common reference point and to imply that they are actual, not standard. However, the conversions can be used for actual volume flow at any point.

Table 30-2
Data Registers Used by Program 30

00	not used	05	lbm/min	10	N·m/kg	
01	not used	06	kg/h	11	hp	
02	not used	07	ICFM	12	kW	
03	psia	08	m³/h	13	°F	
04	kPa	09	ft-lbf/lbm	14	°C	

Table 30-3
Program 30: Definitions of User-Defined Keys, SBR x^2, and SBR $\sqrt{x}$

A	PSIA to KPA	A'	KPA to PSIA
B	LB/M to KG/H	B'	KG/H to LB/M
C	ICFM to M3/H	C'	M3/H to ICFM
D	FEET to NMKG	D'	NMKG to FEET
E	HP to KW	E'	KW to HP
SBR x^2	DEGF to DEGC	SBR $\sqrt{x}$	DEGC to DEGF

Program 30 Usage

Program 30 is executed by using the user-defined keys, SBR x^2, and SBR $\sqrt{x}$, the definitions of which can be found in Table 30-3.

Note that the calculator must be repartitioned to 719.29 before loading or keying in the program.

Sample Problem 30-1

Convert the following:

50 psia to kPa
400 KPa to psia
1500 lbm/min to kg/h
35,000 kg/h to lbm/min
50,000 ICFM to m^3/h
75,000 m^3/h to ICFM
45,000 ft-lbf/lbm to N·m/kg
125,000 N·m/kg to ft-lbf/lbm
2500 hp to kW
5000 kW to hp
100°F to °C
40°C to °F

Sample Problem 30-1: User Instructions

Step	Procedure	Enter	Press	Display
1.	Partition calculator.	3	2nd OP 17	719.29
2.	Load program.			
3.	Convert 50 psia to kPa.	50	A	
4.	Convert 400 kPa to psia.	400	2nd A'	
5.	Convert 1500 lbm/min to kg/h	1500	B	
6.	Convert 35,000 kg/h to lbm/min.	35000	2nd B'	
7.	Convert 50,000 ICFM to m^3/h	50000	C	
8.	Convert 75,000 m^3/h to ICFM.	75000	2nd C'	
9.	Convert 45,000 ft-lbf/ lbm to N·m/kg	45000	D	
10.	Convert 125,000 N·m/ kg to ft-lbf/lbm.	125000	2nd D'	
11.	Convert 2500 hp to kW	2500	E	
12.	Convert 5000 kW to hp.	5000	2nd E'	

(continued on next page)

Sample Problem 30-1: User Instructions continued

Step	Procedure	Enter	Press	Display
13. Convert 100°F to °C.		100	SBR x^2	
14. Convert 40°C to °F		40	SBR $\sqrt{x}$	

Sample Problem 30-1: Program Printout

```
  50.0    PSIA      45000.    FEET
 344.7    KPA      134505.    NMKG

 400.0    KPA      125000.    NMKG
  58.0    PSIA      41820.    FEET

1500.     LB/M       2500.    HP
40827.    KG/H       1864.    KW

35000.    KG/H       5000.    KW
 1286.    LB/M       6705.    HP

50000.    ICFM       100.0    DEGF
84950.    M3/H        37.8    DEGC

75000.    M3/H        40.0    DEGC
44144.    ICFM       104.0    DEGF
```

Program 30 Listing

000	03	3	017	04	04	034	22	INV
001	69	OP	018	03	3	035	58	FIX
002	17	17	019	03	3	036	02	2
003	76	LBL	020	03	3	037	06	6
004	11	A	021	06	6	038	03	3
005	98	ADV	022	02	2	039	03	3
006	42	STD	023	04	4	040	01	1
007	03	03	024	01	1	041	03	3
008	65	×	025	03	3	042	69	OP
009	06	6	026	69	OP	043	04	04
010	93	.	027	04	04	044	43	RCL
011	08	8	028	43	RCL	045	04	04
012	09	9	029	03	03	046	58	FIX
013	04	4	030	58	FIX	047	01	01
014	08	8	031	01	01	048	69	OP
015	95	=	032	69	OP	049	06	06
016	42	STD	033	06	06	050	22	INV

Program 30 Listing continued

051	58	FIX	101	06	06	151	06	06
052	69	OP	102	22	INV	152	58	FIX
053	00	00	103	58	FIX	153	00	00
054	91	R/S	104	69	OP	154	69	OP
055	76	LBL	105	00	00	155	06	06
056	16	A'	106	91	R/S	156	22	INV
057	98	ADV	107	76	LBL	157	58	FIX
058	42	STO	108	12	B	158	69	OP
059	04	04	109	98	ADV	159	00	00
060	55	÷	110	42	STO	160	91	R/S
061	06	6	111	05	05	161	76	LBL
062	93	.	112	55	÷	162	17	B'
063	08	8	113	93	.	163	98	ADV
064	09	9	114	00	0	164	42	STO
065	04	4	115	03	3	165	06	06
066	08	8	116	06	6	166	65	×
067	95	=	117	07	7	167	93	.
068	42	STO	118	04	4	168	00	0
069	03	03	119	95	=	169	03	3
070	02	2	120	42	STO	170	06	6
071	06	6	121	06	06	171	07	7
072	03	3	122	02	2	172	04	4
073	03	3	123	07	7	173	95	=
074	01	1	124	01	1	174	42	STO
075	03	3	125	04	4	175	05	05
076	69	OP	126	06	6	176	02	2
077	04	04	127	03	3	177	06	6
078	43	RCL	128	03	3	178	02	2
079	04	04	129	00	0	179	02	2
080	58	FIX	130	69	OP	180	06	6
081	01	01	131	04	04	181	03	3
082	69	OP	132	43	RCL	182	02	2
083	06	06	133	05	05	183	03	3
084	22	INV	134	58	FIX	184	69	OP
085	58	FIX	135	00	00	185	04	04
086	03	3	136	69	OP	186	43	RCL
087	03	3	137	06	06	187	06	06
088	03	3	138	22	INV	188	58	FIX
089	06	6	139	58	FIX	189	00	00
090	02	2	140	02	2	190	69	OP
091	04	4	141	06	6	191	06	06
092	01	1	142	02	2	192	22	INV
093	03	3	143	02	2	193	58	FIX
094	69	OP	144	06	6	194	02	2
095	04	04	145	03	3	195	07	7
096	43	RCL	146	02	2	196	01	1
097	03	03	147	03	3	197	04	4
098	58	FIX	148	69	OP	198	06	6
099	01	01	149	04	04	199	03	3
100	69	OP	150	43	RCL	200	03	3

(continued on next page)

Program 30 Listing continued

201	00	0	251	06	6	301	04	4
202	69	OP	252	03	3	302	01	1
203	04	04	253	02	2	303	05	5
204	43	RCL	254	03	3	304	02	2
205	05	05	255	69	OP	305	01	1
206	58	FIX	256	04	04	306	03	3
207	00	00	257	43	RCL	307	00	0
208	69	OP	258	08	08	308	69	OP
209	06	06	259	58	FIX	309	04	04
210	22	INV	260	00	00	310	43	RCL
211	58	FIX	261	69	OP	311	07	07
212	69	OP	262	06	06	312	58	FIX
213	00	00	263	22	INV	313	00	00
214	91	R/S	264	58	FIX	314	69	OP
215	76	LBL	265	69	OP	315	06	06
216	13	C	266	00	00	316	22	INV
217	98	ADV	267	91	R/S	317	58	FIX
218	42	STO	268	76	LBL	318	69	OP
219	07	07	269	18	C'	319	00	00
220	65	×	270	98	ADV	320	91	R/S
221	01	1	271	42	STO	321	76	LBL
222	93	.	272	08	08	322	14	D
223	06	6	273	55	÷	323	98	ADV
224	09	9	274	01	1	324	42	STO
225	09	9	275	93	.	325	09	09
226	95	=	276	06	6	326	65	×
227	42	STO	277	09	9	327	02	2
228	08	08	278	09	9	328	93	.
229	02	2	279	95	=	329	09	9
230	04	4	280	42	STO	330	08	8
231	01	1	281	07	07	331	09	9
232	05	5	282	03	3	332	95	=
233	02	2	283	00	0	333	42	STO
234	01	1	284	00	0	334	10	10
235	03	3	285	04	4	335	02	2
236	00	0	286	06	6	336	01	1
237	69	OP	287	03	3	337	01	1
238	04	04	288	02	2	338	07	7
239	43	RCL	289	03	3	339	01	1
240	07	07	290	69	OP	340	07	7
241	58	FIX	291	04	04	341	03	3
242	00	00	292	43	RCL	342	07	7
243	69	OP	293	08	08	343	69	OP
244	06	06	294	58	FIX	344	04	04
245	22	INV	295	00	00	345	43	RCL
246	58	FIX	296	69	OP	346	09	09
247	03	3	297	06	06	347	58	FIX
248	00	0	298	22	INV	348	00	00
249	00	0	299	58	FIX	349	69	OP
250	04	4	300	02	2	350	06	06

Program 30 Listing continued

351	22	INV	401	00	00	451	69	OP
352	58	FIX	402	69	OP	452	06	06
353	03	3	403	06	06	453	22	INV
354	01	1	404	22	INV	454	58	FIX
355	03	3	405	58	FIX	455	02	2
356	00	0	406	02	2	456	06	6
357	02	2	407	01	1	457	04	4
358	06	6	408	01	1	458	03	3
359	02	2	409	07	7	459	69	OP
360	02	2	410	01	1	460	04	04
361	69	OP	411	07	7	461	43	RCL
362	04	04	412	03	3	462	12	12
363	43	RCL	413	07	7	463	58	FIX
364	10	10	414	69	OP	464	00	00
365	58	FIX	415	04	04	465	69	OP
366	00	00	416	43	RCL	466	06	06
367	69	OP	417	09	09	467	22	INV
368	06	06	418	58	FIX	468	58	FIX
369	22	INV	419	00	00	469	69	OP
370	58	FIX	420	69	OP	470	00	00
371	69	OP	421	06	06	471	91	R/S
372	00	00	422	22	INV	472	76	LBL
373	91	R/S	423	58	FIX	473	10	E'
374	76	LBL	424	69	OP	474	98	ADV
375	19	D'	425	00	00	475	42	STO
376	98	ADV	426	91	R/S	476	12	12
377	42	STO	427	76	LBL	477	55	÷
378	10	10	428	15	E	478	93	.
379	55	÷	429	98	ADV	479	07	7
380	02	2	430	42	STO	480	04	4
381	93	.	431	11	11	481	05	5
382	09	9	432	65	×	482	07	7
383	08	8	433	93	.	483	95	=
384	09	9	434	07	7	484	42	STO
385	95	=	435	04	4	485	11	11
386	42	STO	436	05	5	486	02	2
387	09	09	437	07	7	487	06	6
388	03	3	438	95	=	488	04	4
389	01	1	439	42	STO	489	03	3
390	03	3	440	12	12	490	69	OP
391	00	0	441	02	2	491	04	04
392	02	2	442	03	3	492	43	RCL
393	06	6	443	03	3	493	12	12
394	02	2	444	03	3	494	58	FIX
395	02	2	445	69	OP	495	00	00
396	69	OP	446	04	04	496	69	OP
397	04	04	447	43	RCL	497	06	06
398	43	RCL	448	11	11	498	22	INV
399	10	10	449	58	FIX	499	58	FIX
400	58	FIX	450	00	00	500	02	2

(continued on next page)

Program 30 Listing continued

501	03	3	544	13	13	587	13	13
502	03	3	545	58	FIX	588	01	1
503	03	3	546	01	01	589	06	6
504	69	OP	547	69	OP	590	01	1
505	04	04	548	06	06	591	07	7
506	43	RCL	549	22	INV	592	02	2
507	11	11	550	58	FIX	593	02	2
508	58	FIX	551	01	1	594	01	1
509	00	00	552	06	6	595	05	5
510	69	OP	553	01	1	596	69	OP
511	06	06	554	07	7	597	04	04
512	22	INV	555	02	2	598	43	RCL
513	58	FIX	556	02	2	599	14	14
514	69	OP	557	01	1	600	58	FIX
515	00	00	558	05	5	601	01	01
516	91	R/S	559	69	OP	602	69	OP
517	76	LBL	560	04	04	603	06	06
518	33	X²	561	43	RCL	604	22	INV
519	98	ADV	562	14	14	605	58	FIX
520	42	STO	563	58	FIX	606	01	1
521	13	13	564	01	01	607	06	6
522	75	-	565	69	OP	608	01	1
523	03	3	566	06	06	609	07	7
524	02	2	567	22	INV	610	02	2
525	95	=	568	58	FIX	611	02	2
526	55	÷	569	69	OP	612	02	2
527	01	1	570	00	00	613	01	1
528	93	.	571	92	RTN	614	69	OP
529	08	8	572	76	LBL	615	04	04
530	95	=	573	34	ГX	616	43	RCL
531	42	STO	574	98	ADV	617	13	13
532	14	14	575	42	STO	618	58	FIX
533	01	1	576	14	14	619	01	01
534	06	6	577	65	×	620	69	OP
535	01	1	578	01	1	621	06	06
536	07	7	579	93	.	622	22	INV
537	02	2	580	08	8	623	58	FIX
538	02	2	581	95	=	624	69	OP
539	02	2	582	85	+	625	00	00
540	01	1	583	03	3	626	92	RTN
541	69	OP	584	02	2	627	00	0
542	04	04	585	95	=	628	00	0
543	43	RCL	586	42	STO	629	00	0

Bibliography

American Gear Manufacturers Association, *AGMA 421.06 AGMA Standard for High-Speed Helical and Herringbone Gear Units,* Washington, D.C.: AGMA, January 1969.

American Petroleum Institute, *API Standard 613 Special-Purpose Gear Units for Refinery Services,* Second Edition, Washington, D.C.: API, February, 1977

Ibid., *API Standard 617, Centrifugal Compressors for General Refinery Services,* Fourth Edition, Washington, D. C.: API, November 1979.

American Society of Mechanical Engineers, *ASME PTC 10-1965 Compressors and Exhausters,* New York: ASME, 1965.

Ibid., *ASME PTC 19.5;4-1959 Flow Measurement,* New York: ASME, 1959.

Ibid, *ASME Steam Tables,* Fourth Edition, New York: ASME, 1967.

Ibid., *Fluid Meters Their Theory and Application,* Sixth Edition, edited by Howard S. Bean, New York: ASME, 1971.

Baljé, O. E., "A Study on Design Criteria and Matching of Turbomachines: Part B—Compressor and Pump Performance and Matching of Turbocomponents," *Journal of Engineering for Power,* Transactions of the ASME, Series A, Vol. 84, New York: ASME, January 1962.

Baumeister, T., E. A. Avallone and T. Baumeister III, *Mark's Standard Handbook for Mechanical Engineers,* Eight Edition, New York: McGraw-Hill Book Company, 1979.

Elliott Company, *Compressor Refresher,* Jeannette, PA: Elliott Company, 1975.

Ibid., *Engineers Guide to Modern International Units of Measurement for Rotating Machinery,* Bulletin Q49, Jeannette, PA: Elliott Company, 1975.

Ibid., *Quick Selection Methods for Elliott Multistage Centrifugal Compressors,* Bulletin P-25S-Rev, Jeannette, PA: Elliott Company, 1981.

Gas Processors Suppliers Association, *Engineering Data Book,* Ninth Edition, Fifth Revision, Tulsa, OK: GPSA, 1981

Ibid., *SI Engineering Data Book,* Tulsa, OK: GPSA, 1980.

Ingersoll-Rand Company, *Compressed Air and Gas Data,* Third Edition, Washington, NJ: Ingersoll-Rand Company, 1980.

Keenan, J. H., F. G. Keyes, P. G. Hill, and J. G. Moore, *Steam Tables (English Units),* New York: John Wiley and Sons, Inc., 1969.

Lapina, R. P., "Can you Rerate Your Centrifugal Compressor?," *Chemical Engineering,* New York: McGraw-Hill Publications, January 20, 1975 (originally written for the CAGI Technical Article Program).

Ibid., *Estimating Centrifugal Compressor Performance—Process Compressor Technology Volume 1,* Houston: Gulf Publishing Company, 1982.

Ibid., "A Quick Approach to Estimating Hydrocarbon *K*- and *Z*- Values for Compressor Applications," *CAGI Technical Digest,* Vol. 13, No. 2, Cleveland: Compressed Air and Gas Institute; and *Chemical Engineering* (as "How to Estimate Compressibility Factors and Specific Heat Ratios for Hydrocarbon Gases") New York: McGraw-Hill Publications, Feburary 8, 1982.

Ibid., "Single-Stage Centrifugal Compressor Performance Curves—Get More Out of Them," *CAGI Technical Digest,* Vol. 9, No. 2, Cleveland: Compressed Air and Gas Institute; and *Chemical Engineering* (as "How to Use the Performance Curves to Evaluate Behavior of Centrifugal Compressors"), New York: McGraw-Hill Publications, January 25, 1982.

Nelson, L. C., E. F. Obert, "Generalized Compressibility Charts," *Chemical Engineering,* New York: McGraw-Hill Publications, July 1954.

Thermodynamics Research Center Hydrocarbon Project, "Selected Values of Properties of Hydrocarbons and Related Compounds," College Station, TX: Thermodynamics Research Center, Texas A&M University, 1981 (loose-leaf data sheets extant, 1981).

Transamerica DeLaval Inc., *DeLaval Engineering Handbook,* Third Edition, edited by Hans Gartmann, New York: McGraw-Hill Book Company, 1970.

Van Wylen, G. J., and R. E. Sonntag, *Fundamentals of Classical Thermodynamics,* Second Printing, New York: John Wiley and Sons, Inc., 1968.

Index